To the McKeogh family

With very best wishes.

A.B. Morrow

8th November 2010

Farming in County Fermanagh

Development in the Twentieth Century

By Samuel B. Morrow

Published by Samuel B. Morrow, Enniskillen, 2010.

ISBN 978-0-9566997-0-1

Contents

Acknowledgements

Acknowledgements

This book could not have been written without the help of a number of organisations and very many people. The Vaughan Trust has been most supportive in its funding to assist with the costs involved in the production, printing and marketing of the book. The Trustees' enthusiasm for the project was most encouraging at all times.

Former and present staff members of the Department of Agriculture and Rural Development were most helpful in supplying information and photographs. I am particularly indebted to three former colleagues Messrs Lytle, McEwen and McGirr. Sam McEwen and Stanley Lytle and Mrs Jane Elliott readily agreed to proof read the script and furthermore came up with many constructive suggestions. Bernard McGirr undertook the daunting task of digitising a large number of colour slides dating from the early 1950s.

Records of information were readily made available or accessible by staff from the following establishments: the Department of Agriculture and Rural Development (DARD) office at Inishkeen House; Enniskillen Campus of the College of Food and Rural Enterprise; the DARD library in Dundonald House; Economics and Statistics Division of DARD, Enniskillen Library, County Fermanagh Farming Society; The Impartial Reporter; the Public Record Office, Belfast; The Ulster Farmers' Mart Company; National Library of Ireland, NI Folk and Transport Museum; West Ulster Farmers Limited; Electricity Supply Board (IR); Ford Motor Company Ltd, Irish Agricultural Museum and Hampshire County Council Museums and Archive Service. The help of the staff of Enniskillen Library, especially Margaret Kane and Marianna Maguire, was invaluable.

Others who supplied photographs, reference material or other services included: Mr Alex Acheson, Mrs Linda Adams, Miss Jayne Armstrong, Mrs Ruth Armstrong, Mr Derek Alexander, Mr Peter Archdale, Mr Richard Bennett, Sister Edel Bannon, Mr and Mrs Noel Baxter, Mrs Debbie Black, Mr Patrick Blake, Harold Bothwell, Mr Mackey Breen, Viscount Brookeborough, Mr David Brown, Mr Robert Brownlee, Mr Ross Brimstone, Mr Edwin Bruce, Mr Johnny Burke, Mrs Stella Campbell, Mr Leslie Campbell, Mr Jim Carmichael, Ms Eileen Cassidy, Mr and Mrs Richard Chambers, Mr Ken Conn, Mr and Mrs Cecil Cooke, Ms Alisa Courtney, Mr John Courtney, Mr Nicholas Coyle, Mr Charles Crawford, Mr Joe Crawford, Mrs Heather Crawford, Mr and Mrs William Crawford, Mrs Carol Crooke, Miss Dane, Mr Brendan Delany, Ms Fiona Dickson, Mrs E. Dickson, Mr and Mrs W. Dickson, Mr Brian Donaldson, Mr Norman Dunbar, Mr and Mrs W. Dunn, Miss Dora Elliott, Mr George Elliott, Mr James Elliott, Miss Margaret Elliott, Mr and Mrs Mervyn Elliott, The Earl of Erne, Miss Rosaleen Falconer, Mr Ronnie Farrell, Mr Basil Fawcett, Mr George Fawcett, Mr David Fawcett, Mr Malcolm Finney, Messrs D and S. Gallagher, Mr Andrew Glendinning, Mr Alun Goodall, Miss Olwen Gormley, Dr Harry Gracey, Mrs Carol Graham, Mrs Margaret Higham, Mr Victor Graham, The Very Rev John Hay, Mr Bob Haycock, Mr John Hetherington, Mr Harold Hamilton, Mrs D. Hanna, Mr Ian Hill, Mrs Rosemary Houston, Mr Ian Irwin, Mr Steven Irwin, Mr Jack Johnston, Mr Noel Johnston, Mr Stuart Johnston, Miss Susan Jordan, Mr William Johnston, Mr James Kerr, Mr and Mrs Bertie Kerr, Mr Robert Kettyle, Sir John Langham, Mrs Bernadette Leyden, Mrs Betty Little, Mr Ivan Loane, Mrs Anne Loane, Professor Eric Long, Mr Leslie Long, Mr Connor Maguire, Mr Frank Maguire, Mr and Mrs Tom Maguire, Ms Grace Maloney, Mr John McVitty, Mr Alan Morrow, Dr James Morrow, Mrs Marie Morrow, Mrs Marion Maxwell, Mr Seamus McAlinney, Mr Joe McAloon, Mr Seamus McCaffrey, Mr and Mrs Robin McCullagh, Mr Michael McCullagh, Mrs Breege McCusker, Mr Thomas McCusker, Dr W. McLauchlan, Ms Jacqui McGarrity, Mrs Teresa Mc Girr, Ann McGrath, Dr Patrick McGurn, Mrs Michelle McKenna, Mr Michael Murphy, Mr William Neely, Mr Donagh O'Neill, Mrs Ann Orr, Mr Malachy McRoe, Mr Phil Peattie, Mr Joe Pat Prunty, Mr Derek Quinton, Ms Sharon Quinn, Mrs Bronagh Reilly, Mr Frankie Roofe, Mr Douglas Rowe, Mrs R. Rutledge, Mr Jim Stevenson, Mrs Diane Stevenson, Mr Andrew Strutt, Mrs Alison Stronge, Canon J. Stewart, Mr and Mrs Bertie Swan, Mr Frank Tisdall, Mrs M. Veitch, Mr Ian Wilson, Mr Alan Warnock, Ms Lorna Watson, Mrs Maureen West, Mr and Mrs Jim West, Mr Bill Wilson, Mrs Edith Wilson, Mr Ian Wilson, Mrs Majella Woods.

The photographs, unless otherwise acknowledged, were mainly supplied by past or present members of staff of the Ministry/Department of Agriculture or Department of Agriculture and Rural Development and are copyright. Miss Jayne Armstrong, Dr Patrick McGurn and Messrs Sam McEwen, Stanley Lytle, Bernard McGirr, Nicholas Coyle, Alan Warnock and Connor Maguire deserve special mention in this regard.

Introduction

Agricultural development has been an important feature in every century since man arrived in County Fermanagh after the last Ice Age but the changes that occurred in the twentieth century are among the most significant. The passing centuries presented many challenges for those who had to earn a living from the land. Most farmers in Fermanagh were tenants in the nineteenth century and consequently the landlords, who owned the land, had a considerable influence on the farmers' wellbeing and welfare. When farmers became owners of the land they farmed, through the payment of Land Purchase Annuities under the Land Acts of the late nineteenth and early twentieth centuries, they took added responsibility for the development of their businesses. Increasingly, they came under the influence of Government agricultural policy and support measures. The first major step in providing support for farming by Government came through the Agriculture and Technical Instruction Act passed by the Dublin Government in 1900. The main thrust of this Act was the provision of an advisory and educational service for farmers together with measures to encourage them to keep improved livestock and produce better crops.

The establishment of the Fermanagh County Committee of Agriculture in 1901 laid the foundation for developments that were to come in the twentieth century. During that century farmers faced the challenges of economic depression, two World Wars, a transition from mixed farming to specialist production and replacement of the horse by the tractor. Other changes occurred which required farmers to be more competitive. Towards the end of the century increased competition from European and world wide producers necessitated increased productivity and efficiency. Quality of produce and efficiency and effectiveness of marketing also took on a new significance.

Credit must be given to those people and organisations that laid the foundations in the nineteenth century for what took place in the twentieth century. In County Fermanagh the leading landlords and the farming societies made a valuable contribution to agricultural development. It can indeed be claimed that they established a model for agricultural development in the rest of the island of Ireland. It is therefore appropriate that these nineteenth century developments in County Fermanagh should constitute the first two chapters in the book. The support given to farmers during the twentieth century through education, advice, financial and other support measures from Government and other organisations has been significant. The details of these contributions and the role of those personalities who instigated and led these initiatives are highlighted. Advances in crop and animal husbandry and developments in technology and in farm business management, together with Government policy initiatives, all contributed to shaping farming activity over the century.

The most significant changes in the pattern of agricultural production occurred during and after the Second World War. The chapters in this book which follow that dealing with the Second World War give details of the developments in mechanisation, technology, advances in crop and animal husbandry, business management, Government schemes and other factors that enabled progress in County Fermanagh farming to be achieved during the succeeding years of the century.

Chapter 1

The contribution of County Fermanagh Farming Societies in the early nineteenth century

The landlords of County Fermanagh and the farming societies in the county made a very significant contribution to the development of agriculture. It can be claimed that they established a model which laid the foundation for the rest of the island of Ireland. This chapter deals in particular with the contribution made by Lord Erne, Crom Castle, and the Fermanagh Farming Society.

Agricultural societies were well established in Fermanagh and adjoining counties in the early part of the nineteenth century. Their primary purpose was to assist those engaged in improving the standard of farming. The Clones Farming Society was flourishing in 1835 and held its agricultural show on 23rd September of that year. A report in *The Impartial Reporter* of that event stated that it was the *surviving branch of that admirable institution, The Erne Society, which gave a decided impulse to the improvement of the farmers of this neighbourhood in agricultural science, good taste, and profitable pursuits.* The report went on to state that hopes are still entertained of seeing that institution (The Erne Society) again established and manifesting its usefulness throughout the district. The press report of the Clones Farming Society of 22nd September1841stated *that Society had now subsisted for ten years after the suppression of The Erne Society for some unknown reason.* The Erne Society, which held its meetings under the auspices of such men as Lord Enniskillen, Lord Blaney and Mr Archdall, was formed around 1819 and embraced the counties of Monaghan, Fermanagh and Cavan.

John Creighton Esq of Crom Castle ran a comprehensive show and other competitions for his tenants in Lisnaskea. This was well established by 1835. Livestock and other items for exhibition were shown in Lisnaskea in August of that year and in succeeding years. In addition to the livestock and exhibits at the show there were also farm based competitions. At the dinner in Lisnaskea following the 1835 show the Rev J. G. Porter of Belleisle returned thanks to John Creighton Esq. He stated that it would be his hope that the rest of the Fermanagh landlords would follow the Creighton example. He said that he would endeavour to do so. This was probably the seed that led to the establishment of the Fermanagh Farming Society.

The first reference to the establishment of the Fermanagh

Rev J. G. Porter of Belleisle (Courtesy of Mr Joe Crawford).

Farming Society is recorded in *The Impartial Reporter* of 13th October 1836. The report indicated that there was a large attendance of the aristocracy and landed proprietors. John Creighton Esq was placed in the chair, who in a short speech explained the benefits derived from farming societies. The report reads: *He said their objectives were in every way calculated to benefit the landlord and tenant, and incite in the farmer a laudable spirit of emulation, which would eventually tend to improve the circumstances and regenerate the country. At the periodical shows the landlords mingled with their tenantry, and for the time were farmers like them, encouraging them by their presence and improving them by example. He concluded by expressing a hope that all would cordially unite in forwarding the interests of the projected society, which he hoped would be shortly placed on a permanent footing, and in such position as to be capable of doing much good.*

The following noblemen and gentlemen put down their names as subscribers to the Society:

Wm Hugh Barton Esq	M. Jones Esq
John Creighton Esq	W. C. Jones Esq
Enniskillen	Col R. L. Dickson
Lord Belmore	Henry Gresson Esq
Lord Cole	E. M. Archdale Esq

Hon A. H. Cole	Wm. Hassard Esq
George Lendrum Esq	John Collum Esq
Mervyn Archdall Esq MP	Rev J. G. Porter
Edward Archdall Esq	James Daniel Esq
Colonel Hugh Montgomery	James Lendrum Esq
Rev John Richardson	S. Armstrong Esq
Henry M. Richardson Esq	Wm. D'Arcy Esq
John Deering Esq	Rev Hugh Hamilton
William W. Deering Esq	Rev Butler Brooke
Sir A. B. Brooke	Robert Haire Esq

The committee of the Fermanagh Farming Society met on 13th October 1836 and agreed that members of the Society would be those who subscribed not less than £1 5s 0d. Any person wishing to become a subscriber must be recommended by two subscribers at a general meeting. The county was to be divided into three districts where a branch or branches may be formed. The districts were as follows: Number 1 - Magherstephanny, Coole and Clankelly; Number 2 - Lurg and Tirkennedy together with part of Magheraboy on the east side of the lake and the contiguous parts of Tyrone and Donegal. The third district was Knockninny, Clanawley and that part of Magheraboy on the west side of the lake. The subscribers to the general Society, who shall possess property in each district, shall form the committee of that district.

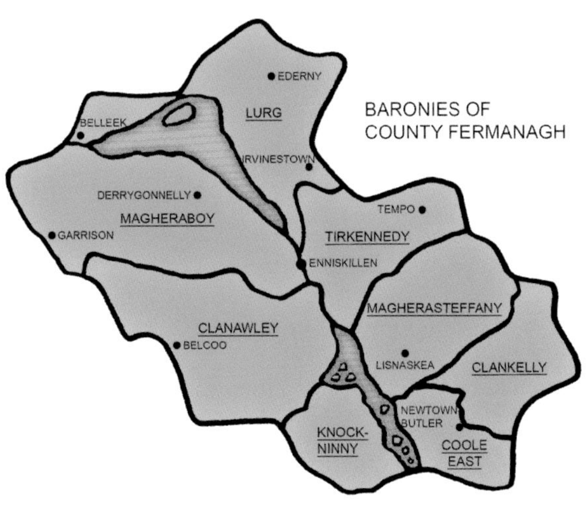

The following were requested to call a meeting of Number 1 district to collect subscriptions and carry the objects of the society into effect:

Sir Arthur Brooke	Robert Graham Esq
John Creighton Esq	Rev John Richardson
Colonel Montgomery	John Hamilton Esq
George Brooke Esq	John Armstrong Esq
Rev Grey Porter	

The members allocated to Number 2 district were:

Rev Grey Porter	William Daniel Esq
William D'Arcy Esq	Colonel Barton
Henry Richardson Esq	Edward Barton Esq
Rev John Richardson	Rev Edward Stack
Rev William West	Charles Archdall Esq
Edward Archdall Esq	William W. Deering Esq
Rev Arthur Irvine	Simon Armstrong Esq

The following had responsibility for Number 3 district:

Lord Cole	Michael Jones Esq
John Creighton Esq	William Jones Esq
Rev Loftus Read	Alexander Hassard Esq
Rev Hugh Hamilton	Rev John James Fox
Thomas Nixon Esq	John Deering Esq
William Hassard Esq	Montgomery Armstrong Esq
Edward Archdall Esq	William Hall
Rev Thomas Ovenden	John Brien Esq
Henry Richardson Esq	Charles Fausset Esq

The principal object of the Society was the encouragement of industry and an improved system of farming amongst the tenantry of the county. It was resolved that all money premiums (prizes) would be given only to farmers making the principal part of their income from farming purposes alone. Honorary premiums were *to be adjudged to members of a higher class.* Subscribers only were allowed to compete. Two events were to be held each year at Enniskillen – a ploughing match at the spring meeting and a general show of cattle at the autumn meeting. George Wood Esq was appointed secretary.

The Early Years

The Fermanagh Farming Society's first show of livestock was held in Enniskillen on Friday 9th September 1837 in *the new market yard*. Eight of the 26 classes were for horses. Ten classes were for cattle and four for sheep and four for pigs. The gentry of the county were very prominent among the prize winners. The report of the show in *The Impartial Reporter* stated that *the arrangements for the exhibition under the superintendence of G. Wood Esq can not be spoken of in too honourable terms. They were most admirable in every particular.* Dinner was provided on show day at 5.30pm for members of the Society. With reference to the dinner the report stated that *a number of the gentry and respectable farmers sat down to an excellent dinner in the White Hart, Edward Archdall in the chair; when the evening, as well as the early part of the day, passed over in greatest harmony, and many very useful suggestions were given for the further improvement and well-being of the Society.*

District shows were an established feature in 1838. The Lurg District meeting was held in Irvinestown on 6th September. A prize was offered for the best crop of *artificial grass* but on this occasion there were no competitors. There were classes for cattle and pigs. Edward Archdall Esq was the presiding officer at the dinner following the show at which 60 sat down to an excellent meal in the market house. One of the speakers, Henry Richardson Esq, commented on the tardy progress of improvement in this country compared to Scotland where he said the land was inferior, the climate not so good, and the rents in most cases higher, and yet the farmers lived in much greater comfort. The Fermanagh Farming Society show in Enniskillen was held on the 19th September 1838 with the usual range of stock and separate classes for landlords and farmers.

Financial problems appeared as an issue at the general meeting of the Society in Enniskillen on Thursday 24th October 1838. The chairman, John Irvine of Rockfield, was requested to write to defaulting subscribers to pay their arrears immediately. Each district was asked to raise £30 in an effort to overcome the arrears amounting to £109:15:0. The spring ploughing match was arranged for March. A £3 prize was to be offered at the next show for the best laid out and fenced farm with farmhouse best arranged as to suitable offices, garden, hay and stack yard, and dung heap. A premium or prize was to be given to a farming servant of a subscriber who shall produce to the judges *the best character for honesty, sobriety and length of service.* The 1840 show in Enniskillen was held on Tuesday 29th September whereas the Knockninny district held its event on Wednesday 2nd September and the Lurg district show was on 17th September. The Tirkennedy branch had its show in Lisbellaw on 28th September.

In 1842 the Fermanagh Farming Society's spring ploughing match was held on 22nd February with 14 ploughs in the field. The classes involved the ploughing of half a rood (statute measure) within two hours *in the best manner with a pair of horses, mules, bulls, or oxen in reins.*

Progress

The Fermanagh Farming Society general show of stock was held in the Corn Market, Enniskillen, on 26th September 1843 and on 24th September in the following year. There were medal classes for which prize money funded by the Royal Agricultural Society of Ireland, ranging from £2

The 1837 Show was held in Enniskillen's new market yard (centre foreground) (Courtesy of National Library of Ireland).

Florencecourt clay drainage pipe dated 1857.

10s 0d to £1, was also given. As well as livestock there was a prize for the best firkin of butter. The classes were open to General Members of any branch of the Society. At the presentation of awards in December the judges made complimentary remarks. They said that the state of agriculture among the nobility and gentry was of the most improved kind and that the class of farmers inspected shows clearly the progress produced and benefits conferred by the Society. They also referred to the liberality of the Royal Agricultural Society in the sponsoring of premiums or prizes. The judges commented on the yields of crops inspected. The turnip class was won by George Lendrum Esq of Jamestown. The judges referred particularly to the drainage work being carried out. They stated that The Earl of Erne had drained 21 statute acres since 1st November 1842 using tiles manufactured at Crom. They viewed the introduction of clay tiles as a matter of great importance as stones were not always readily available for the purpose.

They also said that Henry M. Richardson Esq of Rossfad had drained 10 acres using stones and Folliot W. Barton Esq of Clonelly had drained 38 acres with stones and as a consequence he was awarded the Royal Agricultural Society's medal.

The Lisnaskea Shows

The Crichton (family name spelling changed from Creighton) Annual Farming Meeting was held on 7th September 1838 in Lisnaskea. Prizes were presented for the spring ploughing match. One special prize presented on the day was given to Charles McManus. His prize was the tenancy of a ten acre farm as a reward for *his successful industry in having kept upon three acres of land two cows and one heifer through the means of green crops.* A special event of that day in Lisnaskea was the presentation of *a splendid piece of plate* to Mr Crichton. *The Impartial Reporter's* description of the scene prior to the presentation gave a good impression of the esteem in which Mr Crichton was held by the tenantry. It read: *and so great was the anxiety to witness this matchless tribute of esteem and gratitude, that for some hours, all approaches to it, were most difficult. It was not so much its extreme elegance, its classic proportions, or its superb richness that charmed and riveted their attention, as the moral lustre of so noble an offering.*

Prizes were also presented at the show held on 25th August 1840 for the spring ploughing match. One prize was a beautiful little plough with iron mould board made by *that clever farming implement maker, McCabe of Lisnaskea, upon which was a label 'A reward for an industrious man'. The industrious man is named Somerville from Lisbellaw, who, with two well fed asses and a bad plough made very good work at the ploughing match and though no tenant, or otherwise entitled to the reward, Mr Crichton generously, and with the most amiable feeling now presented Somerville with this plough.*

Agricultural advisers

The Crichton ploughing match in early March 1842 was significant in that Colonel Crichton addressed the gathering of farmers at the prize giving. In his address he referred to his agricultural advisers, Messrs Andrew Mair and William Milne, whom he had brought over from Scotland to advise tenants on good farming practice. The Colonel's address was as follows: "*I am glad to hear from the agriculturists that you are really bestirring yourselves; and that in one district where the land is wettest there are miles of drains made this year. This is what I call going to work like men; and, I do think I read in many of your countenances that, for the future you will follow my advice. We have seen that you have benefited others by setting them a good example where they have been wise enough to profit by it: you must bear in mind that I have taken from you almost every excuse for not becoming good farmers by providing you with an agriculturist to instruct you – good seeds to stock your land with, and an agricultural library where you can always borrow books that will inform you of all that has been done, and is still doing by the intelligent and practical farmers of this and other countries. I have laid out lime kilns on different parts of the estate for your use: and here I am, your landlord, ready and willing, and happy to assist and further the interests of the industrious in every way in my power.*"

Lisnaskea's big event

September 1842 witnessed a big event for the Lisnaskea Farming Show. The Earl of Erne, standing on the steps before the Temperance Coffee Hotel, received the address from the tenantry, read by George Shegog Esq, on his accession to the Earldom of Erne (he succeeded his uncle as the Third Earl). The meeting was not only important because of the celebrations in relation to the landlord's elevation but also due to cash premiums being competed for which were offered by the Royal Agricultural Society. In addition, the Crichton estate premiums, or prizes, were in the form of farm implements. After the Earl had encouraged those present to drain their land, gather manure, improve the breeds of cattle and grow green crops, a Clydesdale stallion, four fine bulls of the Durham, Devon and Ayrshire breeds, and newly imported Scotch pigs were then paraded for the inspection of the tenantry. His Lordship informed his tenants that the animals were procured for their use.

John, Third Earl of Erne (Courtesy of The Earl of Erne).

In September 1844 Lord Erne again took the opportunity of addressing his tenants at the Lisnaskea Show when presenting the awards. He stressed the need for work stating: "*Be assured that industry is the poor man's riches, and without industry no man can prosper – it is the little ingredient that is so much wanted in the Irish character.*" Lord Erne then went on to state that the purpose of establishing the premiums was to improve agriculture. He said that after examining the successful farming systems in Scotland he had decided that green crops and rotations were best suited to his small farmers. Though Lord Erne had been using this system on his estate for eight years he had found difficulty in getting his tenants to adopt it.

References:

Files of *The Impartial Reporter* and *Fermanagh Herald* held in Enniskillen Library.

Livingstone, Peadar, *The Fermanagh Story,* Watergate Press, Enniskillen (1977).

Chapter 2
The Fermanagh Farming Societies after the Famine and Ireland-wide developments

The Famine brought home to those with responsibility the need to improve the standard of livestock and crop husbandry and general management on small farms. Landlords had a particular responsibility and many initiatives were taken in County Fermanagh. The value of demonstrations and agricultural shows was fully appreciated. In addition, the help that advisers and instructors could give tenant farmers was being realised. Lord Erne of Crom Castle was a leader in this field and practices employed by him would come to be adopted throughout Ireland at the end of the century.

The 1847 Lisnaskea show and Lord Erne's criticism of some landlords

The report in October 1847 of the Lord Erne's Show at Lisnaskea highlighted the quality of stock and produce. It stated that there were cattle that could not be surpassed by any others in the Province. The specimens of green crops were of the most admirable description. Some of the 'Red Norfolk' turnips grown at Crom Castle weighed 20lb. Some of the potatoes of the 'lumper' kind grown by Thomas Creighton weighed 1lb 9oz each. Payment of rents resulting from the effects of the famine was obviously an issue as Lord Erne, in his address, dwelt at some length on the topic. After encouraging them to adopt his agricultural system he said with reference to the landlord's role: "*Is it not better for him thus to encourage them to exertion – to teach them what to do, and deal leniently with them, than go and reside in England or the Continent and leave them*

Crom Castle
(Courtesy of The Earl of Erne).

and their interests to the tender mercies of the bailiffs. By the former course he is rendering the tenants able to pay him – and he will have it – but those who pursue the latter one, injure themselves as well as their tenants. A persecuted tenantry can never be satisfactory in their payments. When they are not allowed to defer disposing of their crops until they could do so advantageously, but are prosecuted and put to expense when they chance to run a little in arrears, it is impossible that they can remain solvent. When a man owes some arrears which have accumulated upon him through the means of some calamity or unforeseen circumstance, could anything be more unfeeling than to institute proceedings against him for those arrears, without allowing him time to retrieve the loss which he had sustained. For instance, what could be more heartless in a landlord than to involve his tenant in law expenses this year in trying to enforce on sight the payment of those arrears into which the famine of last year had inevitably forced him! If there be any guilty of this inhuman conduct, it would be well for them to abandon it even at the eleventh hour. They would there be serving themselves as well as their tenants, and they would be depriving the 'Times' and those other English journals that write against the Irish landlords in the aggregate, of their most powerful arguments." In conclusion Lord Erne said: "*I would beg of you to ponder seriously on what I have told you and if you wish to reside in your native land and not be going to America, where there is misery enough without you, you will attend to my advice and that of my agriculturists. As for my own part I shall always be willing and anxious to forward your interests in every possible way.*"

New beginnings

By 1861 the Fermanagh Farming Society had ceased to exist. However, the value of such an organisation had not been forgotten. *The Impartial Reporter* of 3rd October 1861 drew attention to a show that was to be held in Lisbellaw the following day. The report read as follows: *Our local readers will scarcely need to be reminded that on to-morrow there will be an effort made, in Lisbellaw to establish a County Fermanagh Agricultural and Cattle Show. If the effort prove to be successful, it will be the accomplishment of a very desirable development. It is too bad that Fermanagh should be without a county farming society. By whose fault it was that the old society was allowed to pass out of existence we are not prepared to say; but if the effort to revive it prove a failure through the fault of any one or more, that person or persons will have a good deal to answer for to the county. The present show and the project with which it is connected we owe to Mr Porter; we trust they will be successful – that the show of tomorrow will be a good one – and that a county society, which is much needed, will be established on a permanent basis. Such a society would, we presume have two competitions in the year, one a ploughing-match, and the other such a show as Mr Porter has now started. We understand that there is a good deal of interest felt in this competition, and we hope it will prove generally satisfactory.*

In the following week's newspaper there was a full report on the Lisbellaw Show. It read as follows: *On Friday last, the first show of the resuscitated Fermanagh Farming Society was held in a field at Lisbellaw.* Despite the poor weather on the day the reporter was full of praise for the event and attendance stating: *there was a good show, and the things exhibited – livestock, and farm and dairy produce, were prime – fine milch cows, good promising heifers, cabbages like turf kishes, monster turnips, mangels, carrots etc etc, and butter of most tempting appearance. The visitors in spite of the weather, were numerous, and the show was held, by all we heard speak on the subject, to be a decided success.* Like previous Farming Society shows there was a dinner following the event. The press report stated: *Mr Black of the hotel in Lisbellaw, furnished for half a-crown a dinner equal to any we have seen for half-a-guinea, with plenty of punch for all who chose to drink it; Mr Porter gave an ample supply of venison and wine; the Messrs Forde of Lisbellaw, were at much trouble, and we presume, not without expense, in assisting at the getting up and carrying out of all connected with the show.* Another feature in the paper extolling the virtues of the show stated: *it was a shame that Fermanagh was so long without a county farming society. For years past there has been no farming society at all in this county.*

Success from 1870

By 1870 farming societies in Fermanagh were thriving again holding autumn shows. Lisnaskea Farming Society held its event that year on Wednesday 21st September. As well as classes for the various types of livestock there were those for an assortment of woollen and linen articles of clothing. Prizes were also offered for the neatest and best kept farms, for butter and for servants of good conduct and long service. Magheraboy Farming Society held its first show in October 1870. That event was in connection with the estates of The Marquis of Ely and Hugh De Fellenburg Montgomery Esq and was held in a field belonging to Mr A. Johnston near Churchill. The livestock and farm classes were similar to those at Lisnaskea. The livestock show was followed by athletic events. In 1880, Lisbellaw had a flower, vegetable and poultry show. The Fermanagh Farming Society held its show in the market yard in Enniskillen on Friday 27th August. All livestock classes were in two categories – Gentlemen's Class and Farmers' Class. There was also a class for the best kept farms taking into consideration the farm buildings, freedom from weeds, fences, stock of manure, turnips especially, clover, vetches and ryegrass. The Honorary Secretary was Henry Mervyn Richardson.

Lord Erne's advice regarding the Vaughan Charity's estate

The success of the two Scottish agricultural advisers employed by Lord Erne as early as 1842 was a continuing feature on the Crom Estate and with his tenant farmers. These men obviously made quite an impact as the Earl was keen that a similar strategy should be employed on the Vaughan Charity estate at Tubrid, Kesh. He submitted a plan to the Board of Governors at Tubrid in 1868, a plan similar to that which he had recently employed on his own estate. In December he had the tenants assembled in the school at Tubrid and lectured to them on improving their farms and houses.

Vaughan Charter School.

He also gave each of them a pamphlet on agriculture and gave printed tickets to the Land Steward to be filled up by him when he visited each tenant. The following October he re-assembled the tenants, and, having read their tickets, divided them into two classes and gave three premiums in each, amounting in total to £10. He stated: "*I feel quite confident that if the Board will give to Mr Maude and myself the power of carrying out this system, the whole appearance of the estate will soon be changed ... I need hardly say that I think it is our duty to nurture the tenantry of Tubrid estate as well as the boys in the school. I am therefore about to ask them to give five per cent of the rental to Mr Semple, Mr Maude and myself, as a commission to lay out on the estate for three purposes: in providing premiums for the best kept farms, to assist in slating houses, installing windows and doors, creating farm roads and improving farm offices and dwellings.*" The following year the Land Steward reported that the Earl of Erne's plan with respect to premiums had been carried out to good effect.

Lord Clarendon's advisory service for farmers following the Famine

The failure of the potato crop was widespread throughout Ireland in the years 1845 to 1847 but was particularly so in the south and west. As a consequence, a system for agricultural advisory work among small farmers was created. At its peak, over 30 agriculturists were engaged to instruct, advise and assist the small farmers, mainly in the south and west of Ireland to improve their apparently hopeless situation. This was claimed to be the first agricultural advisory service in Ireland. This scheme was reputed to be the brain-child of Lord Clarendon who had been appointed as the Lord Lieutenant of Ireland in 1847. However, as already outlined, John Crichton Esq (later Lord Erne) of Crom Castle in County Fermanagh had an advisory service for his tenants as early as 1842. Perhaps Lord Clarendon got his idea from County Fermanagh.

Lord Clarendon.

Clarendon's scheme was to use the Royal Agricultural Society in Dublin (established in 1731) and its links with local societies as the main structure for bringing some agricultural instruction to small farmers in the south and west. He proposed that the Society should appoint a small number of travelling lecturers who were later known as *'itinerant agricultural instructors'*. During 1847 these instructors were to visit small farmers and give them sound practical instruction. With regard to the methods used by the instructors, Lord Clarendon said that their advice should be "*couched in clear but simple language, and might, in some cases, be usefully illustrated by practical demonstration.*" Their main topics at lectures and demonstrations were to be drainage and subsoiling, rotations and the adoption of green crops, and the economy of using manure allied to the house feeding of livestock. Ten instructors were appointed initially. On January 1st 1848 Lord Clarendon wrote as follows: *The experiment has answered far beyond what could have been expected, for the Priests support it, and the Farmers are grateful for it ... I believe that this agricultural instruction is a step taken in the right direction, and I should grieve that it were abandoned, or not extended for want of funds ... Such instruction is quite within the pale of legitimate interference and if I could send forth 500 instructors instead of ten I would do so for I now see that it would answer, and I believe that before next summer we might change the whole face of the country, and to a great extent the habits of the people.*

Establishment of Department of Agriculture and Technical Instruction

The success of these early initiatives led the Government in Dublin to consider how agriculture could be improved throughout the island of Ireland. This led to the appointment of the 'Recess Committee' in spring 1896. The members of that committee recommended in their report, produced in August 1896, that a Ministry of Agriculture and Industries should be established. The recommendations were accepted and the Ministry of Agriculture and Technical Instruction was operational in 1899. The Hon Horace Plunkett, the third son of Lord Dunsany, Dunsany Castle, County Meath, who had established the co-operative movement in Ireland, was appointed executive head of the new Department with the title of Vice-President.

Under the Act, County Committees of Agriculture were appointed and were financed by the Department with some contribution from the county councils. One of the recommendations from the 'Recess Report' was that the new department should appoint travelling instructors to advise farmers on improving their farming activities.

References:

Files of *The Impartial Reporter* held in Enniskillen Library.

Jackson, Claire and Michael, *A History of the Vaughan Charity.* William Trimble, Enniskillen (1985).

Jones, Gwyn E., *The original agricultural advisory service: Lord Clarendon's practical instructors in mid-nineteenth century Ireland.* A paper presented at The Fourth International Seminar on Extension Education held in Ireland in August/September 1979. Agriculture Extension and Rural Development Centre, University of Reading.

Daly, Mary E., *The First Department – A History of the Department of Agriculture.* Institute of Public Administration, Dublin (2002).

Chapter 3
The County Committee of Agriculture

The passing of the Act in the Dublin Parliament, which established the Department of Agriculture and Technical Instruction in 1899, could be considered as the foundation on which agricultural development was based throughout the greater part of the twentieth century. This Act valued the importance of education and training and of sound scientifically based advice in the development of the Irish farming industry. The organisations through which these services would be provided to the farming community were the County Committees of Agriculture. Each county was to have an agricultural committee employing agricultural, poultry and horticultural instructors. Horace Plunkett, the vice president of the Department of Agriculture and Technical Instruction, when referring to the role of the instructor described him as "the guide, philosopher and friend of farmers".

COUNTY OF FERMANAGH.

REPORT

County Committee of Agriculture

AND

Joint Committee

of Technical Instruction

FOR

THE YEAR 1906.

First Report.

Fermanagh County Committee of Agriculture

Fermanagh County Council met in the Court House, Enniskillen, on the 4th January 1901, and as required under the Agriculture and Technical Instruction Act of 1899, appointed a County Committee of Agriculture. The new Committee was required to operate in the county *A Scheme for improvement of cattle and horse breeding and proposed agricultural experiments.* The experiments were to be carried out on oats, turnips, mangolds, potatoes and flax. Livestock improvement was to be achieved through the payment of premiums for high-class sires – stallions, bulls and rams. The breeds of cattle were to be Shorthorn, Red Poll, Aberdeen Angus and Hereford. To finance the scheme £400 was to be provided from rates and an equal sum from the Department of Agriculture.

Sir Douglas Brooke of Colebrooke, Chairman of the County Committee of Agriculture 1901 (Courtesy of Viscount Brookeborough).

First Report

The first report of this Committee was produced for the year 1906. Commenting on the publication *The Impartial Reporter* stated: *This report bears splendid testimony to the work of the county committees and instructors, and tell of an advance in the methods of working of which could obtain no such proof elsewhere.*

The report pointed out that a Committee was appointed by Fermanagh County Council in 1901. The Committee was unable to procure an Agricultural Instructor until November 1905, when William Smyth was appointed, and as a consequence annual reports were not issued owing to the absence of results of experiments and demonstrations which were regarded as an important part of the work. The Chairman of the twenty-eight member committee was Sir Douglas Brooke of Colebrooke.

Other members were: The Earl of Erne KP, HML; Viscount Corry; Jeremiah Jordan JP, MP; E. M. Archdale DL, Riversdale, Ballinamallard; Rev John Hall, Garvary; Patrick Crumley JP, Enniskillen; Hon Cecil Corry, Castlecoole; Edward Mitchell, Derryvullan, Enniskillen; Thomas W. West, Mullyduff, Newtownbutler; Edward Archdale DL, Castle Archdale, Irvinestown; John McHugh, Pettigo; John Lendrum JP, Cleen, Fivemiletown; James McManus, Rathkeelan, Maguiresbridge; William Teele, Dunbar; John Smyth, Mullaghbrady, Rosslea; John B. Frith JP, The Cross, Enniskillen; James O'Donnell, Brookeborough; James Hall, Drumclay; Felix P. Smyth JP, Johnstown, Clones; James W. Johnston JP, Newtownbutler; Rev James E. McKenna CC, Enniskillen; R. W. Strathearn JP, Killesher, Florencecourt; Frank Coulson, Drummully, Clones; Joseph Ball, Drumcullion, Ballinamallard; Joseph Beatty, Lisbellaw; Thomas Morrow, Donagh, Lisnaskea and Patrick Blake, Derrylin.

Mr W. H. West was appointed as Secretary to the Committee in 1901. A Poultry Instructor was appointed in 1902 and an Instructor in Horticulture in 1904.

Mr W. H. West
(Courtesy of Mr and Mrs J. West).

In 1906, the total spent by the County Committee on agricultural development was £1,884. The salaries of the instructors, their expenses, and cost of running the experiments were as follows: agriculture - £350, poultry - £207, and horticulture and bee keeping - £261. Awards for farm competitions amounted to £72. Livestock improvement was an important element of the Committee's work and the premiums and awards were allocated for the breeding improvement of horses, cattle and pigs. The allocation for nominations to mares was £140, twenty-nine premiums to bulls were worth £390, and seven premiums to boars amounted to £35. Flax was an important crop and prize money in respect of competitions was £25. Agricultural shows were subsidised to the value of £150 and home industries and skilled labour received £30 in support.

Agricultural experiments in 1906

A wide range of experiments and demonstrations was carried out by William Smyth, the Agricultural Instructor. These included the fertilising of meadow hay, where it was shown that a balanced mixture of nitrate of soda, superphosphate and kainit (potash) gave a significant increase in yield and that the value of the extra hay was considerably more than the cost of the fertiliser. The demonstration plots were on a number of farms including those of James Keenan, Drumbargy, Bellanaleck; James Spence, Clonelly; Bernard Gallagher, Meenmore; John Rusk, Brookeborough; John Eaves, Kesh; R. Rusk, Cavanaleck; William Spence, Moyglass; Andrew Moore, Breagho; John Moore, Moorelough; Joseph Johnston, Killyfole; P. Mulligan; Rathkeeland; Crozier W. Phair, Feddans; B. Martin, Manor Highgate; James Crozier, Dring House; and William Baxter, Tatnaboda. Another experiment involved the fertilising of pasture using potassic superphosphate applied at the rate of six cwt per acre. The farms used were those of Charles Keown, Portinode, Kesh; John Armstrong, Clonearm; James McDonnell, Tedd, Irvinestown; Robert Somerville, Corlough and Hubert Reid, Brookeborough. Potatoes, mangolds and turnips, which were important root crops grown at that time, were the subject of fertiliser and related trials carried out on the farms of Patrick Mulligan, Rathkeeland; John Johnston, Goblusk, C. Erskine, Brookeborough, F. Howe, Tubrid; Joseph Johnston, Killyfole; James McElroy, Knockmacmanus; William Baxter, Cooneen; William Nixon, Waternerry; B. T. Kerr, Tattenamona; William Hunter, Ballyreagh; Edward Scollan, Boa Island; R. Scott, Lisbellaw; A. Savage, Lisboy; William Lyttle, Ballyreagh; Henry Keys, Drumbulkin; William Johnston, Bosallagh; George Knight, Donagh,; Joseph Knox, Shanmullagh; R. Maxwell, Ballyreagh; R. Clarke, Cortrasna; Thomas Cox, Largy and R. Lyttle and James McBrien, Oakfield. The varieties of potatoes grown in the experiments included:

Old Champion, Up-to-Date, Bruce and *Northern Star.* With regard to spraying of the potato crop to prevent blight, Mr Smyth advised that in an area where potatoes were grown in drills it would be a good idea for a few farmers to join together and buy a 'horse spraying machine'.

Management

In summarising his report for the year, Mr William Smyth stated: *If a farmer desires to get as much profit as possible from the money expended on manures he should attend as well to the other conditions which are favourable to the growth of the crop. It is possible to have the land well supplied with every manurial ingredient in the best form and yet the crop may be unsatisfactory. Manure can only fulfil its own function, which is to supply food to the growing plant. If the land is badly tilled or in need of drainage or lime, or if bad seed is used, and the farmer imagines he can remedy these deficiencies by the purchase of a few bags of artificial manure he will find himself mistaken. It is only by attention to all the above points that the best results will accrue.*

Scheme of prizes for Cottages and Small Farms 1906

The County Committee organised a competition for cottages and small farms. The judge for this competition was James Bradshaw. The Cottage Section was judged on the basis of cleanliness and general order of the cottage and premises, cultivation of garden, variety of vegetables, fruit and flowers, arrangements of manure heap, bees (seldom kept), general management and care of livestock, and general.

The Small Farm Section was judged taking into consideration the cleanliness, order and economy in the dwelling houses and offices, judicious character of cropping, efficiency of cultivation, arrangement of manure heaps, and provision for collection of liquid manure, cultivation of garden, varieties of vegetables and fruit trees, general condition of land under grass, care of fences, watercourses, judicious planting of shelter belts etc, freedom from weeds, especially grasslands, stackyards and headlands, cultivation of headlands, management and care of livestock and poultry. In his comments Mr Bradshaw stated that points requiring attention were neatness etc in dwelling houses,

Cottage belonging to Mrs Helen Finlay, Toneywall, Derrylin, typical of many in the early to mid 20th century.

inside of byres, fowl houses and pig stys, care of manure heap, greater use of permanent grasses and keeping of accounts. He emphasised that very little attention is paid to the keeping of accounts. In connection with the handling of manure, he noted that in far too many cases the rain water from nearly all buildings is allowed to run down into the heap or alongside it. This should be remedied at once by the use of spouting along the eaves of the buildings.

Poultry Scheme

During the period 18th November 1905 to 16th March 1906, the Poultry Instructor, Mr J. E. Ferris, delivered 59 lectures with an average attendance at each of 45. He also made 292 advisory visits to farmers and others interested in poultry keeping. In addition, he visited each of the egg and turkey stations five times. He stated that 1,393 settings of eggs had been distributed from the egg stations. He gave credit to the Co-operative Egg Societies for raising the price of eggs in the localities in which they exist. The breeds of poultry kept by the egg distributing stations were: *Black Minorcas, White Leghorns, Buff Orpingtons, Brown Leghorns,* and *White Wyandottes. Indian Runner* ducks were kept on six of the 14 stations.

Buff Orpington pullets.

Premium bulls and Premium boars

The County Committee operated Premium Bull and Boar Schemes. These animals were located on farms throughout the County to which farmers could bring their female stock for mating. Those who had Premium Boars were: William Wilson, Ashfield; William Wilson, Depot, Enniskillen; William R. Thompson, Keeran, Irvinestown; Thomas Bussell, Toolin, Maguiresbridge; John W. Swindells, Mullaghsillogagh; Sir Douglas Brooke, Colebrooke; Samuel Coulson, Bellmount, Magheraveely and John Deering, Cloghan, Derrylin.

Those who kept Premium Bulls were: William Garvin, Corry; William J. Maye, Gorteen; James West, Scotsborough; Earl of Erne, Crom Castle; Robert Egerton, Deerpark; Thomas W. West, Mullyduff; Rowland Hurst, Tullyraine; Andrew O'Dolan, Rushin; Patrick McCauley, Derrylin; William Wilson, Ashfield; John Graham, Tamlaght; E. M. Archdale, Riversdale; Joseph Ball, Drumcullion; Crozier W. Phair, Feddans; John Sheridan, Sallysgrove; Noble Johnston, Monea; Rev John Hall, Garvary; Folliott W. Barton, Clonelly; David I. Johnston, Doraville; William Armstrong, Ballindullagh; Hugh J. Stewart, Edenbane; William Morrison, Coolane; William Bryans, Moorelough; John A. Beatty, Killykeeran; Montgomery Moore, Curraghmore; and Sir Douglas Brooke, Colebrooke. All bulls kept were of the Shorthorn breed apart from five, which were Polled Angus.

Horse Breeding Scheme

The names of the registered stallions in Fermanagh were *Ben Gartley, Colonial, Coylton, Goschen, Height O'Fashion, Sir Keith,* and *Spook.* There were 54 services of nominated mares. *Colonial* was the most popular stallion having served 31 nominated mares.

STALLIONS FOR 1908.

THOROUGH-BRED STALLION. 'Ravenscroft.' Registered under Department of Agriculture. Sire of winner Champion Cup, Sligo, 1907 (one of his first produce).

CLYDESDALE STALLION 'Height o' Fashion.' Registered under Department of Agriculture. Sire of best foal at Enniskillen, '04, '06 and '07, also of 1st and 2nd in three year olds, two year olds, and foals in '07.

HACKNEY STALLION. 'Terrington Conjuror' by Lord Drewton 2nd, first London, in '99, dam 9075 Lady Crompton, winner of over nine firsts at leading English shows.

For particulars apply
E. M. ARCHDALE,
Riversdale, Ballinamallard.
9451

Advertisement in local press for stallions in 1908.

Flax Scheme

The Committee held a show of scutched flax in Lisnaskea (practically the only flax-growing district in the county at that time). Prizes were offered for the best flax, and to the scutchers and employees who turned out the prize lots.

Growing flax crop.

The show was held on 30th January 1907. In the class for farmers with a valuation of under £15 the prize winners were; 1st William Irvine, Drumgoon; 2nd Robert Graham, Drumgowna; 3rd Thomas McGinnity, Derrymea.

In the class for farmers with valuations between £15 and £50 the prizewinners were: 1st William Kerr, Corfannon; 2nd Joseph Watson, Toolin; 3rd Mrs Gillece, Kilturk. In the over £50 valuation category Thomas Morrow of Donagh was the winner with the Representatives of John Martin, Cornashannel, coming second and William Bryans, Moorlough, third. The scutchers' prizes in class A were won by: 1st and 2nd Tully Mills (proprietor J. Morrison); 3rd prize Boyhill Mills (proprietor, George Hazlett). In class B the 1st and 2nd prizewinners were as in class A with Donagh Mills (proprietress, Mrs Knight) coming third. In class C the order was 1st Donagh Mills; 2nd Boyhill Mills and 3rd Donagh Mills.

Horticulture and Bee Keeping

The instructor in horticulture and bee keeping was Mr Peter Brock who said that from 1st November 1904 he had visited all districts in County Fermanagh, giving lectures on farms, gardens, orchards and apiaries. He reported that the main horticultural activity in the past was the growing of apples where soil conditions were suitable. He added that in the majority of cases the trees were worn out, moss and lichen laden and in unprofitable condition and that the general standard of husbandry was poor.

Orchards

The planting of new orchards under his direction started during the winter of 1904-5 in the Brookeborough and Crieve Hill districts where nearly 800 apple trees were planted. The largest orchards of around one acre were planted with Bramley Seedlings. He said that the method of establishing profitable orchards on tillage land, while being intercropped and worked between the trees with horse labour, was being well exemplified by Mr R. Noble, Lisboy; Mr H. Greene, Cleffany, and Mr J. Montgomery, Tullykeneye. Mr Brock had also considerable success in encouraging farmers to grow other classes of fruit including pears, plums, gooseberries, blackcurrants, raspberries and strawberries and all sorts of vegetables. He also had a number of demonstration gardens and encouraged tree planting. He referred to the planting of London Plane trees in Brookeborough and stated that this was a 'standing testimony' to the good taste of Sir Douglas Brooke. Mr Brock promoted the planting of shelter belts and recommended the Austrian Pine as one of the best shelter trees ever introduced. Another tree recommended for this purpose was *Giant Arborvitae.* He referred to the large belt of 14,000 larch and 2,400 Scotch Fir planted by Mr Nixon, Belcoo, at Gardenvale.

During the 1905-6 season 2303 apple trees, 24 pear trees, 56 plum trees, 390 gooseberry, 66 blackcurrant and 250 raspberry bushes were planted. Mr Brock referred to success in the Rosslea area where, under the influence of the Rev P. K. Lynch CC, 600 apple trees had been distributed among residents by Mr P. Murray, Principal, Cordoole National

School. Similar enthusiasm for fruit growing had been started among the farmers around Killadeas encouraged by the Rev J. R. Gumley, rector of the local Church of Ireland parish from 1892 until 1911.

In his report, Mr Brock stated that Fermanagh had been notable for the number of people who kept bees in straw skeps. However, due to lack of knowledge many lost their bees through starvation during the adverse seasons of 1902-3-4. The summer of 1905 proved to be one of the best seasons that beekeepers had experienced in many years. He had visited 113 beekeepers during 1905 and 76 of these kept bees in bar-frame hives. In 1906 he visited 178 persons who kept bees in bar-frame hives, possessing altogether 473 stocked hives.

County Fermanagh Technical Instruction Scheme

This Scheme was administered by a separate committee from that of the County Committee of Agriculture. It was made up of members from Enniskillen Urban Council and Fermanagh County Council. The objectives of this Scheme were to provide, by means of County and Itinerant Teachers, instruction in lace-making, crochet-work, needle-work, manual work, domestic economy, and hygiene. The sum of £855 was spent on this work in the year ending July 1906. The instructors were Alexander McKibbin (Manual Instruction) and Louisa S. Gaine (Domestic Economy Instructress).

Reference:

Report of the Fermanagh County Committee of Agriculture and Joint Committee of Technical Instruction for the year 1906.

Newly planted orchard at Brownlee's farm, Legmacaffrey, Newtownbutler.

Chapter 4
Agricultural development 1900-1914

The establishment of the Department of Agriculture and Technical Instruction in 1899 gave great encouragement to Irish farmers. The services provided through the County Committees of Agriculture helped farmers with their crop and livestock husbandry and business development. The spread of knowledge through lectures, classes, demonstrations and farm advisory visits by the instructors employed by the County Committees contributed to the efficiency of farm production. Marketing of agricultural produce, so as to obtain the maximum return to the farmer, presented a considerable challenge. In the early years of the century, much effort went into improving the marketing of agricultural produce in an attempt to get better returns for the farmer. Butter and pork were the two commodities that received particular attention in the early part of the century. For an understanding of butter production and marketing during the early years of the twentieth century, it is important to know the background to the development of the many creameries in County Fermanagh.

Horse powered churn preserved on Mr Basil Fawcett's farm at Tully, Churchill.

Mr Basil Fawcett.

Importance of butter

Milk production has always been a significant enterprise on County Fermanagh farms. In the absence of substantial centres of urban population, which would provide a market for liquid milk, the only economic way of getting a financial return from milk in the early days was through the manufacture and sale of butter. For most of the nineteenth century, butter was produced on individual farms and then sold in the butter markets. There were well-established butter markets in the main towns in the county. An area in Enniskillen, where craft shops thrive today, is still known as the Butter Market.

Farm made butter was variable in quality and this was reflected in the wide range of prices received for the product. Furthermore, churning was a labour intensive operation and was carried out usually by the women of the household except on larger farms where the scale of production merited mechanically driven churns, which were powered usually by donkeys or ponies.

Creameries, where milk supplies were brought by farmers for churning into butter, offered the potential of a more consistent quality product which would fetch a higher price in the market place. In addition, it would relieve the women on the farms of a time consuming and demanding chore. It was not until the late nineteenth and early twentieth century that creameries were developed in County Fermanagh.

Church Street and High Street Enniskillen in 1900 (Courtesy of National Library of Ireland).

Scotch Store (Courtesy of National Library of Ireland).

Mr Porter Martin after delivering milk to Monea Creamery (Courtesy of Mr George Elliott).

Butter marketing

During the nineteenth century, butter was exported from Fermanagh to London and Liverpool. Dealers bought the butter in markets in the main towns in the county and exported it to the centres in England. As early as 1843 concern was being expressed about the poor prices being obtained for butter produced in Fermanagh compared to that obtained for Dutch butter in the London market. A feature in *The Impartial Reporter* stated that every year Fermanagh exported butter to the value of £300,000 but was losing £75,000 by not getting the best prices. At the end of the nineteenth century, Irish butter in the English market was attracting significantly lower prices than that imported from Denmark and Sweden because of the difference in quality. The Danish and Swedish butter differed from Irish butter in that most of it was produced under controlled conditions in creameries rather than on farms.

The Scotch Store

The Scottish Co-operative Wholesale Society Ltd (SCWS) established a depot in Enniskillen in 1885. The SCWS supplied retail co-operatives in Great Britain with butter, poultry, eggs and pig meat. It dealt directly with farmers and therefore cut out the numerous dealers and agents who were normally involved in the transactions between the farmer and the retailer and therefore had the potential to give the farmer a better price for his produce. The SCWS store in Enniskillen was involved initially in improving the marketing of butter produced on Fermanagh farms but then moved on to producing butter from its new creamery on the Sligo Road in Enniskillen.

The new creamery, together with its collecting stations at Bellanaleck, Florencecourt, 'S' Bridge (now the Ballyreagh Band Hall) and Gola, was operational in 1898. Four further collecting stations were established by the SCWS during the next decade. These were at Gardiner's Cross, Blacklion, Glenfarne and Monea.

Co-operation potential

The Honourable Horace Plunkett was the leader of the co-operative movement in Ireland which developed at the end of the 1880s. He maintained that the best way to get most return from the market was when producers collaborated to process and market their milk in co-operatives under producers' control.

He established an organisation called the Irish Agricultural Organisation Society Ltd (IAOS) to promote and co-ordinate the co-operative movement. This body had a considerable impact on the development of the milk processing industry in Fermanagh as in other counties in Ireland.

Sir Horace Plunkett in later life.

The first Fermanagh creamery

A meeting in Ballinamallard in March 1897, attended by a representative of the IAOS, led to the establishment of Fermanagh's first co-operative creamery. Mr E. M. Archdale Esq DL of Riversdale was Chairman of the meeting and subsequently President of the Society. Mr W. H. West JP of Mullaghmeen was appointed Secretary. There was good support from the farmers around Ballinamallard. Money was raised, the new creamery was built and butter making started during 1897. The Ballinamallard creamery subsequently built an auxiliary creamery at Coa in 1899 where the milk was skimmed, with the cream being taken to Ballinamallard for churning. The example shown by Ballinamallard encouraged other areas. Co-operative creameries were built at Irvinestown, Derrygonnelly and Springfield and these commenced production in 1898. Springfield had two milk collection centres at Boho and Letterbreen. Kinawley Co-Operative Creamery which opened in 1899 had a collection centre at Macken and received cream from an independent unit at Swanlinbar. In the same year, the Erne Dairy Society opened its creamery in Kesh with a milk collection centre at Pettigo where the milk was skimmed and the cream forwarded to Kesh for churning. The Pettigo collection centre became independent from Kesh in 1907 and became a butter-making unit on its own.

President of Kinawley Co-Operative Society, Mr Henry Breen and family in 1906 (Courtesy of Mr Mackey Breen).

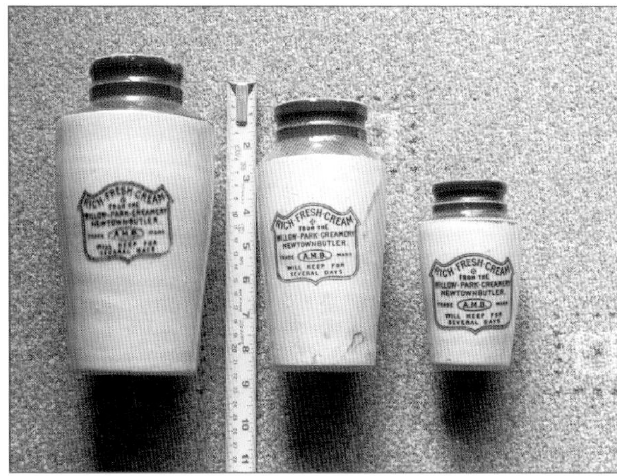

Willow Park Cream jars. (Courtesy of the Very Rev John Hay, Dean of Raphoe).

Development in the South of the County

A privately owned creamery, known as Willow Park Creamery, which was established in Newtownbutler, was in production by 1897 but ceased operating in 1910. This creamery specialised in the production of preserved cream marketed in stone jars.

Lisnaskea Co-Operative Creamery opened during early 1899 and like many other creameries provided a horse drawn milk collection service to encourage suppliers from outlying areas. The price received in Lisnaskea by suppliers in June 1899 was 3¼ d per gallon, with a premium of up to a ½ d per gallon for above-average butterfat.

Brookeborough and Fivemiletown

An auxiliary creamery that separated milk was established at Brookeborough in 1899. The cream was taken to Fivemiletown Co-operative Creamery for butter making. The Brookeborough unit, which had been established under the leadership of Sir Douglas Brooke, amalgamated with Fivemiletown Creamery in 1902 to form the Fivemiletown and Brookeborough Co-Operative Agricultural and Dairy Society Ltd. The Brookeborough unit closed down in 1942 with all milk from the area being transported to Fivemiletown.

Belleek to Rosslea

The year 1899 also witnessed the opening of a creamery at Belleek with two auxiliaries at Garrison and Whealt. Further independent auxiliary creameries were built around that time at Lack, Rosslea, Wheathill and Termon. Rosslea amalgamated with Clones in 1902 and Wheathill joined with Springfield at the same time. In 1904, a new producer co-operative creamery in Lisbellaw was opened in the village and continued in production until 1942.

Mr Patrick Falconer JP, Tawneyreagh, President of Lisbellaw Co-Op (Courtesy of Miss Rosaleen Falconer).

Transport

The large number of creameries, auxiliaries and collection centres was required in the early years in order to provide easy accessibility for producers. When the creameries were built, there was no motorised transport and the milk was brought to the centres by donkey or horse transport.

Producers who lived close to the centres normally transported their own milk. Those slightly further away would co-operate and share the transport responsibilities. Most creameries organised transport with the costs being deducted when payment was being made.

Dairy and Cowsheds Order

Concern was expressed at the Springfield Creamery annual meeting of shareholders in January 1909 regarding the implementation of the Dairies and Cowsheds Order made by the Local Government Board. It applied only to creamery suppliers and not to those who produced butter on the farms. This Order was aimed at improving the hygienic standards of milk production particularly for butter manufacture, which was the main output from the creamery. Congratulations were forthcoming from Mr Clifford, representing the Irish Department of Agriculture, on the nature of Springfield's balance sheet. He said that the price paid for milk was their highest to-date and one of the highest he had ever seen. The prices paid by Springfield in 1907 and 1908 were 4.21d and 4.52d respectively per gallon.

Winter milk production

Mr Clifford then dealt with winter dairying. He said that so long as Irish creameries produced butter only during nine months of the year they would never be able to compete with the Danish farmer and take their proper place at the top of the great British market.

The topic of winter milk production was still very much a live issue in August 1913. The Ulster and Connaught members of the Irish Creamery Managers' Association, meeting in Bundoran under the chairmanship of Mr Timony of Belleek Creamery, passed the following resolution:- *That this Conference is of the opinion that inasmuch as without all-the-year round dairying Ireland can never hope to obtain the position in the British market to which her geographical situation entitles her, it is incumbent on the Department of Agriculture to give more liberal subsidies for experiments in winter dairying, and in the growing of foods on the farm. We are also of the opinion that in order to produce the best results such subsidies should be concentrated on one or two creameries, and should be such as would not fail to induce the suppliers of these creameries to produce as much milk during the winter as in the summer months in order that it could once and for all be placed beyond doubt whether the production of winter milk paid or not.*

Success

The Butter and Margarine Act of 1906 provided for the registration of butter factories and all premises where butter was blended. The Act, among other things, specified the maximum amount of water to be contained in butter. The experience of the co-operative creameries in those

Boho creamery closed in 1941. Kathleen McCaffrey is leading the donkey and cart (Courtesy of Mr George Elliott).

An early photograph of Derrygonnelly Creamery (Courtesy of Mr Basil Fawcett).

early years was very positive. The butter produced in Fermanagh under the creamery system soon established a good reputation. In all-Ireland butter making competitions in 1910, Fermanagh creameries took three of the first five places and in 1912 Derrygonnelly and Springfield creameries took first and second places out of 95 entries from all over Ireland. The price received by farmers for their milk was estimated to be about 25 per cent higher than when the milk was processed into butter in the farm kitchens.

Marketing of Pigs

The price obtained by producers for their pigs was a concern from the early years of the century. In October 1907 a report by Mr W. H. West JP, Secretary of the County Fermanagh Committee of Agriculture, stated: *"I have ascertained the prices at which pork is purchased in our local markets and the wholesale prices charged by bacon curers for the same article, and the margin of profit seems enormous and out of all proportion to the cost of curing"*. He continued: *"Considering the fact that farmers have no protection in the shape of co-operative bacon curing societies, same as they have in other countries, I think this matter should have the attention of the Department of Agriculture"*. In 1912, Mr West raised the issue of the marketing of pigs at a meeting of the Enniskillen District Conference of the Co-Operative Agricultural and Dairy Societies. In his address he stated: *"Under the present conditions the producer has no control over the market, he is bound to take what he gets for his produce, he has no means of knowing whether he is getting the current market price of his article or not, nor does he know what particular market may be a bad one or otherwise. During the last year, the price of pork varied from 4s to 6s per cwt. from one market to another, on several occasions without any apparent reason and without any corresponding fluctuation in the price of bacon. Trade or industry under these conditions could not possibly succeed because of its unfairness to the producer and is bound to do incalculable harm to any industry. Such a state of affairs is a disgrace to the intelligence of the co-operator of this county."*

Mr West then went on to suggest that as a first step a buyer should be appointed by the co-operatives who would liaise with purchasers in Great Britain and that he would organise the purchase and transport of carcases or live pigs directly.

Nothing further appears to have been done about the marketing of pigs for many years. Sir Horace Plunkett, when addressing a large gathering in the Townhall, Enniskillen, in October 1912, made the case for improvement in the marketing of pigs when he stated that this was the greatest challenge facing farmers. He went on to emphasise the need for farmers to have their own co-operative marketing organisation. Despite the approval of the earlier meeting, which Mr West had addressed, and the support of Sir Horace Plunkett, little effective action seems to have been taken at that time.

Agricultural production from 1900 to 1914

In Ireland as a whole, agricultural output rose by 36 per cent during the period 1900 to 1914 and this growth was shared equally between arable and livestock production. On the eve of World War I, poultry accounted for nine per cent of agricultural output. Exports of beef and mutton showed a phenomenal increase from 6,000 cwt in 1904 to over 320,000 cwt by 1912. This increase was offset to some extent by a fall in bacon exports.

The overall Irish pattern of production was not replicated in County Fermanagh. Cattle numbers showed a significant increase from 98,639 in the year 1900 to 104,485 in 1914. Total sheep numbers decreased from 11,942 to 8,655 whereas pig numbers remained similar at a total of just over 20,000. Poultry showed a substantial increase from just under 518,000 to almost 741,000 by 1914. Cropping showed a marginal increase from almost 29,000 acres to just under 30,000 acres. The two major crops were potatoes and oats.

Department of Agriculture and Technical Instruction for Ireland.

OATS FOR SEED.

As there appears to be some misapprehension on the subject the Department wish it to be understood that the maximum prices for Oats set out in the Grain Prices Order, 1917, do not apply to Oats sold and used specifically for seed purposes.

Owing to the threatened **Shortage of Feeding Stuffs,** and the consequent need for a further large increase in the area under Oats in Ireland in 1918, farmers should reserve their best samples of grain to provide seed for this increased area.

It is most important that every prospective grower of Oats should make sure of having sufficient seed for the area he intends to put under the crop this year.

DUBLIN, JANUARY, 1918.

5 927 K.A A.

Seed oats for 1918.

Potatoes showed a decrease from 13,056 acres in 1900 to 11,140 in 1914 whereas oats declined by almost 2,000 acres from just over 16,000 acres in 1900. Flax was grown but not in a significant quantity at around 250 acres over the period.

Foot and Mouth Disease

During the first decade of the twentieth century and in the years immediately preceding the First World War, farmers and the agricultural industry had to contend with an outbreak of Foot and Mouth Disease. Restrictions on imports of hay and straw from countries with Foot and Mouth Disease were introduced in 1908. The disease developed in Ireland in 1912 and affected a number of counties including Fermanagh. Details of the impact of the disease in Fermanagh are to be found in Chapter 21.

Sir Horace Plunkett's departure from the Department of Agriculture and Technical instruction

Sir Horace Plunkett who had done so much for developing the co-operative movement in Ireland and establishing the Department of Agriculture and Technical Instruction was a casualty of Unionist/Nationalist political differences that developed in the Irish Parliament in May 1907.

Local displeasure at Sir Horace's removal from his Departmental Office was voiced at a meeting of the Fivemiletown and Brookeborough Co-Operative Agricultural and Dairy Society's annual meeting in May 2007. A resolution was passed which read as follows: *That this meeting desires to express its sense of services of Sir Horace Plunkett to the farmers of Ireland by the introduction into this country of agricultural co-operation to which this Society owes its existence and its regret at his removal from the post of Vice President of the Department of Agriculture and Technical Instruction.* The proposer added: "*The removal of Sir Horace from the position was nothing short of a national misfortune.*" He said: "*They all knew what he had done, and how many co-operative societies had been established since he took up the work. None but a gentleman with the enthusiasm which had been displayed by Sir Horace Plunkett could have succeeded in doing half as much as he had done. It was not only a misfortune to this country that he should be removed, but it was a disgraceful act on the part of the powers that be to remove a gentleman who has done so much for the country and whose work will remain a monument in the country to him when the name of Sir Horace Plunkett was forgotten.*"

Similar sentiments were expressed in a resolution passed by the Tyrone County Committee of Agriculture on 1st May 1907. It read as follows: *That this committee desire to express their sense of the eminent services rendered to the cause of technical education in this country by Sir Horace Plunkett, and regret his removal from office as Vice President of the Department of Agriculture and Technical Instruction.*"

Despite Sir Horace's removal from the Vice Presidency of the Department he continued to champion the cause of agricultural co-operation through his involvement in the Irish Agricultural Organisation Society.

Sad loss

Sir Douglas Brooke, who was the first Chairman of the Fermanagh County Committee of Agriculture, died in November 1907, aged 42 years. As well as his role in the County Committee of Agriculture, he was also Honorary Secretary of the Fermanagh Farming Society. When referring to his death and his role in the County Committee of Agriculture *The Impartial Reporter* referred to the County Committee, under his chairmanship, as having - *done so much to advance agriculture and horticulture in this county.*

References:

Files of *The Impartial Reporter* and *Fermanagh Herald* held in Enniskillen Library.

Chambers, Dr George, *The Rise and Fall of an Indigenous Industry: Milk Processing in County Fermanagh from the Seventeenth Century until the Present Day.* Fermanagh History and Society. Geography Publications edited by Eileen M. Murphy and William J. Roulston. Dublin 2004.

Advertisements shown have been copied from the files of *The Impartial Reporter.*

Chapter 5
The First World War

Great Britain declared war on Germany and her allies on 4th August 1914. Immediately, British naval power and her shipping lanes came under threat from German submarines and surface ships. Many vessels carrying desperately needed supplies, including food, were being sunk each week crossing the Atlantic.

The German submarine menace on the sea lanes – a sinking cargo ship.

Imports of cheap American grain, which previously constituted an important element in pig, poultry and cattle feeds, were very much curtailed and there was the need for increased home production of food and more self-sufficiency. The production of food became a vital war necessity. Arable cropping received particular encouragement. Compulsory tillage was in force towards the end of the war and Government regulations, under the 'Defence of the Realm Act', covered nearly every aspect of farming. These changed circumstances had a significant impact in County Fermanagh as elsewhere.

Early British Government policy

In 1914, advice was offered to the farming community on the need for increased food production and especially for an increased area of cereals. Farmers were encouraged to plough up grassland and grow grain crops. At the same time, they were asked not to reduce stock numbers and refrain from slaughtering immature breeding animals. Contracts were agreed with South American meat companies and in 1915 with Australia and New Zealand for securing a supply of meat. In 1915 in Ireland there was, for one year only, a government guaranteed price for wheat and oats as an incentive for increased production. The vulnerability of the British food supply was being assessed at this time. It had been shown that Germany could produce 90 per cent of that country's population energy needs as a result of its higher proportion of arable crops compared to 40 per cent in Britain. There was a sharp deterioration in food prospects for the UK during the summer and autumn of 1916. The greatest threat came from the comparative failure of the North American wheat harvest of 1916 where yields were down by one third compared to the previous year. North America had supplied over half of Britain's imported grain. In November 1916, it was agreed to give Irish farmers a guaranteed price for oats to stimulate production of that crop for the use of army horses. It was not until December 1916 that the British Government adopted an interventionist policy with regard to agricultural production.

Advice to farmers

Farmers were being advised in the summer of 1914 to resist the temptation to respond to increased prices for livestock by selling their breeding stock. Likewise, they were advised to resist selling all their grain crops, as new seed for the next season may not be available. On 14th August 1914 the Agricultural Instructors, including those from Fermanagh, were summoned to Dublin to a special meeting to discuss what steps could be taken to increase food supply. The need for increased production and the role of catch crops, sown after the harvest of early potatoes and flax, was being emphasised. Mr William Smyth, the Instructor in Agriculture for County Fermanagh, wrote an article in the local press in September 1915 encouraging farmers to sow catch crops for feeding livestock in spring. The crops recommended to be sown were hybrid turnips and winter rye and vetches. Increased flax production was also being encouraged, as it was feared that imports from the Continent and particularly Russia would be curtailed or cease altogether. At that time, only one quarter of the flax required by Irish flax spinners was produced in Ireland. A report by the Departmental Committee on Food Production in Ireland in 1915 was appealing for an increase in the area under tillage, not only with a view to

Mr Thomas Maguire (Courtesy Mr Tom Maguire).

Army horses at the front

Some of the stabling at Munville (Courtesy of Mr Tom Maguire).

the direct production of more human food, but also to increasing the amount of fodder available for cattle. It was also advocating the improvement of breeding stock of all kinds and emphasising the need for more machinery and implements. The 1915 'Maintenance of Livestock Act' followed and placed a ban on the slaughter or export of in-calf heifers and cows, pregnant sows and lambs.

Impact on milk production

Demand for home produced butter rose sharply from 1914 until the end of the First World War. Supplies from overseas were curtailed and consequently milk prices trebled from four pence to almost 13 pence per gallon between 1913 and 1921. In May 1914, the Fivemiletown and Brookeborough Co-operative Agricultural and Dairy Society Ltd reported that for the year 1913 the average price paid for milk was 4.31 pence per gallon. It took 2.41 gallons of milk to make a pound of butter and the price received for the butter was 12.33 pence per pound. In 1914 the average price paid for milk was a record 4.87 pence per gallon for Lisnaskea Creamery.

Demand for horses

The First World War created a new demand for horses for military purposes. The horses were required by the army for the transport of weaponry and other supplies. Mr Thomas Maguire of Munville, Lisnaskea, had the largest agency trading in horses in Ireland at that time.

The trade in Irish bred horses for military purposes had started earlier with the Boer War where, in addition to their transport role, horses were required by the cavalry. Other equines were also in demand at that time. Mr Maguire sent an agent to Letterkenny to buy horses. Much to Mr Maguire's surprise, and initial displeasure, a telegram was received from the buyer asking him to meet the seven o'clock train in Lisnaskea to receive 72 mules. There was some relief when the agent explained that he had met an army officer on the train on the way to Letterkenny who had assured him that mules were very much in demand for transport purposes in the difficult terrain in South Africa. The mules were subsequently sold to the army at a reasonable profit.

Mr Maguire bought horses from all over Ireland and they were assembled for onward sale at Munville. Captain King, of the North Irish Horse, made a purchase of horses in early August 1914 from Mr Maguire, which received press publicity and was regarded to be a record at that time. The sum of £2,850 was paid for this particular batch of horses. Best quality hay and oats for feeding cavalry horses were also in demand.

In 1917 and 1918, as many as 1,200 horses were sold each fortnight from Munville to the British army. When the sale day was set army personnel, including a colonel and a complement of other ranks including veterinary surgeons, attended. Each animal was individually assessed in front of the colonel, who was seated in what the Maguires called 'the Colonel's box', at the centre of the display area. The horses were transported to and from Lisnaskea by train. By 1918 there were over 791,600 horses owned by the British Army. The bulk of these were used for transport purposes with 186,500 being cavalry or riding horses.

Binders in Ballinamallard

By 1916, the difficulty in importing feeding stuffs was having a major impact. Yellow or maize meal, or Indian meal as it was more commonly called, imported from North and South America had previously been the main element in pig and poultry diets and in the hand feeding of both dairy and beef cattle. This meal had increased in price from 13 shillings to 28 shillings per cwt and was difficult to obtain. The pressure was on to grow more crops at home. The need to plough more land was paramount. Shortage of labour was advanced as a major obstacle and the virtues of self-binders for harvesting cereal crops in the Ballinamallard area were being advanced. Mr E. M. Archdale DL, when addressing a co-operative conference, said that his binder which cost him £30 was doing the work of 20 men. Mr W. H. West, Secretary to the County Committee of Agriculture and also an extensive farmer, showed how he saved 20 acres by having one. He claimed that a binder could work in any field conditions where an ordinary mower could operate. He stressed that small farmers could co-operate in acquiring such a machine.

Fertiliser was also scarce and the value of burnt lime as an aid to soil fertility was being advanced. Farmers in Fermanagh were encouraged to use burnt lime and to get their lime kilns, which it was claimed had not been used for fifty years, back into commission again.

The 1917 Irish Food Production Scheme

The 1917 Irish Food Production Scheme related to compulsory tillage, which required every occupier of arable land to cultivate in 1917 a portion equivalent to one-tenth of his holding if his land was not tilled in 1916. For those who had cropped some of their land in 1916 they were required to cultivate one-tenth of their holding in addition to the area cropped in the previous year subject to a maximum of half the total area. Farms of under 10 acres were exempt. The scheme was administered through the County Committees of Agriculture. The County Committees were empowered to employ their Instructors full-time in the Scheme of Food Production.

Guaranteed prices had been set for cereals and potatoes. Mr W. H. West, Secretary of the Fermanagh County Committee of Agriculture, organised meetings at centres throughout the County in February 1917 *to form local committees and to give such information as may be possible as to carrying out the law in this urgent and important matter and the procuring of the necessary implements and labour.* The Government fixed prices for the 1917 crop as follows: wheat 60s per quarter of 504lbs and oats 36s 6d per quarter of 336lbs. The price for potatoes delivered to the boat averaged around £6 per ton. Lower prices applied to sales from September to the end of January with the higher prices applying from April onwards. Loans were granted for purchase of implements and machinery. In March 1917, there were only 70 tractors in Ireland but within six months tractors numbered 300 and by September 1918 there were 640.

Horse drawn binder in action at Cooke's of Thomastown, Enniskillen (Courtesy of Mr and Mrs Cecil Cooke).

Horse drawn binders still feature each year at the vintage display at Moynalty, County Meath.

Tillage and Guaranteed Prices

The following advertisement appeared in the local newspapers in January and February 1917 entitled - *Food Production in Ireland, 1917.*

FOOD PRODUCTION IN IRELAND, 1917.

FARMERS TO THE RESCUE!

National Duty — Through various effects of the War, a great extra quantity of food grown at home this year is absolutely necessary to secure our population against the danger of privation. The farmer alone can supply that need.

Guarantee Against Loss — To secure him against risk of loss in performing this vital duty the Government have guaranteed him a fixed or contract price for wheat, oats, and potatoes of the 1917 crop.

Means of Production — The Department of Agriculture have taken special measures to ensure that a supply of seeds, manures, and implements will be available in Ireland for the extra tillage. Loans for seeds and manures are being made available by the Local Government Board through the Rural and Urban District Councils for holders under £10 valuation; and loans for implements and machinery will be provided by the Department for other holders.

Compulsory Tillage — Under the Defence of the Realm Act occupiers who hold ten acres or more are required to cultivate in 1917 **one-tenth of the arable land on their holdings in addition to their tillage area of last year.** That is, if you hold, say, 40 acres of which 30 are arable you must till the same amount that you tilled last year **and three acres in addition.**

Arable Land — Means land which is cultivated or can be cultivated. Every farmer knows just what portion of his land can be cultivated. Therefore, do not wait for an inspector to tell you. Go ahead and

PLOUGH NOW — With the horses and the ploughs at present in the country. **We have enough of both** in most districts. Motor tractors are good, but there are few of them yet in Ireland, and a supply may not get here in time. Don't wait for them. Use the horse and plough at once.

Seed is being kept for you to purchase. Loans will be provided. Manures are being mobilised. Consult your County Committee, your County Agricultural Instructor, and the Department. Get to work on your arable land. Leave the appealing and the asking for exemption to others.

THERE NEED BE NO SCARCITY OF FOOD IF THE IRISH FARMERS DO THEIR DUTY, AND THEY WILL.

Department of Agriculture and Technical Instruction for Ireland, DUBLIN, January, 1917. 2313

The Chief Secretary of the Dublin Government addressed the problem of food shortage in January 1917. Under his direction, powers were conferred on urban councils to encourage tillage on land over which they had control. Furthermore, they were empowered to acquisition land in the neighbourhood of towns for laying out in allotments. The local councils in Fermanagh responded by indicating their intention of facilitating loans to occupiers of land valued at £10 or less for tillage requisites to a maximum of 12 cwt of seed potatoes, 3 cwt of oats, 6 cwt of artificial manure. Tenants of labourers' cottages had lower limits of requisites eligible for loans.

Ploughing the land

Early ploughing became a requirement. Originally, under the 'Tillage Order', ploughing was to be underway by 25th March 1917 but this was then brought forward to 28th February. The ploughing date did not mean that ploughing had to be complete at that time. The War Office Inspectors were visiting farms and those farmers who had not started ploughing by 28th February were liable to prosecution under the 'Defence of the Realm Act' and a fine of £10 per acre. In the case of defaulters, land could be taken from them and given to others to cultivate.

Horses did most of the ploughing.

Exemptions under the scheme were few. Arable land was defined as any land *fit for cultivation.* Non-arable land included: land subject to flooding, sand hills, land covered with whins, land which could not be cultivated – forests, plantations and orchards. There was a clause through which exemption could be sought by applying to the Department before 28th March. The clause read as follows: *that the cultivation of the holding or class of holdings would be of less service for the production of food than the use of the holding or class of holdings in some other manner in which the same is being used or proposed to be used.* Mr W. H. West at a meeting of farmers in Enniskillen said: "*it would be practically impossible for any farmer in this part of the country to prove what is required in this paragraph. An acre of oats is worth £16, and an acre of potatoes worth about £40. What farmer is there who can prove that by keeping his acre under grass, that it will be more productive than potatoes or even oats at £16 per acre?*"

As well as the compulsion on farmers to cultivate the additional tenth over and above the area cultivated in 1916 there was an appeal to do more than the minimum.

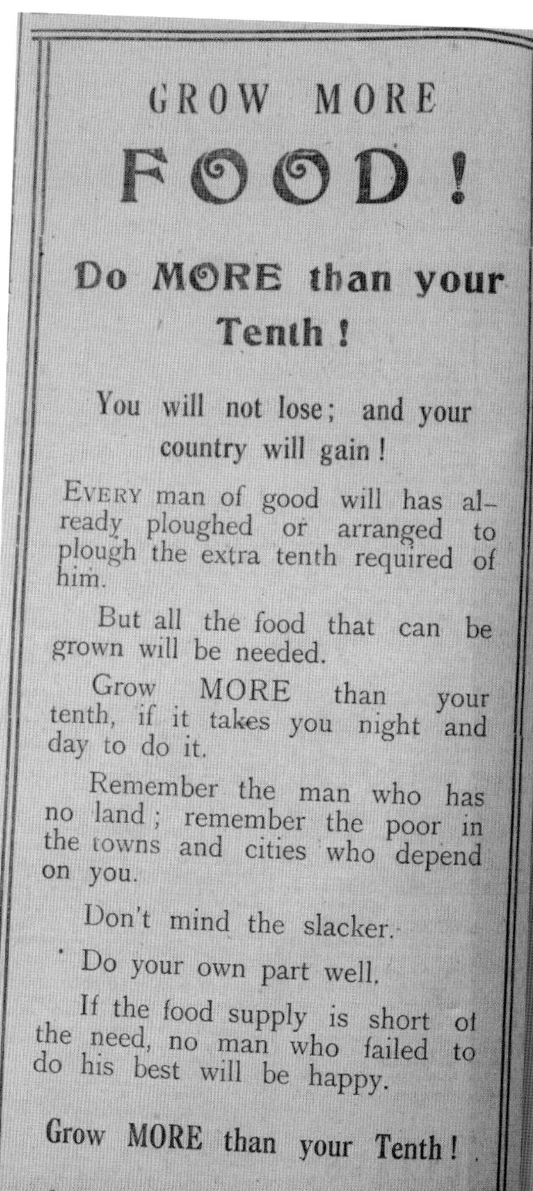

GROW MORE

FOOD!

Do MORE than your Tenth!

You will not lose; and your country will gain!

EVERY man of good will has already ploughed or arranged to plough the extra tenth required of him.

But all the food that can be grown will be needed.

Grow MORE than your tenth, if it takes you night and day to do it.

Remember the man who has no land; remember the poor in the towns and cities who depend on you.

Don't mind the slacker.

Do your own part well.

If the food supply is short of the need, no man who failed to do his best will be happy.

Grow MORE than your Tenth!

—J 2386 K.A.A.

1917 advertisement – Grow More Food.

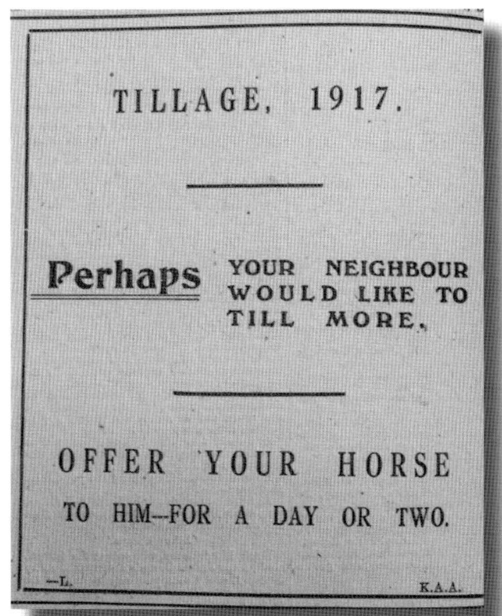

TILLAGE, 1917.

Perhaps YOUR NEIGHBOUR WOULD LIKE TO TILL MORE.

OFFER YOUR HORSE TO HIM—FOR A DAY OR TWO.

—L. K.A.A.

Farmers were encouraged to lend their horse to a neighbour if he required it.

Furthermore, neighbours were encouraged to lend their horses to those who did not have the resources to undertake the cultivation required.

Migratory workers

The Department of Agriculture and Technical Instruction ran a scheme in spring 1917 entitled - *Migratory Labour*. It provided a pool of labourers for seasonal employment for tillage operations in Ireland. These workers would return to their own districts at the end of the season. Ploughmen were available at 25 shillings per week with board and lodgings. General labourers earned 15 shillings per week, again including board and lodgings.

The 'Food Production Act' of 1917 introduced an Agricultural Wages Board, with representatives of employers, workers and trade unions, which had the power to fix minimum wages and other conditions of employment for farm workers. The Act also introduced a temporary suspension of land purchase and redistribution under the Land Acts.

The British Corn Production Act

Meanwhile, the 'British Corn Production Act' of 1917 marked a new departure in the agricultural policy of Great Britain. It aimed not only at securing an increase in supplies of food for the duration of the war but also *to effect in the interests of national security, such permanent improvement in the agricultural industry as would secure to those engaged in it a fair return in future years for their labour and capital.* The Act set guaranteed prices for wheat and oats and export of these crops was controlled by licence. Compulsory tillage was not introduced in Great Britain until 1918.

Fermanagh's concerns

A large meeting of farmers met in Enniskillen Townhall on the afternoon of 23rd January 1917, under the chairmanship of Mr E. M. Archdale DL MP, to consider the Government's compulsory tillage scheme. A comprehensive report of the meeting was carried in *The Impartial Reporter*. Mr Archdale in his introduction said: "*In the history of their county that there never was a time when it was more necessary for every one to put their shoulders to the wheel. Daily the German submarines were sinking 5,000 tons of shipping, and if that continues till the end of the War there would be no possible way of getting their food stuffs from Canada and the United States, to keep them alive. So at home, they must do their utmost to grow all the food they can, and keep starvation from their doors. As regards the Department's Scheme, there was one clause about compulsory tillage, which affected a great many people in this county. Last year the Government appealed to them to put in extra crops. The season was bad, and those that put in extra crops in reply to that appeal had severe loss. He himself had to throw some stacks of hay in the dung heap. There was no use in tilling unsuitable land, but there was suitable land that should be tilled if they had the men, horses and implements, and above all the manure. Unless they had the manure, they would only be leaving the land poorer than before, and have in the end a wilderness of weeds. Prices had been fixed for one year. What was the good of that? Prices should be guaranteed for four years. Then the farmer would have something to look forward to and to encourage him to till his land".*

The Rt Hon Edward Mervyn Archdale (right) with his brothers Frank and Jack. Mr Jack Porter Archdale changed his surname to Porter when he inherited the Porter family estate at Belleisle.

Mr Archdale then dealt with the declining imports of eggs and other farm produce into England from abroad and pointed out that now the Irish people had a great opportunity of capturing part of that trade. Big prices were being paid for pork, but it hardly paid the farmer due to high prices of potatoes and feeding stuffs. He referred to shortage of labour in England and in France but stated that in Ireland they had plenty of able fit men to work and urged them in the hour of necessity to answer the call of the Government willingly and to do what they could to help the country.

The Rev John Hall, Chairman of the County Committee of Agriculture, said that the matter before them was one of grave importance and he begged to remind them that the Department's Scheme was compulsory. He criticised the timing of the scheme (25th March) and said that the Scheme should have been in the hands of the people in October last. However, he said: "*Now that they had the Scheme it was for them to make the best use of it , and even if it were not compulsory there was loyalty enough amongst them to do their best and fall in with the ideas of the Department."* Mr Chamberlain spoke about duty. He said: "*Fermanagh had already nobly done its part in the war, and in this question of tillage they must also do their duty. None of them had ever been called upon to do his best – and today that was what was being demanded of them. Let them put their heart into their work and do more than has been done in the past."* He recalled reading doggerel lines some days ago:

In days gone by a gentleman was a man who kept a gig,

But now a patriotic man was the man who kept a pig.

Not all present were in favour of compulsory tillage. Mr John Ward of Innishkeen, said that there was a lot of land in Fermanagh unsuitable for tillage, and many farmers cultivated already as much as they could manage. An advance of 10 per cent on last year for many farmers was utterly impossible. If more were tilled it would be impossible to save the extra crops put in. A resolution was then proposed by Mr Robert O'Hara, which expressed appreciation for the need for extra tillage but opposed the compulsion to cultivate unsuitable land – the result of which would be greater economic loss rather than gain. The resolution also contained the consideration that Government should be encouraging those with suitable land and equipment to produce the extra required. Mr O'Hara said that most of their land was only suitable for fattening stores and finishing fatstock. Mr Ben Maguire seconded the adoption of the resolution but expressed the hope that all would do their best and that every man should do his best and crop all he could.

Mr Henry Lyons, a Tyrone man born and bred, said: "*that after 40 years of experience of farming in Fermanagh, if he had followed on the lines of tillage in Tyrone, to which he had been brought up, he would that day be in the workhouse. He tried corn, potatoes and flax, and everything else that he used to grow in Tyrone. It was impossible. In Tyrone, the rain had little effect on the land; in Fermanagh after one night's rain, a horse and plough could not go on the land for a week. The compulsory tillage scheme would result in large numbers of cases in that county of very serious loss.* He concluded by saying: *"they were bound to be patriotic and do their best".*

Need for sacrifice

Mr W. Copeland Trimble stated that he was a small landowner. He said: "*they were all concerned in the one business, and they all desired to do what was good for the country in the present crisis. They might sometimes have to do things that they did not like. Many of them had already made sacrifices for the good of the country. They might have to make greater sacrifices, then in God's name let them not be talking about tilling a bit of grassland, if by doing so they could produce more food. They were warned that they would have privation; tickets for sugar and meat were near; they might have to face starvation. His father had told him that he would*

have been unable to feed his family in the days of the great famine of '47, only for the vegetables and produce that he had got from his garden. They now had to do what was best for the county, not only to feed the people at large but to feed their own children. Millions of tons of shipping were going to the bottom of the sea, and instead of purchasing food from abroad they could not get it to buy owing to failure of transport, and they must produce it at home".

Mr Trimble then went on to refer to differences in the farming conditions in the east and west of the county. He said that it would be unreasonable to expect those in the east of the county to carry the total burden of extra tillage. He believed that all should contribute.

Mr W. Copeland Trimble.

After further debate, Mr O'Hara's resolution was withdrawn. Mr J. Porter Porter DL then moved a second resolution, pledging support to the Government, that they would do their utmost to produce more food-stuffs in the coming spring. He acknowledged the differences in land quality but said that they must all do their best. Mr J. B. Frith seconded the resolution, which was supported by Mr J. Dunlop of Lisbellaw.

Rev Father T. Maguire CC commented: "*the Department would not act in a tyrannical manner. It would be a terrible disgrace to farmers of Fermanagh if Mr O'Hara's resolution had gone forth. Let them remember that at the close of the War prices would fall and there would be a time of financial stress, and produce of the land was what they would have to fall back upon and not on cattle.*"

Rev John Hall added: "*that the scheme was not perfect. If it would be proved that land was unsuitable for tillage and it would be better not to break it up, a farmer would not be compelled to till it. There was bread and money in it.*"

Mr Porter Porter's resolution was unanimously adopted and the meeting was concluded with cheers for the Chairman.

Food supply

The food supply deteriorated further in February 1917 when Germany launched an unrestricted submarine war on all ships, including neutral ones, which were heading to Allied ports. The United Kingdom then concentrated its acquisition of imported food from North America. A Ministry of Food was established to regularise domestic distribution of food supplies. Maximum prices and rations for certain foodstuffs were set and the price of bread was subsidised.

THE OATS CROP OF 1917.

The Government have informed the Department that the War Office will buy Oats in Ireland for Army purposes on and after 15th November, when this year's crop will be fit for Army purposes, and that they will be prepared to pay at the rate of 38s 6d per quarter of 312 lbs. on rail or in store, for clean, sound Oats in good condition.

This price is equivalent to

24s 2d

PER BARREL OF 14 STONES.

Farmers should, therefore, stack and thatch their corn, and keep it in the rick at least until the date mentioned (15th November), threshing out as little as possible in the meantime. This will improve the keeping quality of the grain and make it fit for Army purposes.

TO SECURE THE ABOVE PRICE, KEEP YOUR OATS IN RICK UNTIL 15th NOVEMBER, AND WHEN THRESHING SEE THAT THE GRAIN IS PROPERLY CLEANED.

Department of Agriculture and Technical Instruction, Dublin.

V.7 K.A.A.

Oats for Army horses

Oats were in demand for feeding army horses during the winter of 1917. The War Office undertook to buy oats for Army purposes on and after 15th November at a price of 38s 6d per quarter of 312lbs (equivalent to 24s 2d per barrel of 14 stones) on rail or in store, for clean sound oats in good condition. Farmers who wished to avail of this trade were asked to keep their oats in thatched stacks until 15th November before threshing in order to improve the keeping quality of the grain.

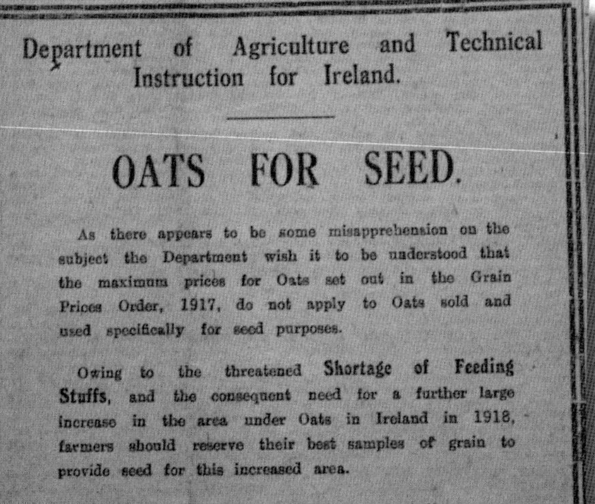

Department of Agriculture and Technical Instruction for Ireland.

OATS FOR SEED.

As there appears to be some misapprehension on the subject the Department wish it to be understood that the maximum prices for Oats set out in the Grain Prices Order, 1917, do not apply to Oats sold and used specifically for seed purposes.

Owing to the threatened **Shortage of Feeding Stuffs,** and the consequent need for a further large increase in the area under Oats in Ireland in 1918, farmers should reserve their best samples of grain to provide seed for this increased area.

It is most important that every prospective grower of Oats should make sure of having sufficient seed for the area he intends to put under the crop this year.

DUBLIN, JANUARY, 1918. K.A.A.

The challenges of 1918

Additional cropping was required for the 1918 season. With the German offensive early in 1918 seriously threatening food supplies, a Supplementary Order was issued which required those farmers with more than 200 arable acres to till 20 per cent over the amount tilled in 1916. Those with under 200 arable acres had to till five per cent more being a total of 15 per cent more than in 1916. This announcement came with the warning that a reasonable effort this year will not be enough. The full percentage will be strictly required from everybody. Farmers were asked in January 1918 to ensure that they had adequate horse power for dealing with the additional cropping required.

The slaughter or export of milk cows, young heifers, calves and ewes in lamb was prohibited and licences were required for the export from Ireland of milk, butter, oats and potatoes. In 1918, the Ulster Farmers' Union sent a deputation to the Irish Food Control Committee in Dublin to point out the serious position of farmers due to the very high prices of feeding stuffs and labour, which made it unprofitable to produce pork or beef.

HORSES FOR EXTRA TILLAGE.

Farmers are advised to provide themselves without delay with the HORSES which they will require to deal with the tillage operations and harvest of this year.

Horses suitable for agricultural purposes have for some time past been retained in the country under embargo, and this has resulted in a good supply of these animals being now available.

Farmers should, therefore, make their purchases without delay.

If they do not buy at once the may have difficulty later in procuring suitable animals.

DEPARTMENT OF AGRICULTURE AND TECHNICAL INSTRUCTION, DUBLIN, JANUARY, 1918.
5 3893 K.A.A.

THE TILLAGE WANTED.

THE Department have issued an Order requiring an extra quantity of tillage from holders of 200 arable acres and upwards making a total of 20 per cent. over the amount tilled in 1916 on these holdings.

The holder of a farm of less than 200 arable acres is required to till five per cent. more than last year, being a total of 15 per cent more than in 1916.

'Reasonable Effort' this year will not be enough. The full percentage will be strickly required from everybody.

Moreover so urgent has become the need for more food that the Department appeal both to the occupiers of the larger holdings and to all others, down to the smallest cultivators to till as much as possible over the amount actually required by the Tillage Order.

To accomplish this great task not a day should be lost. The plough should be kept going every fine hour. Bad weather may be ahead.

Department of Agriculture and Technical Instruction, Dublin, Feb., 1918
4114 13 K.A.A.

An appeal in February 1918 was also made for more tillage in the following terms: *Moreover, so urgent has become the need for more food that the Department appeals both to the occupiers of the larger holdings and to all others, down to the smallest cultivators to till as much as possible over the amount actually required by the Tillage Order. To accomplish this great task not a day should be lost. The plough should be kept going every fine hour. Bad weather may be ahead.*

The Department of Agriculture and Technical Instruction appears to have enforced Compulsory Tillage Orders more actively in 1918 than in the previous year. In 1918, it was reported that their inspectors had entered farm holdings for that purpose in 24 counties.

Rotational cropping

In April 1918, the Department issued a notice about *rational cropping*. It referred in particular to the risks of taking a third grain crop in succession after grass. It recommended a proper rotation, suggesting swedes or turnips for the third year grown with artificial manures. Basic slag was stated to be as suitable as superphosphate. It also stated that liquid manure if suitably employed would save the purchase of sulphate of ammonia which was becoming scarce and dear. Nitrate of soda was available without licence providing not more than 6 cwt were purchased. It was stated that hay was likely to be in short supply and in keen demand next season. Farmers should therefore use nitrate of soda as a top dressing for meadows. Farmers were also advised to have their threshing machines overhauled at once. Machinery agents were also being pressed to place their orders for machinery for the remainder of the 1918 season and for the spring tillage operations in 1919. An appeal in October 1918 was issued exhorting landowners to make their farms self sustaining. Due to the shortage of hay, farmers were authorised to feed oats to all classes of stock.

Cropping areas and stock numbers during the War

The following table shows the trends in cropping areas and livestock numbers in County Fermanagh during the War years and in 1919.

During the early years of the war and prior to the introduction of compulsory tillage, the area of cropping in Fermanagh remained more or less static. It was not until compulsory tillage was introduced in 1917 that a significant increase in the cropping area was recorded. Under the 'Compulsory Tillage Order' of 1917, farmers were compelled to plough up for cropping ten per cent more than the area cropped in 1916. Despite the reservations expressed by farmers at meetings about the difficulty of increasing the tillage area, Fermanagh farmers responded splendidly and in 1917, the acreage under the plough had increased by 38 per cent. Potatoes increased marginally but the greatest increase was in the area of oats (53 per cent increase) and flax (67 per cent increase). The increase in the area of crops was accompanied by a decrease in cow numbers but other numbers of cattle were maintained. Pig numbers suffered due to a shortage of suitable feed. Oats is not a suitable feed for pigs because of its high fibre content but potatoes would have been used extensively for that purpose. Poultry numbers also suffered but not to the same extent as pigs. Potatoes and oats were acceptable feeds for poultry.

The area under cultivation increased further in 1918 when the 'Tillage Order' compelled farmers to cultivate an area 15 per cent (or 20 per cent on larger farms) greater than in 1916. Fermanagh farmers increased the area under cultivation by over 12 per cent compared to 1917 giving a 56 per cent increase over the 1916 area.

The area cultivated in Fermanagh in 1918 represented just under five per cent of the total area cultivated in Northern Ireland. This reflects the relatively small area of what can be regarded as arable land in Fermanagh compared with other counties.

Table 5.1 Farming activity 1914 - 1918

	1914	1915	1916	1917	1918	1919
Cattle	**104,485**	**102,589**	**104, 868**	**104,134**	**100,268**	**99,119**
Cows and Heifers in milk	**40,291**	**40,276**	**40,118**	**39,615**	**37,104**	**36,013**
Sheep	**8,655**	**9,919**	**10,489**	**11,740,**	**11,394**	**10,326**
Pigs	**20,085**	**16,387**	**17,936**	**10,649**	**12,121**	**13,162**
Poultry	**740,876**	**729,598**	**773,011**	**620,858**	**682,159**	
Horses	**9,348**	**8,440**	**9,945**	**9,289**	**9,648**	**9,670**
Potatoes (acres)	**11,140**	**11,302**	**11,483**	**13,702**	**14,337**	**11,877**
Oats (acres)	**14,047**	**14,080**	**14,289**	**21,929**	**25,478**	**22,264**
Barley (acres)	**7**	**6**	**8**	**22**	**34**	**9**
Flax (acres)	**249**	**388**	**865**	**1,449**	**2,178**	**1,646**
Total crops	**29,804**	**30,148**	**30,460**	**42,310**	**47,630**	**39,370**

Source: Economics and Statistics Division, Department of Agriculture and Rural Development.

Inquiry into decline in milk production during the War years

Milk supplies to Fermanagh creameries over the war years showed a considerable decline. Supplies were as follows:

Table 5.2 Milk production 1914 -1918

Year	Milk received (gallons)	Increase/Decrease
1914	10,321,126	
1915	10,748,940	4.10% increase
1916	10,851,343	0.95% increase
1917	9,581,343	11.60% decrease
1918	8,394,610	12.30% decrease

The total decrease from 1914 to 1918 was 18.7 per cent. Professor Wilkinson, Royal College of Science and the Department's Inspector for Connaught, Fermanagh and South Tyrone, gave evidence at the Department's Inquiry into the decline of dairying held in Enniskillen in November 1919. A report of the proceedings was carried in *The Impartial Reporter*. The Inquiry was called because of the decline in butter exports from Ireland during the period 1914 to 1918. Exports during this period had declined from 42,786 tons to 19,901 tons. Professor Wilkinson attributed the decline mainly to the loss of imports of butter (3,000 tons), increased manufacture of cheese, and increased home consumption due to the absence of fat bacon and scarcity of margarine.

In so far as the drop in milk supplies to Fermanagh creameries was concerned the Professor attributed this to the hard winter of 1916/1917 together with a scarcity of hay and imported feeds. The increase in home made butter making due to high prices was also another factor. Milk production over the years of the war had dropped due to heifers replacing cows at a higher than normal rate and the shortage of feeding stuffs. Milk supplies had dropped by a similar percentage in Britain and Denmark.

Mr James McElroy, Drumwhinney, Kesh, at the Inquiry complained about the price paid by the creameries for milk. He said he received 13d per gallon in winter and 10d in summer. In response it was pointed out that in 1912 milk was only worth 3½d per gallon.

Mr W. H. West, Secretary, County Committee of Agriculture, gave evidence at the Inquiry. He farmed 300 acres and stated that he used to keep 15 to 16 cows. He found that in 1917/1918 they did not pay. He ceased milk production and put in store cattle. He said that counting a yield of 400 gallons per cow and the current price of milk store cattle were worth £80 per year more than the cows. He said the stores were less trouble. He stated that the common breeding bull was now the Roscommon bull. There were 120 of them in the county and the intention was to raise good stores with milking quality as a secondary consideration. He said that the Agricultural Committee offered farmers dairy bulls but the farmers did not prefer them.

Professor Wilkinson indicated that the future of dairying depended on increasing the yield per cow and only manufacturing highest grade milk products. He said it only paid to keep and feed the best animals. He compared Ireland with Denmark. In Ireland, the average yield per cow was 450 gallons compared to 600 in Denmark. Irish butter fetched 1d to 2d per lb less than Danish butter. He called for increased yields and better quality milk products.

Impact of prices

Compulsory tillage obliged farmers to increase their area of cropping but there is little doubt that much of the additional tillage was in response to increased prices. Government was well aware that war time prices for agricultural produce would not be sustained in peace time. In 1920 prices for agricultural commodities were approximately three times the 1913 level. As early as 1915, the Department of Agriculture and Technical Instruction issued a warning to farmers relating to current prices. It read: *The present high prices will by, an inevitable law, be followed at the close of war by a period of low prices, depression and perhaps distress.* Farmers were advised to *clear all debts, accumulate savings for the rainy days ahead, and refrain from additional borrowing.* This was sound advice and reflected what was to come very accurately.

End of the War

The war ended on 11th November 1918 but the difficulties facing the farming community would intensify and continue for many years. At the end of the war the Department of Agriculture and Technical instruction lifted the requirement for the additional five per cent tillage imposed in 1918. Compulsory tillage continued for the 1919 and 1920 seasons but was revoked early in 1921.

Before leaving the 1918 year behind it is worth commenting on the success of a Fermanagh crop grown during that year. Because of the huge war demand for linen, and the loss of imports of flax, flax production in Ireland was an important enterprise. On the 28th November 1918, the Lisnaskea flax market constituted a record both in quantity and in price. There were 40 tons of fibre, all of which graded within the prescribed range of prices – 35s to 45s per stone, realising the grand total of £13,000. The graders were pleasantly surprised at the quality of the flax in the market. The workmanship of some mills was the subject of complimentary remarks, the graders referring to the quality and marketable appearance of a few choice lots as *all that is to be desired.*

References:

Files of *The Impartial Reporter* and *Fermanagh Herald* held in Enniskillen Library.

Daly, Mary E., *The First Department – A History of the Department of Agriculture.* Institute of Public Administration. Dublin (2002).

The advertisements shown have been copied from the files of *The Impartial Reporter.*

Chapter 6
Depression and distress

The dire economic conditions predicted to follow the ending of the First World War sadly became a reality. As indicated in the previous chapter the Department of Agriculture and Technical Instruction (DATI) in 191 had issued the following statement: *The present high prices will by, an inevitable law, be followed at the close of War by a period of low prices, depression and perhaps distress. Farmers were advised to - clear all debts, accumulate savings for the rainy days ahead, and refrain from additional borrowing.*

The 1920s and early 1930s would prove to be the most challenging time for farming during the twentieth century. Poor demand and low prices for home produced farm commodities characterised this difficult period in farming. Poor and unorganised marketing of agricultural produce together with competition from cheap imports and a lack of effective Governmental price support mechanisms were major factors. This combined with a number of very wet seasons created serious problems for farmers in County Fermanagh. The levels of world food production increased rapidly after the war with correspondingly lower prices and this made imports to the United Kingdom particularly attractive to an urban industrial society. Home farm production had to compete with these low cost imports.

Superimposed on these constraints was the partition of Ireland with effect from 1922. This meant that a new administration system was dealing with the farming community as with all other sections of the population in the six counties of Northern Ireland.

Map of Northern Ireland.

Depression

The 1920s and 1930s were economically very difficult for farmers. Prices for produce were poor and farmers had difficulty in paying their bills. In 1921, the Ulster Farmers' Union (UFU) reported that prices were down to pre-war level and were continuing to fall. The payment of rates on farmland was a considerable financial burden at that time. It was claimed by the UFU in 1921 that the payment of rates in some cases was a greater burden than rent that had applied when most farmers were tenants. Apart from the difficulty in raising the money to pay the rates farmers resented paying them on their land. They believed that the improvement of roads, which was funded from the rates, was largely for the benefit of motor traffic. In fact, they claimed that the improved roads were too slippery for their main form of transport which was horse power.

Early marketing challenge

In February 1920 the UFU in Enniskillen, whose Chairman was Mr W. H. West (also Secretary of the Fermanagh County Committee of Agriculture), was concerned about marketing of agricultural produce. It was said that no other produce was marketed in such a slipshod manner as farm produce. Mr West stated that farmers must establish a society in the North of Ireland whereby they could market their produce to best advantage. It was claimed that at Christmas 1919 turkeys were 1s 10d per pound and in London they fetched 4 shillings. The producer was being 'fleeced up to his face' and they should see that this was put an end to. Mr West also claimed that flax in England was making £600 per ton whereas in Ireland they had to content themselves with £300 to £370 per ton. The price of butter was controlled by Government at a level which left its production uneconomic. Immediate decontrol of the price of Irish butter was sought, so that producers could compete with their British counterparts where decontrol had already been implemented. This and other major issues for farmers would face the new administration for Northern Ireland.

The new administration for agriculture

Following the partition of Ireland, under the Government of Ireland Act 1920, powers in relation to agriculture were transferred to the Ministry of Agriculture for Northern

Ireland. The Rt Hon E. M. Archdale MP PC DL, of Crocknacrieve, Ballinamallard, County Fermanagh, was appointed Northern Ireland's first Minister of Agriculture. In December 1921, in the Northern Ireland Parliament, £19,887 was allocated to defray the salaries and expenses of the Ministry of Agriculture and £19,049 for agricultural services.

Rt Hon E. M. Archdale MP PC (Courtesy of Mr Peter Archdale).

There were 75 officials who were taken over from the Department of Agriculture in Dublin on 1st January 1922. Among those were three agriculturists who would make a considerable impact on Northern Ireland agriculture during the following years. These were Messrs John Getty, Harry Cuthbertson and J. G. Rhynehart.

The County Committees of Agriculture, which had been set up under the Agriculture and Technical instruction Act of 1889, retained responsibility for advisory work and agricultural development under the Northern Ireland Ministry of Agriculture's supervision. Mr W. H. West, who had been Secretary and Organiser of the County Committee of Agriculture on its formation in 1901, under the Dublin Government's Department of Agriculture and Technical Instruction, was appointed Secretary and Organiser by the Fermanagh County Committee of Agriculture under the new regime. In 1922, Mr West, who had also been Assistant Secretary to the late Fermanagh Grand Jury from 1899, was appointed Secretary to the Fermanagh County Council. Mr West would continue to give outstanding service to the Committee until his death in 1935.

Rates

The members of the new Parliament in Northern Ireland, together with the UFU, were very active in presenting the farmers' case. Captain The Hon Harry Mulholland raised the plight of farmers in the Northern Ireland House of Commons in May 1923. In appealing for relief on rates, he gave details of the reduced prices for agricultural produce since the war. He said hay was then £15 per ton but is now £3 to £4; cows were formerly £60 a head, now they were £18; horses had been worth from £100 to £150 a head whereas they were now down to £30. Potatoes were £10 per ton but were now 10s. He said most farmers in Northern Ireland were facing insolvency. Some relief on rates on land had been granted in 1898 and through pressure from the UFU, the amount of this relief was doubled in 1924. This relief was worth about £20,000 per year to Fermanagh farmers.

Pork

Meantime, in March 1924, at the Fermanagh County Committee of Agriculture, serious concerns were raised about the marketing of pork and particularly the variability in price from one week to the next. Fluctuations from 80s to 64s per cwt within a two-week period were quoted. This meant a significant loss of income to those farmers who had the misfortune to present their pig carcases on a day when prices were depressed. The economics and methods of pig feeding were discussed again at a meeting of the County Committee in August 1924. The merits of dry versus wet feeding were discussed and were to be the subject of a farm experiment to be held on the farm of Mr Charles Graham, Drumack. In a general comment Mr West, Secretary, said that pigs paid well. He quoted the case of a Springfield farmer, who had kept accurate records, whose pigs left £3 net profit per pig after four months' keep. This farmer obviously sold his pigs on a day in the market when the higher prices were being paid.

Bad season

The summer of 1924 was extremely wet. Whilst crops generally suffered, in Mr West's view, turf presented the greatest problem. He said in the autumn of 1924: "*It is, perhaps, the matter that will affect the largest number of people in the county directly. The turf is as wet today as at the beginning of the summer, and the amount that can be saved will be as nothing to the needs of the people. You may say there is no turf, and it is a very dark prospect for the country people*

this winter. Unless there are extraordinary and unforeseen opportunities in the next few weeks for drying out the sods, I am afraid the situation will be such as to require some public action."

Staff changes and the Committee's educational role

The death of Mr Smyth, the County Fermanagh Committee of Agriculture's first Agricultural Instructor, was recorded in June 1919. At that time, warm tributes were paid to his service by Committee members. It was stated that he gave most useful instruction to farmers. He was most industrious and took a great interest in his work. All the farmers had a great respect for him and consulted him when they were in difficulty. Rev Canon MacMahon PP said that regarding their crops he hoped they would be able to get a man *"as good as Mr Smyth or nearly as good"*. Mr D. T. Ritchie was appointed as Mr Smyth's successor.

There was good news at the Fermanagh County Committee of Agriculture meeting in March 1924, when Mr J. J. McFerran from Rasharkin was appointed to serve as Instructor in the Garrison area. Mr William Graham of Rathfriland was also appointed Instructor to serve in the Rosslea area. There were four applicants for the new additional post of Agricultural Instructor. Mr W. M. Cameron, Ballinrees, Macosquin, Coleraine, who had just finished his course at the Royal College of Science, was appointed at a salary of £150 and locomotion expenses. At the same meeting the sum of £112 for demonstration plots was also approved, half of which was to be allocated to Mr Ritchie and the other half divided between the Instructors in Rosslea and Garrison.

Educational role

The County Committee was told in April 1925 that its role was educational. Mr John Getty of the Ministry of Agriculture reminded members that they had the interests of every one in the county to look after and cater for. This advice was given when members were debating whether they would appoint a horticultural instructor in succession to Mr Brock. Mr Getty said that the horticultural instructor was the only person that the labourers and small farmers could get advice from and as a consequence improve their standard of living.

The Secretary, Mr W. H. West, stated that Mr Brock had been the most useful officer they had and he not only dealt with horticulture but also with forestry. It then emerged that the cost of the County Committee schemes including premium bulls, the poultry schemes and the work of the instructors cost £2,600 per year. The county contributed £980 of this amount through the rates (1d in the £).

Turf as a source of heat for cooking and heating was vital in the 1920s.

Mr D. T. Ritchie (Courtesy of Department of Agriculture and Rural Development).

Mr John Getty (Courtesy of Department of Agriculture and Rural Development).

Distress in 1925

In February 1925, conditions in the Eshnadarragh, Rosslea and the Carnmore districts of South Fermanagh were regarded as extremely serious due to the previous year's bad weather. Urgent and prompt measures were required to deal with the situation. The mountainous districts were the worst as the people there had no food, no crops, no seed and no turf. A sum of £250 was granted by the County Council to enable the Relieving Officer in the Lisnaskea Guardians district to give financial support to families in these districts. A sum of 12s 6d per week, for a two month period, was given to the needy families. Consideration was given to the construction of a road in the district that would give much needed employment when men would earn 18s to 20s per week. In the meantime, the attractions of a new life in Canada were being promoted.

CANADIAN FARMS FOR BRITISH FAMILIES

The British and Canadian Governments have entered into an Agreement to advance funds for the settlement of Families from the United Kingdom on Improved Farm Lands in

CANADA

The Land of Opportunity for the experienced Farm Hand and Household Worker.

In every Province in Canada there are Prosperous Farmers who began life as labourers on the land.

There is a steady demand at good wages in all parts of Canada for Household Workers who can cook.

For full information regarding settlement schemes &c., apply to Dept. 10, Canadian Government Offices, 1, Regent Street, London, S.W. 1, or to Dep. 31, Canadian Government Emigration Office, 15/19, Victoria Street, Belfast. 2415

Advertisement for land in Canada.

Problems in the West

The south of the county was not the only area where the poor seasons had given rise to serious problems for those working the land. Farmers from the Derrygonnelly and Churchill areas of Fermanagh met in May 1925 in Derrygonnelly, under the chairmanship of Mr John Wilson, Bunnahone, to consider the crisis in the farming industry. Reference was made to the bad seasons, death of cattle and loss of crops. The meeting passed a resolution seeking relief from Government of a year's land purchase annuities, which could be added on at the end of the 68½ year lease period. In addition, a loan was sought for restocking purposes for those who had a heavy loss of cattle. It referred particularly to flooding in the Sillees River valley leading to the ruination of the grass, hay, crops and the deaths of cattle through fluke. The resolution when referring to conditions stated: *This is twice as bad a year for us as the long famed 1846. In that year, potatoes were the only failure, while this year crops in flooding and mountainous districts were almost a total failure, while in addition we lost our hay, our fuel, and our cattle, while the £1 note now has not the purchasing power eight shillings had then.*

Our cause is a just one, our case is desperate, and we hope and trust that it will not be necessary for our claims and negotiations to be marred by feeling or pressure. And we ever hope and pray that the good feeling that has always existed between us may ever continue unbroken.

Mr John Wilson
(Courtesy of Mrs Edith Wilson).

A similar meeting was held in Springfield in the same month under the chairmanship of William Hamilton of Enniskillen. Part of the Chairman's address, as reported in *The Impartial Reporter*, read as follows: *Since the black year of 1846, farmers have never been up against such a problem as they were up against to-day. The problems that were facing*

them to-day were manifold. They have had three years of very bad weather. It has been almost impossible to put a crop in and equally impossible to get it out with a profit to the farmer. They had just passed through a terrible time due to the disease of cattle caused by fluke. Their best cattle had been wiped out, and the small farmer, with farms depleted of stock, could not raise the money to keep his family going. They were met there to raise their voices and let those who represented them in Parliament know that they were expected to stand by the farmer.

Thomas Elliott JP supported what the Chairman had said. He stated that the milk supply to Springfield Creamery had decreased last year by 175,000 gallons. Mr William Spence appealed for farmers to join the UFU. Mr John Connor said that he had recorded the losses suffered by farmers within a mile of Springfield and some of them had lost stock and produce to the value of £200. A resolution was passed calling on the Government to suspend the payment of Land Purchase Annuities for two years and to make loans available to farmers.

Fluke treatment

Fluke in cattle and sheep was a very serious problem at that time aggravated by the number of very wet seasons. Mr John Fawcett of Rossculton, Springfield, had recorded in his notebook in 1922 a *Fluke Cure* for cattle. The formula for the cure read as follows:

First day:	*naggin of brandy*
Second day:	*drachm Tartar Emetic*
Third day:	*half ounce of Nitre*
Fourth day:	*half ounce of blue stone*
Fifth day:	*one iron spoonful of sulphur*
Sixth day:	*half a wine glass of vinegar on a pint of buttermilk whey.*

These treatments were to be combined with good nourishment of the animal.

Better weather

The year 1926 was an improvement as far as weather and production were concerned. Milk output increased in 1926. Professor R. H. Wilkinson, Inspector of the Ministry of Agriculture, in April 1928, at a meeting of Fermanagh Creamery Managers, said that a good grass year meant millions of gallons of milk to the county. He stated that the milk yield in 1926 was 20 to 25 per cent more than in 1925 and that 1927 showed a further substantial increase.

A harvest report in September 1927 indicated that hay was of good quality although some August saved hay suffered some damage from the weather. The grazing season was regarded as exceptionally good. The cereal crops, including oats and wheat, were classed as heavy. There was little blight on potatoes and there were excellent yields of good quality tubers. Turnips and mangolds, after a difficult start, were doing well.The flax crop generally was excellent with high yields and good quality.

Despite the good harvest conditions in 1927, *The Impartial Reporter* regarded the farming community as *being down and out.* This was attributed to the bad years and the livestock losses through diseases which followed. Due to their impoverished condition, farmers had not enough stock to eat their present supply of grass and were unable, due to poverty, to obtain more cattle. *The Impartial Reporter* was appealing to the Ministry of Agriculture to give the farmers assistance to recover from their deplorable condition.

A Government response to the crisis was the availability of cheap loans to those who had lost stock as a result of the poor seasons. The 'livestock replacement loan' was put into operation to meet a very special emergency and the loans were confined to those who had losses of livestock from October 1924.

The family farm in Fermanagh in the 1920s

Despite the wider economic problems, many farmers still managed to rear families well although there were few luxuries. Mr George Cathcart gave a detailed account in 1979 of life on his family farm at Scandally, Derrygonnelly, in the 1920s.

Mr George Cathcart OBE JP (Courtesy of Mrs Marion Maxwell).

He stated that he had been born on an average Fermanagh farm of some sixty to seventy acres. His account of farming activity and family life was as follows.

A farm of that size would be considered by the Ministry of Agriculture as being barely viable and yet my father and mother raised ten of us with a reasonable standard of living. This was possible because of the system of mixed farming practised in Fermanagh at that time. On our farm we kept fifteen cows, milked by hand, and their calves reared to year-olds when they were sold. A few sows producing young pigs for sale and fattening. A flock of about twenty sheep producing lambs and wool. Two to three hundred hens on free range producing eggs for sale. A few geese and a gander rearing 20 to 25 goslings and a flock of 20 to 25 ducks and with a bit of luck 20 to 30 turkeys reared for the Christmas market and not forgetting the two horses kept to do the farm work. Although the horses consumed a lot of grass, hay and oats (these being produced on the farm) they were very economical compared with the cost of tractors and fuel today. Production from the land was grass to feed the stock in the summer and hay for winter keep. Four or five acres of oats providing feed for the horses, egg laying stimulation for the hens, oatmeal for the porridge, and straw for feeding and bedding, and seed for the following year. Potatoes were grown for home consumption and for seed for the following year. A half acre of early seed potatoes, called Flounders, which were sold to neighbouring farmers each spring for the production of first early potatoes. A half acre of turnips was grown for cattle feeding and as vegetables for the house. A small area of other vegetables was grown for house consumption mainly cabbage, onions, beans, peas, parsnips and carrots. An orchard of about a half acre existed with cooking and eating apples, pears, plums, gooseberries and black currants and not forgetting a plot of rhubarb.

Most farms at that time were self sufficient in fuel for heating and cooking, mainly turf and home grown timber for firewood. However, the plot of bog on our farm was not of good quality turf and ours were obtained from a mountain bog about twelve miles away.

While the horses provided motive power most of the work was done by the family, supplemented by a farm labourer who was hired on a half yearly basis at £10 for the summer and £8 for the winter plus board and lodgings. Most farm labourers placed as much store by how they were fed and kept as the money they received.

A turf fuelled hearth fire.

You will by now have some idea of the comprehensive nature of production on the farms of Fermanagh at that time. The net result was that apart from the purchase of a 10 stone pack of flour, tea, sugar, salt, paraffin oil, candles, and the occasional roast of beef, the entire family was sustained by what was produced on the farm. The open hearth fire was the only method of heating and cooking. The main cooking utensils were the metal pots and kettle hung on the iron crane crook and the three legged pot oven in which the bread was baked and in which the turkeys, geese and chickens were roasted. This oven stood on three short legs on the open hearth with coals underneath and on the lid and I can still smell the rich aroma coming from that oven when my mother removed the lid with a pair of tongs to see if the roasting had been complete. The bread was baked every day and the bag of flour was soon used up with the size of our household.

The oats when harvested were stacked in the farmyard and during the winter a stack at a time would be built in on the barn loft for threshing on a wet day when it was not possible to do any outside work. The threshing was done, of course, by two men with old wooden flails then used for the purpose. The grain was sent to the nearest corn mill with some to be crushed for cattle feeding but always enough to be ground into oatmeal to provide enough meal for the porridge to provide the family with supper all days of the year. The quantity of potatoes grown ensured there was enough for the family needs and sufficient seed for planting the following year.

Most of the milk produced was sold to the local Co-operative Creamery for separation and butter making and the skimmed milk was returned to the farm for feeding to the calves and the pigs, while enough was kept at home to provide the family with home-made butter and wonderful buttermilk for drinking.

All the poultry were hatched on the farm and after replenishing the laying flocks all the rest were consumed in the household which meant that there was always an ample supply of roast chicken, roast duckling, and roast goose with of course the traditional turkey at Christmas. The remainder of the turkey flock was sold before Christmas providing my mother with some well earned spending money for the festive season.

Twice yearly one pig was chosen to be fed until it weighed at least 3cwt when it would be slaughtered by a neighbour who was an adept hand at this work and after hanging for a few days this man returned one evening and butchered the pig carcase and laid it in salt on a flagstone floor to be cured into bacon. What I can remember so well about this operation was that the trimmings of the cutting process, called griskins, when laid on the pan provided the loveliest fry imaginable. Another by-product was the pig's bladder which when properly dried could be inflated to make a football, which we as boys appreciated very much.

The eggs were sold to a local egg exporter who had acquired the great art of packing them in wooden boxes in straw in such a perfect manner that they could be transported to England in complete safety and, of course, there was an everlasting supply for all purposes in the household.

However, the outstanding example of self sufficiency on the farm was that not only was the whole family amply fed but they were partially clothed as well because part of the yearly wool clip sold to the Lisbellaw Wool House in Enniskillen was sent by them to Galashiels in Scotland where it was manufactured into material and returned to the farm where it was used to provide suits for my father and the boys of the family and skirts for my mother and the girls.

Those were memorable and happy days on the farm when every member of the family played their part and even the youngest member found something useful which they could do and I remember with great pride when I mastered the art of holding a skein of wool on my two outstretched hands while my mother wound it into a ball of appropriate size for the knitting of the socks.

Land Acts

The UFU was very active in promoting the completion of land purchase. Under the Land Acts, at the end of the nineteenth and early twentieth centuries, farmers were entitled to buy-out the land that they farmed from the landlord from whom the land had previously been rented. It was 1925 before the final Land Act was passed at Westminster when the Government guaranteed the issue of 4½ per cent Bonds to buy out 1,000,000 acres of land. Those farmers who were still tenants had the opportunity of buying-out their farms. The Government advanced the purchase price and those who bought out their land repaid the Government by way of Land Purchase Annuities. These repayments were normally less than their previous rent. However, finding the money was not always easy. The financial situation on farms in 1926 was very difficult. Sir Charles Falls, MP, who lived at Derryinch, Enniskillen, led a delegation from Fermanagh to meet the Prime Minister in February 1926 urging him to take some steps to relieve the farmers in the County. The Prime Minister was informed as follows: *As a result of three bad seasons over the last three years the majority of farmers are in a hopeless financial condition, and many of the best class are making arrangements to sell their farms at any price and to emigrate with their families, while the less desirable people are being financed from some unknown source and are buying up every farm on offer for sale.*

In November 1927 Mr R. Irvine, Clerk of Lisnaskea Rural District Council, wrote asking the Government to extend the Land Purchase Annuity repayments over a longer period of time. In his letter, he referred to the depression in cattle and pork trades and stated that: *farmers were on the verge of bankruptcy.*

Deterioration

By 1928, the economic conditions had deteriorated even further. The UFU Council was informed by its Executive that: *Farmers are passing through the worst time they have ever experienced in recent history.* Final success in relation to rates on farms was achieved in 1928 when Winston Churchill, Chancellor of the Exchequer, promised relief from rates on agricultural land. The UFU pressed for the rates relief being granted in Great Britain to be applied to Northern Ireland. The farming industry was relieved of 75 per cent of its rates burden. Despite this reduction in overhead costs, the situation was reported by the UFU Executive in January 1929 as even more grave, stating: *agriculture is suffering from a greater depression than ever – prices do not cover the costs of production.* Strong representations by the UFU to the Ministry of Agriculture at that time met with a small degree of success in that guaranteed loans at at 3½ per cent interest rate were granted to enable farmers to purchase seeds and fertiliser to put in the next year's crop.

When addressing the House of Commons at Stormont in February 1928, The Rt Hon E. M. Archdale MP for Fermanagh and Minister of Agriculture, said: "*the farmers have been down and out during the last few years*". He continued: "*I hope, and the members of the Government hope – we have the greatest sympathy from the Prime Minister and Minister of Finance – that we will be able to help the farmers in some way, but it is at present almost impossible to help the farmers in Northern Ireland. I have no doubt that they have their backs to the wall, and that they will, by recovery and hard work, and by decent weather this year be able to get money for their produce, which will help them out of their Slough of Despair they are now in*".

Improvement schemes

The Land Improvement Scheme, which provided limited assistance for certain land improvements, was introduced by Government during 1929 (details can be found in Chapter 7). This assistance complemented the Pasture Improvement Scheme, introduced in 1925, which encouraged liming and fertilising to improve grassland output.

Agricultural Credit Act not welcome

In August 1929, an eleven-man Fermanagh delegation, led by Captain T. Verschoyle of Tullycleagh, Ballinamallard, met the Minister of Finance seeking long-term financial facilities on the lines of the Agricultural Credits Act in Great Britain. The delegation pointed out that there was a serious decline in the cattle population in Fermanagh. Furthermore, Mr Browne, an auctioneer and member of the delegation, stated: "*farms were selling at 20 per cent of the price paid for them some years ago.*" A resolution by Fermanagh County Council supporting the concept was not supported by the other County Councils. The Fermanagh based Minister of Agriculture, now Sir Edward Archdale, thought that farmers would be wary of the British scheme since they would be entirely in the hands of the banks or Credit Corporation. The Ministry of Agriculture when dealing with the issue consulted the banks on the availability of credit. The local banks in Fermanagh indicated that the availability of credit through their organisations was not limiting the development of agriculture. They did, however, state that there had been a steady drain on deposits over the past four to five years. One local bank manager, who displayed his ignorance in relation to farming conditions in Fermanagh, stated: "*Farmers are largely to blame – adherence to raising livestock only – fields covered with rushes – little effort to drain their land – entire absence of tillage and fruit. Farming industry at present in the hands of old people as a rule, and complaints are general that young folk will not remain on the land and emigrate at first opportunity.*"

In summing up the situation, the Ministry of Agriculture stated: *On the whole the farming community seems to be rather poorer, and savings diminishing, but it is not apparent that banks are restricting credit in any way.*

Farmers were also pressurising their local MPs for help. A delegation of Fermanagh farmers went to see their MP, Sir Basil Brooke at Colebrooke. Prior to the delegation's visit, Sir Basil wrote on 17th November 1929 to Mr Pollock, Minister of Finance, who had obviously dealt with the Fermanagh group on their visit to Stormont. Sir Basil wrote as follows: *So that if you find yourself unable to grant all they ask would you make it as easy as possible for me to give the answer which burneth away the wrath as they are not an easy lot, but if given good reason are not difficult to appease.*

Milk production 1924 to 1934

By 1924, milk prices had halved from the high level of 1921. Milk prices paid to producers during the year 1929/30 were recorded by Fivemiletown and Brookeborough Co-Operative Agricultural and Dairy Society Ltd as 6.70d per gallon on average and the price received for the butter produced was 19.38d per lb.

For the 1930/31 year the amount paid to producers had dropped to 5.38d per gallon on average and butter fetched 14.73d. For the 1932 year, Springfield Creamery paid on average 4.16d per gallon. Milk prices in Fermanagh dropped even further and by 1934, it was fetching just over two pence per gallon whereas in the east of the Province near the centres of large population milk for the liquid trade was making four times that price.

Professor Wilkinson, the Ministry of Agriculture's Senior Dairying Inspector, when addressing a meeting of the Erne (Kesh) Co-Operative Dairy Society in April 1931, emphasised the need for pasteurising milk received at the creameries, improved grassland and using the right bulls. He also stressed the need for increased production stating that in Northern Ireland "*we don't produce enough butter to supply the city of Belfast, except for a couple of months during the height of summer.*" He stated that during the year 1930 Northern Ireland imported 51,109 cwt of butter and exported 32,381 cwt. He blamed the Irish Free State, where butter was ten shillings per cwt less, for the low prices in Northern Ireland.

The summer of 1931 was not good for milk producers or for creameries. In September 1931, butter was making 118s to 120s per cwt compared to 143s a year earlier. Payment of Land Purchase Annuities by farmers was also presenting problems in 1931. The poorer parts of the country were worst affected. It was stated that Fermanagh, which had been badly hit by flooding and also by poor prices for farm produce, was the worst paying centre. Arrears in County Fermanagh amounted to almost £5,000.

Government loans and depressed prices

Representations continued to be made over succeeding years regarding payment of the Land Purchase Annuities under the depressed economic conditions, which continued through the early 1930s. In January 1933, a delegation from the UFU headquarters, which included Mr James McElroy from Monea, met the Prime Minister, the Minister of Finance and the Minister of Agriculture, regarding the difficulties for farmers in paying the annuities. No relaxation was granted in respect of the payment of annuities. However, the Government offered loans at 3 per cent interest to assist farmers out of their difficulties until new policies, which would raise the price of agricultural produce, became effective.

In December 1933, prices at Enniskillen Fair had dropped from the levels of 1926. The 1926 prices are shown in brackets. Calves were £4 5s (£7 15s); store cattle were 20s to 30s per cwt (38s to 41s per cwt); springing cows were

Irvinestown Creamery in the 1930s (Courtesy of ITEC).

£15 10s (£21); suckers (pigs) were £1 13s (£2 5s) and fat lambs were £1 4s per head. Some costs of production had also dropped by 1933, for example, maize meal was under 9s 10d per cwt whereas in 1926 it was12s 2d.

Pig production and marketing

From the beginning of the century, pigs were an important enterprise on many farms. The Large White Ulster pig was the popular breed. This breed produced good-sized litters. In addition, the pigs grew rapidly and came to maturity sooner than the Large White York breed.

Large White Ulster sow

When trade with England was developing in the mid 1920s the York pig was in greater demand by English buyers and was considered to be more suitable for the pork trade. The English buyers claimed that the Ulster breed was 'too fat and too soapy'. In October 1926, it was stated that that an Ulster pig would fetch about 30s per pig less than a York.

Pig Breeders' and Feeders' Association

It was not until October 1927 that co-operative action was taken by Fermanagh farmers in relation to the marketing of pigs. A resolution was passed at a well-attended meeting in Enniskillen calling on the Northern Ireland Ministry of Agriculture to get legislative authority to compel pork curers to publish the weekly price of pork in advance. Those in attendance decided to form an association to market pigs. Mr W. Copeland Trimble was appointed Chairman of the new organisation and the Honorary Secretaries were Messrs J. A. Cathcart and P. F. Cassidy. Concern was expressed at local prices. In London, the prices were claimed to be double those obtained in Enniskillen. At that time pork in the Enniskillen market was 63s per cwt. The first *live light pig market* was held by Co Fermanagh Pig Breeders' and Feeders' Association on Tuesday 15th November 1927. Live pigs, which would kill out at 80 to 100lb, were to be brought to Bleakley's Slaughter House in Enniskillen. On the Friday of that week, producers were invited to bring heavier pigs killing out at 100 to 120 lb. One hundred live pigs were brought on the first day. The slaughtered pigs were placed in crates, then the crates onto the train, transhipped to the steamer at Greenore and hence to Broadstreet Station, London, the nearest station to the Smithfield market. Later live pigs were exported. In December 1927, it was reported that the Association had a turnover of £1,000 per week. Producers using the service were well satisfied with the arrangements and financial rewards. Mr Trimble, at a meeting in November 1927 at Aghadrumsee, told a gathering of interested producers that by marketing their pigs through the Association 7s to 8s more per cwt was obtained. Mr Trimble said that York pigs were the most suitable breed for the London trade. At the same meeting, Mr W. H. West JP spoke of the helpless condition of farmers being obliged to accept anything tendered to them for a perishable article in the pork market without any option of arranging prices as in other matters. He urged farmers to come together as they had done in Enniskillen to market their pigs to best advantage.

Future of Large White Ulster Pigs

In March 1928, Captain Verschoyle, who had succeeded Mr W. Copeland Trimble as Chairman, presided at his first meeting of the Fermanagh Pig Breeders' and Feeders' Association. He said that since 1st January 150 pigs per week on average had been marketed through the Association by its 129 members. This he said was comparatively small in relation to the 400 to 500 per week going through the Enniskillen market. In view of this, he said it was time for members to consider whether it was worthwhile for the Association to continue. Mr Trimble said that when the Association was formed, pork was only 52s and as they made their efforts, so the price of pork increased. Mr W. H. West, Secretary, County Committee of Agriculture, warned that if the Association failed pork would once again be 52s per cwt. Mr Sydney Smith, Marketing Inspector of the Ministry of Agriculture who was in attendance, addressed the meeting and told them that the English buyers were not going to take the White Ulster pigs indefinitely. He said that the English market required a lean pig such as that produced from the Large White York breed.

Large White York boar.

Concern

By December 1929, two years after its formation, concern was expressed about the future of the Pig Breeders' and Feeders' Association. At a meeting in December 1929, consideration was given to winding up the Association due to apathy and the selfishness of its members. At a reconvened gathering in early January 1930, Captain Verschoyle informed the 60 to 70 members in attendance (out of a total of 376) that the meeting, adjourned from last month, had been called to consider further a resolution which had been unanimously agreed by the Committee to the effect that the Association would be wound up voluntarily under the Companies Act 1908. Captain Verschoyle expressed concern that only 90 members had paid up their five shillings per share and was not hopeful for the future of the Association. After much discussion and encouragement from Mr W. H. West, a vote was taken and by a substantial majority, it was decided to continue with the Association. Captain Verschoyle stated that since the meeting rejected the unanimous recommendation of the Committee the members now resigned and it would be necessary to elect a new Committee. A new Committee was appointed and Mr J. McElroy JP (Monea) was appointed Chairman with Mr C. Graham, who had been the buyer for the Association, being nominated as Secretary and Manager.

Progress

In early March 1930, good progress was reported by the Association at its annual meeting. Mr W. Copeland Trimble said that it was very gratifying to find that the Association, which was supposed to be dead and dying, had recovered and was now in fairly good condition. The number of members had increased to 493. The best testimony to what they had been doing was what had occurred last week. A number of pigs had been sent last Friday to Belfast, and for three of these pigs Mr William Lucy of Monea received £32 14s 6d, net after expenses had been deducted, and Mr Lucy had his cheque the following morning. That showed what the Association could do for its members. They were not tied to any one market. He offered congratulations to the Chairman and his Committee.

The 1931 annual meeting of the Association held in June received a satisfactory report on the year's trading with a profit of £72 and a bank overdraft of only 3s 9d. Concern was expressed by some members that the annual membership levy had not been collected in many cases. However, the Chairman said that in the circumstances the throughput of pigs was the priority. During the year Mr C. Graham, Manager, had died and the responsibility for running the organisation fell largely to the Chairman, Mr J. McElroy. The Chairman indicated that he wished to resign but, after much praise, was prevailed upon at the meeting, under the chairmanship of Mr W. Copeland Trimble, to carry on for a further year. The new committee appointed Mr A. Noble, Glassdrummond, Lisnaskea, as the new Manager and Mr A. Rusk, Cavanaleck, Fivemiletown, as Secretary.

In June 1932, at the Association's annual meeting good progress was reported by the Chairman, Mr J. McElroy. Some diversification had taken place in the Association's operation in that it was now trading in pigs, poultry and wool. Sales during the year were in excess of £7,450.

Change in farming activity from 1917 until 1930 in County Fermanagh

Table 6.1 Livestock and cropping 1917 and 1930

Year	1917	1930
Cattle	104,134	83,976
Sheep	11,740	15,655
Pigs	10,649	18,464
Poultry	620,858	871,149
Potatoes (acres)	13,702	9,494
Total crops (acres)	42,310	24,830

Source: Economics and Statistics Division, Department of Agriculture and Rural Development.

The year 1918 was the peak year for cropping in County Fermanagh during the First World War. By 1930, in the middle of the depression years, the area of crops had dropped to just less than 25,000 acres showing a decline of over 40 per cent in area. The drop in the areas of cereals (45 per cent) was greater than the decline in potatoes, which showed a 31 per cent drop. The decrease in the area of cereals was no doubt due to the increased availability of relatively cheap grain such as maize, which was once again being imported from America and elsewhere in increasing quantities.

The major decline in farming activity during the period was reflected in the decrease in cattle numbers, which showed a drop of over 19 per cent. The poor prices combined with bad seasons and associated disease in cattle both contributed to this significant decline. Sheep numbers increased by one third during the period. Sheep were much less dependent on winter fodder than cattle and no doubt this made them a more attractive proposition during the bad seasons.

Pigs and poultry benefited from the availability of the American grain and both increased substantially over the years. Pigs also benefited from the marketing initiative and increased in number by 73 per cent and poultry showed an increase of 40 per cent.

Sheep were less dependent than cattle on winter fodder.

Accounts

The Ministry of Agriculture introduced a Financial Accounting System for farming at that time. Account books were issued to farmers who agreed to keep records for the information of the Ministry whose staff provided supervision for the keeping and auditing of the accounts. During the year ending 30th September 1931, accounts were kept on 24 farms in Northern Ireland. The profit for that year worked out at about £3 11s per acre. This did not take into account any return on capital invested on the farm.

References:

File re rate relief for farmers, including comment on poor state of agriculture in Fermanagh PRONI.

Cabinet papers PRONI.

Files of *The Impartial Reporter* and *Fermanagh Herald* held in Enniskillen Library.

Ministry of Agriculture for Northern Ireland *Monthly Reports.*

MacLurg, Alistair, *The Ulster Farmers' Union – The History of its first Seventy Years 1917 – 1987.*

Chapter 7
Prospect of better times

There were many years of depression in farming following the end of the First World War. Prices for agricultural produce were very low. This situation arose from cheap imports of food into the United Kingdom, particularly from countries of the Empire and the Dominions. County Fermanagh farmers suffered in this general way but also had the handicap of remoteness from the markets at the main centres of population. Furthermore, there were a number of exceptionally poor seasons from a weather perspective, which made cropping and livestock production extremely difficult. In succeeding years, some hope was kindled with the prospect of controls on imports and better marketing arrangements for farm produce with some assurances regarding prices. Changes in the personalities charged with responsibility for developing agriculture in Northern Ireland and specifically in agricultural administration in County Fermanagh occurred during this era.

The Ottawa Agreement

The British Empire Economic Conference was held in the late summer of 1932 in Ottawa to discuss the economic crisis referred to as the Great Depression. Participants at the conference were representatives of the British colonies and the autonomous Dominions. The outcome of the conference brought new hope to aspects of Northern Ireland agriculture. Sir Edward Archdale, Minister of Agriculture, at a press briefing in October 1932, said: "*The tax of 15s per cwt on butter and 1s to 1s 9d per great hundred on eggs will give much needed assistance to our dairy and poultry industries. Though the benefits Ulster agriculture will receive under the new tariff proposals are undoubtedly substantial, I attach far greater importance to the undertaking, which the United Kingdom Government has entered into in respect of meat. The position which has developed recently with regard to bacon, mutton, lamb and beef has been threatening the whole future of our livestock industry. The enormous imports of bacon and hams, particularly during 1931 and 1932 have made economic production at home impossible. How serious the mutton and lamb position is can be judged from the fact that during this summer the price of Australian and New Zealand mutton and lamb in the London market was as low as 2¾d to 2½d per lb which covers no more than the cost of transport from Australia to London.*" The agreements from the conference enabled the United Kingdom Government to limit and control the imports of frozen and chilled beef, mutton and lamb in such a way as to secure a higher and more stable price level for the home producer. In summing up the Minister said: "*I should like to emphasise the fact that 80 per cent of our agricultural wealth is derived from stock and stock products. Our most important products are eggs and poultry, bacon and hams, cattle, butter, mutton and lamb. Every one of these items will benefit as a consequence of the Ottawa Agreement.*"

Smuggling

One of the consequences in Ireland of the implementation of this agreement was the smuggling of agricultural produce across the border between Northern Ireland and the Irish Free State. There were tariffs and quotas placed on imports of farm produce from the Free State to the United Kingdom. Smuggling of livestock and other commodities into Northern Ireland would be a feature for many years to come.

Guaranteed prices for pigs

After many years of agitation by the Ulster Farmers' Union (UFU), a scheme was agreed between the Pig Industry Council and the United Kingdom Government in 1932, which secured for the English and Northern Ireland farmers the first place in their own markets in Britain. The new scheme gave the farmers, for the first time in 80 years, a guaranteed market for their produce and, best of all, a guaranteed price fixed by the Trade Board in such a way as to give a reasonable margin of profit to the producer. The press report with this announcement indicated that this scheme was one of the greatest boons to Northern Ireland and would give great encouragement to small producers.

Cheap imports

The importation of cheap grain and other farm products made it almost impossible for Northern Ireland farmers to obtain prices for their produce that would cover costs of production. Restriction of imports was demanded otherwise farmers would go bankrupt and tillage would cease. Representations by the UFU to Westminster in partnership with the English and Scottish Farmers' Unions regarding the import of cheap food, which led to depressed prices for home produced commodities, met with some success. The British Government, in response, maintained that control of imports must be accompanied by better marketing of home produced commodities.

Agricultural Marketing Act 1933

After discussions in 1933 between the UFU and the Ministry of Agriculture in Northern Ireland, a marketing Act was passed at Stormont. Sir Edward Archdale, Minister of Agriculture, in introducing the Agricultural Marketing Bill on 14th May 1933 said: "*This Bill does provide our Ulster farmers with the means of securing a just return for their labours without in any way prejudicing the position of the consumer.*" He said that the Bill was an enabling Bill to allow schemes to be formulated for the better marketing of agricultural produce. Under this Bill, the Northern Ireland Pigs Marketing Board was established and a milk marketing scheme introduced. The detailed operation of these schemes is explained in later chapters.

Any advance at this time was welcomed by farmers. In April 1933, at the annual general meeting of the UFU, the previous year was described as *the darkest year in the experience of farmers in a generation.*

Beef Subsidy

Beef producers also had the prospect of better times. Under the Cattle Industry (Emergency Provisions) Act 1934, a subsidy of 5 shillings per cwt in respect of bullocks, heifers and cow heifers (a young animal that has produced one calf) came into operation at the beginning of September 1934. Eligible animals were those that killed out at 52 per cent and were not less than 5 ½ cwt. Subsidy became payable when the cattle were sold and only payable to the producer. The cattle had to be presented at an approved centre where the Ministry's veterinary staff acted as certifying officers. Fairs and markets recognised for the purposes of certification in County Fermanagh were: Irvinestown, Newtownbutler, Enniskillen, Derrygonnelly and Lisnaskea. Fivemiletown, although in Tyrone, would have also served Fermanagh farmers.

Sir Edward Archdale at Riversdale House with his sons (Audley, Nicholas and William) and extended family (Courtesy of Mr Peter Archdale).

Retirement of the Minister, The Rt Hon Sir Edward Archdale MP PC DL

Sir Edward Archdale, Northern Ireland's first Minister of Agriculture, retired in the early winter of 1933. He was a Fermanagh man, born in 1853. His parents lived at Crocknacrieve. His father was Mr Nicholas Montgomery Archdale and his mother a daughter of Rev and Mrs John Grey Porter of Belleisle. Sir Edward was educated at the Naval School, Portsmouth, and entered the Royal Navy in 1866. He had reached the rank of Lieutenant after 14 years service when his father's sudden death, while riding to hounds in County Meath, meant a return to Crocknacrieve in 1880. From that time, he farmed at Crocknacrieve and later at Riversdale and Rossahilly, Ballinamallard. He took a very active part in local affairs as a county gentleman. He was a most energetic member of a family which has had a prominent part in county affairs since the Plantation of Ulster. Sir Edward was High Sheriff of County Fermanagh in 1884 and was elected Member of Parliament for North Fermanagh in 1897 retaining the seat until 1903 when he retired. He again entered Parliament in 1916 as Member for North Fermanagh. He resigned in 1921 to stand for the new Parliament of Northern Ireland and was elected as the Member for Fermanagh and Tyrone. He held this seat until 1929. He was then elected to represent the Enniskillen constituency, from which he retired in 1937. He was appointed Minister of Agriculture for Northern Ireland and a Privy Councillor in 1921 and also served as Minister of Commerce until 1925. From 1925 until 1933, he served as Minister of Agriculture. He was created Baronet in 1928 in the King's Birthday Honours. It was claimed at the end of his Ministerial career that Sir Edward was the oldest Cabinet Minister in the British Empire, if not in the world. In 1934, *The Impartial Reporter* had recorded that the Archdales had represented the county in parliament for over 154 years without a break.

Sir Basil Brooke, Minister of Agriculture for Northern Ireland, 1934 – 1941 (Courtesy of Viscount Brookeborough).

On his retirement, the Fermanagh County Committee of Agriculture passed a resolution in appreciation of his services as Minister. The Committee also copied the resolution to the Prime Minister. Lord Craigavon, in his response, stated: "*I am very much obliged for your kindness in forwarding copy of the resolution unanimously adopted by the County Fermanagh Committee of Agriculture at their meeting on 11th December. Needless to say, my colleagues and I are whole-heartedly with your Committee in the encomiums, which they have passed on our old friend and colleague, who during a long lifetime has so faithfully represented his native county and served Ulster with such conspicuous ability. It is some source of satisfaction to me personally that the county is to have the honour of furnishing the Cabinet with his successor.*"

Sir Basil Brooke's review and vision

During 1934, Sir Basil Brooke succeeded Sir Edward Archdale as Minister for Agriculture. In the early months of Sir Basil Brooke's tenure as Minister, he said: "*The farming community is entering into a complete revolution in agricultural policy, which was entirely changing everything that has happened previously in the country.*"

The Minister of Agriculture, Sir Basil Brooke, with Mr R. J. Fannin, Principal of Greenmount Agricultural College (Courtesy of Mr Derek Alexander).

In May 1935, Sir Basil Brooke, in a Foreword to the Ministry of Agriculture's *Monthly Report*, gave a review of agriculture from the time the first *Monthly Report* was produced in 1923. He wrote: *During the lifetime of the Report, there have been many interesting developments in Ulster Agriculture. The period has two phases, the one of depression and the other of market reorganisation. These phases are not clear-cut. Market reorganisation began as early as 1923, and it would be foolish to assert that since the principal measures of market legislation have been passed depression has disappeared, but the period can be looked at most conveniently as a period of depression and reorganisation.*

In 1925, agricultural prices were still comparatively high. According to the Monthly Report of February of that year the price of milk sold to creameries was between 8¾d and 9d per gallon, the price of wheat was 10s to 12s per cwt, and the price of dead pigs ranged from 87s to 90s per cwt. In February 1932, the price of milk sold to creameries had fallen from 5½d to 3½d per gallon, the price of wheat averaged 6s 5d per cwt, and the price of dead pigs had dropped as low as 50s per cwt. In 1932, therefore, it can be seen that the depression was very severe and that farmers were not getting a remunerative return on their production.

There are two ways of meeting adversity. One is that of Chinese peasants on the banks of the Yellow River, who, I am told, attribute the floods which from time to time sweep away their homes and ruin their crops to the work of an evil spirit and accept their fate with folded hands. The other is the attitude, which distinguishes the British race. While admitting that some of the factors in our hard lot are due to forces beyond our control, we do what we can to set our own house in order and to improve our situation. It was this attitude of mind that produced the Agricultural Marketing Act of 1933, which attempts to meet the depression, which I have illustrated by dealing with those causes, which are immediately controllable. The objects of the Act, out of which the Pigs scheme has emerged, and of the Milk and Milk Products Act which followed in 1934, are to increase the control of producers over the marketing of their produce by setting up boards or councils representative of the industry concerned with a view to securing better quality and therefore more competitive produce, to lower marketing costs by effecting much needed economies, and to raise the price to the producer.

Low incomes

Despite the advances made in marketing agricultural produce, resulting from the 1933 Agricultural Marketing Act, the financial position on farms was far from satisfactory. The financial situation had not improved by 1938 and in November of that year, the UFU magazine was claiming that the farming industry in the Province was still in a worse plight than it had been for a generation. In December 1938, the UFU Council called for the setting up of an inquiry into the causes of the continuing agricultural depression.

The Ministry of Agriculture's *Monthly Report* for 1938 showed that average family earnings for eleven typical Northern Ireland farms in the years 1930 to 1936 varied from nine shillings per week in 1932/33 to £2 10s 0d per week in 1935/36. The value of farmland at that time was also very depressed being worth less than half normal prices. Emigration by farmers to Canada, Australia and New Zealand was commonplace.

The Pigs Marketing Board

The first fruit of the 1933 Agricultural Marketing Act was the formation of the Northern Ireland Pigs Marketing Board (PMB) on 13th September 1933. The Board consisted of 14 members, 11 of whom were elected by registered producers and three appointed by the Ministry of Agriculture. Mr R. Rusk JP, Cavanaleck, Fivemiletown, was elected to represent Fermanagh's interests. The scheme applied to pigs that were sold for curing as bacon. One object of the scheme was to stabilise prices and prevent the violent fluctuations which had been experienced in the past. Grading of pigs, which was initially very contentious, became the basis for payment.

The next significant development was the appointment of a Pig Industry Council, consisting of three members appointed by the Bacon Marketing Board, three by the Pigs Marketing Board and three members appointed by the Ministry of Agriculture. This Council fixed the price of pigs to be sold by the producer, previously set by the PMB. Details of developments in pig marketing are dealt with in Chapter 20.

Depression

Following the collapse of milk prices in the west of the Province in 1934, there was a strong temptation to move milk to the east of the Province to capitalise on the higher liquid milk prices. This development had the potential to undermine the business of the milk producers serving Belfast and also raised the issue of milk quality in relation to liquid consumption. There was also the need to provide a reasonable return to those producers who supplied milk for manufacturing. These pressures led the Ministry of Agriculture for Northern Ireland to introduce measures to protect the quality of the household milk supply and to establish a system which would provide a basis for the development of a sustainable dairy industry throughout Northern Ireland.

Milk Marketing Scheme

The Northern Ireland Milk Marketing Scheme of 1934 gave the Ministry powers to control all milk sales in the Province. The Ministry introduced a system of licensing suppliers with herd disease status and hygienic milk standards. All milk for human consumption had to be from either Tuberculin Tested herds or milk that had been pasteurised. The Milk and Milk Products scheme was aimed at improving the prices paid to producers many

of whom previously depended on what they received for milk used in manufacturing. Producers near large centres of population then received much higher prices as the milk was used for liquid consumption. At that time, only 30 per cent of the milk produced in Northern Ireland was for liquid consumption with the remainder going into manufacturing, mainly butter.

Sir Basil Brooke, Minister of Agriculture, in introducing the Bill in Parliament in June 1934 said: "*A scheme for Northern Ireland must be primarily one for assisting the producer of manufacturing milk, which represents, as I have already said, 70 per cent of our production*". He said that the existing arrangements for most producers meant that the creamery milk supply was down to 3d per gallon and even lower. Sir Basil then referred to the proposals announced recently at Westminster for assisting milk schemes. He said that under the new arrangements it would be possible in Northern Ireland to guarantee for two years a minimum price of 5d per gallon in summer and 6d per gallon in winter to producers of milk which was sent to registered creameries and their auxiliaries. A Joint Milk Council, representing producers, distributors and consumers and with independent members which could determine the retail price of milk, was set up under the Bill. A charge was placed on wholesalers of butter and margarine and this together with a contribution from the Imperial Government went into a Milk Fund from which the guaranteed prices were paid to producers.

Delight in Fermanagh

The Milk and Milk Products Act 1934 made provision for bringing the average price of milk sold for manufacturing purposes up to 5d per gallon during the summer and 6d during the winter. The difference between the price received and the guaranteed price was known as the Equalisation payment. The average prices of milk per gallon sold for manufacturing in Northern Ireland during the months of April, May and June 1934 were 3.7d, 3.3d and 3.0d respectively. For these months, the Equalisation payment varied from 1.3d to 2.0d per gallon, depending on the month, which in relation to the basic price was very substantial. By 20th September 1934, all the Fermanagh creameries had paid out the Equalisation grant under the Milk Marketing Scheme. Farmers were delighted at the outcome. The returns showed that farmers had their average price for milk brought up to over 5d per gallon. A Monea farmer's return was 5½d and one in Kesh received 6d per gallon.

Fivemiletown Creamery in mid 1930s (Courtesy of Mrs Carol Graham).

These payments indicated that these farmers received above the average Northern Ireland basic price for their milk from their co-operative creamery. All creameries reported an increase in milk production. Springfield Creamery had an average increase of 20 per cent over last season. Irvinestown suppliers had increased in number from 350 to 450 in June. Optimism was very much to the fore in the county not only in the case of milk producers but also for cattle rearers.

Milk Standards

The Milk Fund also covered the costs of a twice-yearly veterinary inspection of every cow in the country producing milk for human consumption. The consumer was regarded as all-important and improving the quality of milk from a cleanliness point of view was considered to be a top priority. All milk under this Act was sold according to quality grades. To this end, the Minister proposed to licence three grades of milk, namely A, B and C. All producers required a licence from the Ministry of Agriculture with the exception of Grade D producers who were not permitted to sell milk for human consumption. Grade A milk was required to meet a fairly severe bacterial test and only milk of a high standard of cleanliness passed the test. Grade A milk was bottled on the farm and then sold on to the consumer. The standards were similar to those for milk produced from Tuberculosis Tested (TT) herds and bottled on the farm. Grade B was of a slightly lower bacterial standard than Grade A and could be bottled by the producer or distributor. For Grade C there was no bacterial standard but it was required to pass a cleanliness test. Producers of Grade C and a number of Grades B producers, who could not secure a liquid market for their milk, sent their supplies to the creamery where they not only received the guaranteed price but also a bonus of 1d for Grade C milk and 2d for Grade B milk in respect of purity.

Milk prices

From 16th December 1934 under the Milk Act, minimum prices were set for milk. Grade A had a minimum price of 1s 4½d per gallon and Grades B and C 1s 2½d per gallon. Bottled milk commanded a top-up premium of 1½d per gallon. The prices quoted were those for milk delivered to the distributor's premises. Grade D was not suitable for liquid consumption and received the standard price. During the period May to August 1935, the prices of milk from farms were determined by the Joint Milk Council as follows: Grade A not less than 1s 0¾d; Grade B and C 10¾d. Transport charges were also specified. These financial rewards had a very positive impact on producers and as a result production increased by well over 30 per cent in 1936. In March 1935, there were 4,722 milk suppliers in County Fermanagh out of a Northern Ireland total of 13,511.

Milk quality improvement

As well as the twice-yearly inspection by veterinary officers of the Ministry, certain standards of premises and equipment had to be maintained as laid down by regulation under the Act. Sampling for cleanliness and bacteriological count was carried out by Ministry officers. In November 1935, a feature in the Ministry's *Monthly Report* stated: *there was evidence of a very considerable improvement in the standard of cleanliness of milk now being sold in Northern Ireland. There can be little doubt that this improvement has been due not only to greater care in the handling of milk, but also to the carrying out of alterations in premises and to the adoption of other suggestions made by the Ministry's Veterinary Officers and Milk Inspectors.*

Butter and Cream Marketing Board

The Ministry of Agriculture for Northern Ireland established the Butter and Cream Marketing Board (BCMB) following the introduction of the 1934 Act. The creameries of Fermanagh were represented on the BCMB by Mr Robert G. McCullagh, Manager of Springfield Creamery. The BCMB organisation's existence was terminated in March 1940 following an earlier suspension of its activities.

Death of Mr W. H. West JP

Agriculture in County Fermanagh suffered a severe loss in 1935 through the death of Mr W. H. West JP, who had served as Organiser and Secretary of the Fermanagh County Committee of Agriculture from its inception. Up until his death Mr West had been Secretary of Fermanagh County Council as well as Secretary of the Agricultural Committee. When reviewing Mr West's salary as Secretary of the Agricultural Committee in 1920 the Chairman of the Committee, Rev Canon John Hall, said that he did not think they could get a better man than Mr West. The Department had acknowledged him to be one of the finest Secretaries in Ireland. He never spared himself and he understood what he was doing. Mr West had done sterling work in developing agriculture in County Fermanagh through the efficient and effective administration of the various improvement schemes operated through the County Committee of Agriculture. Mr West appreciated the need for better marketing of agricultural produce right from the beginning of the century and pioneered some very worthwhile and innovative farming co-operative activities. In addition to his public duties, Mr West was an extensive and successful farmer.

When Mr West died his only son, Harry, was still a pupil at Portora Royal School. Harry immediately took over the running of the farm and in time entered politics. He became one of the most popular and successful Ministers of Agriculture in Northern Ireland.

Mr W. T. McClintock's appointment

Following Mr West's death, the Organiser and Secretary post for the Fermanagh County Committee of Agriculture was advertised in 1935. As the Ministry of Agriculture funded the County Committee of Agriculture in large measure, it had specified that a university degree or diploma in agriculture was a requirement for the new post although the County Committee wanted to omit this specification when advertising the post. When it came to consider the candidates for the post, members of the Committee voted 11 votes in favour and seven against the appointment of Mr William Wilson, Ashfield, Lisbellaw. Mr Wilson did not have the qualifications specified by the Ministry and as a back-up position the Committee also took a vote on the candidates who had the appropriate qualifications. There were two applicants with the specified qualifications, Mr William (Bill) T. McClintock BAgr from Cooneen and Mr J. C. (Cecil) Patterson BAgr from Derrylin. Mr McClintock received 14 votes and Mr Patterson got five. The Ministry wrote to the County Committee stating that they could not accept the appointment of Mr Wilson but approved that of Mr McClintock. Mr J. C. Patterson was subsequently appointed the Secretary and Organiser for the County Armagh Committee of Agriculture.

A report in *The Impartial Reporter* at the time of Mr McClintock's appointment stated that, to-date, he had *a very remarkable and successful career.* He was educated at Grogey Public Elementary School (near Fivemiletown) where his father was the Master. He then had his secondary education as a boarder at Methodist College, Belfast. After attending Methody he received a scholarship to attend Greenmount Agricultural College and from there gained a scholarship to study agriculture at Queen's University, Belfast. He graduated with a Bachelor of Agriculture degree and was first in his year. Bill McClintock was a noted athlete. He was Ulster Schools' champion in athletics, and broke the long jump record at Queen's four times (23 feet). He was captain of Queen's University and Northern Ireland athletics teams when on tour in Great Britain, and had the great honour of representing Great Britain in the World University Athletic Championships in Budapest in 1935. Bill was also an excellent rugby player having played on the Methodist College and Queen's first teams. The appointment of Mr McClintock as Secretary and Organiser of the County Committee of Agriculture marked the beginning of a very significant period in the development of agriculture in County Fermanagh.

Mr W. T. McClintock (Courtesy of Mrs Margaret Higham).

Early schemes

When Sir Basil Brooke, Minister of Agriculture (from 1933 until 1941), made a tour of the six counties in October 1935 he referred to the success of the Pasture Improvement Scheme which had been in operation for a period of ten years. He stated that the results were outstanding on the 'manurial and good seed' plots and that it was gratifying to see that in many districts farmers were taking advantage of the lessons demonstrated. The Minister also referred to the success of the Ministry's Land Improvement Scheme, introduced in 1929, which provided assistance for drainage, reclamation and the making and repairing of farm roads. Fencing was added later as an eligible item.

The Land Improvement Scheme

The Land Improvement Scheme had the purpose of relieving unemployment and improving agricultural land. The rate of grant varied between 50 per cent and 85 per cent depending on the Poor Law Valuation of the farmer's property. The original grant covered materials and employed labour engaged through the Labour Exchange but in 1932 the grant on materials was withdrawn. In February 1935 the scope of the scheme was narrowed excluding roads as an eligible item and limiting eligibility to holdings where the valuation did not exceed £60. This was later raised to £75. In April 1937 the rate of grant was increased to 75 per cent of the labour costs where labour was employed through the Labour Exchange and roads were reintroduced as an eligible item. In November of that year flax dams and wells became eligible items. Wells would enable water supplies to be provided to meet the needs of livestock on grassland and permit the farm to be utilised to the fullest extent for grazing and cropping. In May 1938, much to the satisfaction of larger farmers, the scheme became applicable on farms where the valuation did not exceed £200 but the grant on labour was on a sliding scale (50 to 85 per cent) depending on the valuation. At the outbreak of war the scheme was curtailed in September 1939 by reducing the grant to 75 per cent on the smaller holdings. Eligible items under the scheme were limited to those that would facilitate food production and the cultivation of flax. Items like roads, fencing and reclamation were excluded. Whin stubbing continued to be eligible providing the cleared area was immediately ploughed and cropped. These restrictions were withdrawn in September 1940 and the Poor Law Valuation limit was increased to £250 with a sliding scale for the rate of grant depending on valuation. On those holdings with a valuation in excess of £250 tile or stone drainage was eligible at 50 per cent of the cost of labour and materials subject to a maximum grant of £7 10s 0d per acre.

Land Fertility Scheme

The United Kingdom Land Fertility Scheme brought in under the Agriculture Act of 1937 offered a grant of 50 per cent of the cost of lime and basic slag applied to farmland. The Fermanagh County Committee of Agriculture expressed dissatisfaction with the scheme. They stated that grant aid should not be confined only to the use of basic slag and lime. They claimed that other forms of phosphatic fertilisers should be eligible as well as basic slag. Despite the availability of the 50 per cent grant Fermanagh farmers had only applied 1,300 tons of lime in the first year. This was by far the lowest usage of any county. At a County Committee of Agriculture meeting it was stated that 40 years previously practically every farmer had his own lime kiln and that every year burnt lime was applied to the land. Mr McClintock stated: *"In a grazing county like Fermanagh, the beneficial effects of lime are even greater than in other counties. Lime in the soil is a splendid bone builder in grazing cattle and, in addition to its better known benefits, it prevents and eradicates numerous diseases of cattle, pigs, sheep, poultry and also crops."*

References:

Ministry of Agriculture for Northern Ireland *Monthly Reports* held in Dundonald House Library.

Files of *The Impartial Reporter* and *Fermanagh Herald* held in Enniskillen Library.

MacLurg, Alistair, *The Ulster Farmers' Union – The History of its first Seventy Years 1917 – 1987.*

The Armstrong family of Keeranbeg, Magheraveely, having a tea break while stacking corn (oats) in 1935 (Courtesy of Miss Jayne Armstrong)

A crawler tractor drawn binder at work in Makeny in 1938. Left to right Irvine Campbell, Thelma Campbell, Jack Campbell (Courtesy of Mrs Stella Campbell).

Chapter 8
The Second World War

In April 1939, there was a war atmosphere in Enniskillen with citizens being measured for gas masks.

After the outbreak of the Second World War on 1st September 1939 the Fermanagh County Committee of Agriculture, at their meeting on 11th September, responded by passing two resolutions. These covered the need for more cropping and better prices for produce. The first resolution read as follows: *That every farmer in the County be strongly urged to break more land, to grow barley on our lighter soils and oats on the heavier ground, so as to save importing Indian meal and oilcakes from foreign countries.* The second resolution related to the price of flax: *That the Government be strongly pressed to fix a minimum buying price for flax and in every way to encourage the farmer so as to make it worthwhile for the farmer to grow such an essential crop.* Both resolutions in time met with a positive response from farmers and the Ministry of Agriculture for Northern Ireland. Appeals were being made by Government during the autumn to grow more crops, including flax, oats and barley.

Emergency Provisions

With the outbreak of the war the Agriculture (Emergency Provisions) Act (Northern Ireland) was passed, which gave the Ministry powers to increase agricultural production. The staff and services of the County Committees of Agriculture were taken over by the Ministry of Agriculture on what was considered to be a temporary basis. In 1949, the take-over was made permanent. Hence, the Ministry of Agriculture from then had total responsibility for agricultural research, advisory work, education and statutory administration.

The Agricultural Organisers and Secretaries to the County Committees of Agriculture became the County War Agricultural Executive Officers and members of the Ministry's staff. The County Committees of Agriculture continued to act in an advisory capacity to the Ministry and had responsibility for administering the Livestock Improvement Schemes at county level – a role they would retain until 1973 when they were disbanded and replaced by the General Agricultural Advisory Committee, which had a Province wide role. The County Agricultural Executive Officer continued to act as Secretary to the County Committee during its lifetime.

Compulsory Tillage and 'Plough to Victory' campaign

The need for maximum home production of food became an essential. *'Plough to Victory'* became Ulster's slogan. Fermanagh farmers, despite their difficult soil and climatic conditions, responded well and applications for the £2 per acre Ploughing Grant poured in. The Ploughing Grant was to encourage ploughing up of grassland which had been down to grass for at least seven years.

The Compulsory Tillage Order was introduced by the Ministry of Agriculture for Northern Ireland on 15th September 1939. The requirements of the Order were that all occupiers of land with 10 acres or more had to cultivate at least one-fifth of their arable land in 1940. Those occupiers of land who had tillage in 1939 were required in 1940 to cultivate one-tenth of their arable land as well as the equivalent area under crop in 1939 providing that the total was at least one-fifth of the total arable area occupied.

The need for more home-grown food was necessitated because of reduced imports of grain, mainly from North America. Northern Ireland had been very dependent on imported maize or as it was known locally 'Indian corn'. It was claimed that in pre-war days Northern Ireland imported one-sixth of the total maize coming into the United Kingdom.

In October 1939, Sir Basil Brooke, Minister of Agriculture, when addressing the Fermanagh County Committee of Agriculture, informed them that the Secretary of the County Committee of Agriculture, Mr W. T. McClintock, would become County Executive Officer for the collection and collation of information relating to agriculture in respect of the extension of tillage. He would advise upon seed and manure requirements and the provision of tractors to carry out ploughing and other agricultural work. Under him, in charge of rural areas, would be Area Officers who would advise farmers what they should plough.

COMPULSORY TILLAGE

NOTICE TO FARMERS

EVERY occupier in Northern Ireland of 10 acres or more of **arable land** is hereby notified that, under an Order of the Ministry of Agriculture for Northern Ireland made on the 15th September, 1939, in pursuance of powers delegated to it by the Secretary of State, he is required:

(1) If no part of the arable land was cultivated in the year 1939 to cultivate **ONE-FIFTH** of the area of such land in the year 1940.

(2) If any part of the arable land was cultivated in the year 1939 to cultivate in the year 1940 a portion equivalent in extent to the part so cultivated and to **ONE-TENTH** of the TOTAL ARABLE AREA **IN ADDITION**; provided that at least **ONE-FIFTH** of such TOTAL AREA shall be so cultivated.

The "occupier" is the person who is rated, or would be rated or liable to be rated to the poor rate in respect of the holding but for the derating of agricultural land.

No occupier will be required to cultivate in the year 1940 more than half of the total arable area of the holding but he should aim at cultivating the maximum area.

Provision is made in the Order for dealing with **very exceptional** cases where full compliance with the provisions would be impracticable. Such cases can be considered only if full particulars are furnished to the Ministry **not later** than the **30th November, 1939.**

MINISTRY OF AGRICULTURE NORTHERN IRELAND
STORMONT 2689 BELFAST

Compulsory tillage notification.

A youthful Samuel Armstrong of Keeranbeg with a fine pair of horses and a chill plough (Courtesy of Miss Jayne Armstrong).

Few tractors

By November 1939, only 90 tractors and ploughs had been imported into Northern Ireland since the beginning of the war. Sir Basil Brooke, at that time, stated that 1,400 tractors and ploughs were needed to enable another 250,000 acres of crop to be grown in the Province. In January 1940, the Minister stated: *if we are to survive, we must plough.* In a radio broadcast in March 1940, Sir Basil, in encouraging farmers to grow more crops, said: "*the British plough was mightier than the German submarine.*"

In late 1939, hire purchase for the acquisition of tractors became available through the Ministry of Agriculture. In February 1940, demonstrations of working tractors, ploughs and disc harrows, which attracted large numbers of farmers, were held on the farms of Mr F. West, Mullyduff, Newtownbutler; Mr B. Ferguson, Glenlevin, Derrygonnelly; and Mr Lyons, Drumsillagh, Florencecourt. In March 1940, it was reported by Mr W. T. McClintock, County War Agricultural Executive Officer, that there were 50 tractors in County Fermanagh. At the end of 1941, there were 127 tractors and ploughs and 40 disc harrows in the county.

The early response to the Compulsory Tillage Order in Fermanagh was encouraging no doubt due to the £2 per acre Ploughing Grant and the value of the crop. However, there was a patriotic response as well. A Brookeborough farmer, who had 24 acres of poor land, ploughed half of his farm. He stated: "*When men are out in France willing to give their lives for my protection it is the least I can do to try and help the country by raising more crop*".

Publicity

A Tillage Campaign van equipped with loudspeaker, for use throughout Northern Ireland, was supplied to the Ministry by the Gallaghers tobacco factory in Belfast. This van was present in Enniskillen Fair in February 1940 and up to three hundred farmers listened to Mr McClintock while he explained the Tillage Order. He also dealt with the essentials of crop husbandry, including the need for fertilisers not only on crops but also on grassland and meadows. This publicity was repeated at other villages in the county in succeeding months.

Concern was being expressed at this time by the County Committee about the infestation of rabbits in Fermanagh. It was claimed that acres of crops were going to be lost in 1940 due to damage by rabbits. Mr Irwin of Derrygore stated that 1,400 rabbits had been cleared from his land that season but they were now coming in from neighbours' land.

'Produce more food' campaign

Over the next few months, the serious shortage of feedingstuffs was reported time and again. There was a *'Produce more Food'* campaign. Feedingstuffs prices were fixed by Government. Mr McClintock wrote many press articles in the following years in the local press on growing various crops including flax and on the importance of the 'Tillage Order'. There were serious penalties for those who did not meet their commitments under the Order. In December 1940 it was reported that farmers should not expect any feedingstuffs to be imported and that 65,000 tons of feed needed to be produced in Fermanagh, otherwise the county would face starvation. Contractors who had machinery played an important role and charges for work done were regulated. In October 1940 the rates agreed for contract ploughing lea were 25 shillings per statute acre up to the end of December, rising month by month to April when it was 30 shillings. Ploughing stubble was two shillings and sixpence less per acre. The rates for threshing were one shilling and sixpence for a 'clarendo' bag and one shilling and three pence for an 'Indian meal' bag.

Throughout the period of compulsory tillage, the Ulster

War Leaflet No. 1 addressed to Mr Peter McAloon (Courtesy of Mr Joe McAloon).

Mr Peter McAloon (Courtesy of Mr Joe McAloon).

Farmers' Union urged farmers to meet their commitments. In November 1940 the Union appealed to farmers to grow 100,000 acres of flax, in spite of unsatisfactory prices, to demonstrate their 'patriotic propensity'.

Stark warning to Fermanagh farmers

Mr McClintock issued a stark warning at the beginning of March 1941. He said: "*I want to restate the solemn warning of the various authorities, that we need hope no longer for help from across the seas as far as feeding stuffs are concerned. The question then arises what was the extent of that help? The answer will startle every living man.*" The facts were that Fermanagh received more than 65,000 tons of imported feedingstuffs previously and that none could be expected for the 1941/42 winter. Mr McClintock said that with a willing mind and ready hand Fermanagh farmers could rise to the challenge. He said no one could question the wisdom of the Tillage Order and that the severest penalties, under the *'Defence of the Realm Regulations'*, would apply to those farmers who failed to comply. In the meantime, farmers throughout the United Kingdom were being encouraged by appealing to patriotism. Included in the Ministry of Agriculture's *Monthly Report* of 1941 was the following encouragement: *The Battle of Waterloo was said to have been won on the playing fields of Eton, but there is not a doubt that the Battle of the Atlantic will be won on the tilled fields of the United Kingdom if farmers make their greatest effort now.*

Mr T. C. Skelly, a Tillage Officer during wartime.

War Leaflet No.1 (revised October 1941), entitled GUIDE TO FOOD PRODUCTION

A copy of War Leaflet No. 1 was issued by the Northern Ireland Ministry of Agriculture to all farmers in late 1941. The leaflet pictured on page 55 addressed to Mr Peter McAloon, Cortrasna Glebe, Lisnaskea, was issued by the County Agricultural Executive Office in Enniskillen.

The leaflet dealt with the various aspects of Compulsory Tillage and contained a lot of advice on husbandry and information on the crops to be grown for essential food and raw materials. The crops recommended were wheat, oats, barley, mixed crops of oats and barley, field beans, mixed crops of beans and oats, turnips, mangels, cabbage

Mr Winston Churchill.

and kale, carrots, spring cabbage, other vegetables and catch crops. Potatoes also got special emphasis. The leaflet stated: *No other crop can give so high a yield of food per acre as potatoes. Where potatoes are plentiful there can be no risk of hunger of either man or beast.* The importance of potatoes and the need for an increased acreage in 1942 was indicated by the fact that a subsidy of £10 per acre was being paid. Furthermore, there was an undertaking from the Imperial Government to buy all surplus saleable potatoes and to pay fixed prices for them.

Machinery was regarded as essential for undertaking the tillage required in 1942. The Ministry urged farmers to place orders for tractors and agricultural machinery at the earliest possible moment. The Ministry's leaflet stated that a greatly increased number of tractors would be available for the forthcoming tillage programme.

The leaflet gave the names and addresses of the County Agricultural Executive Officers, the Area Tillage Officers and the Horticultural Instructors. In Fermanagh, Mr W. T. McClintock was the County Agricultural Executive Officer and the Tillage Officers named were: Messrs T. Moore, D. T. Ritchie, H. S. Flack, T. C. Skelly and William Tweed. Mr J. C. Johnston was the Horticultural Instructor.

The leaflet also contained an encouraging message from Mr Churchill, Prime Minister of Great Britain. The message read as follows:

"Never before have farmers and farm workers carried such a heavy responsibility as you do in this struggle. Never before have you responded to the country's call as you have done in the last two years.

It is due in no small measure to the efforts you have made, in spite of many difficulties, that we find ourselves to-day in a better position on the food front than at any previous time since the war started.

But there can be no relaxation. Far from it. The enemy's attack at sea will be intensified. The situation demands from each one of us still greater efforts, still greater sacrifices than we have yet made.

Ships that would have brought food to our shores must now be used to meet the urgent needs of ourselves and our Russian allies for aeroplanes and tanks. You can release more ships by growing still more food in this country, and hasten the day of victory. May God speed the plough."

To help with the work on farms the Women's Land Army was organised in Northern Ireland in May 1941 and through it students and servicemen were enlisted to provide help at harvest time. 'Double summer time' was also introduced in the same month but farm workers were permitted to work by 'single summer time' to suit hay making and harvesting.

Beets of flax.

'Farming Front New Offensive'

The Ministry of Agriculture's *Monthly Report* of December 1941 launched *The Farming Front New Offensive.* Farmers were encouraged to co-operate wholeheartedly in launching the new food production offensive and were informed that they were under an obligation to their fellow men to do so. The article stated: *Every farmer and landowner has a*

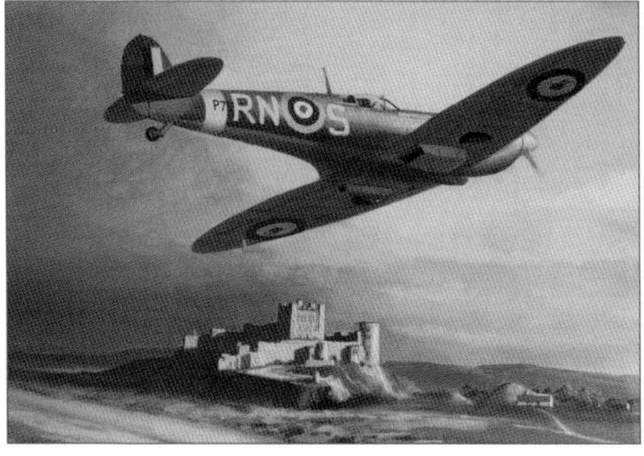

Flax was used in aircraft manufacture and in parachutes.

responsibility to bear and an obligation to fulfill. As custodians of the soil, the farmers and landowners have the responsibility of producing food for their country to the full capacity of the land they own or rent. To do less than that would be to fail to honour their obligations and to fulfill the trust reposed in them by their fellow men.

The launch of this offensive was accompanied by welcome news that there would be a guaranteed market and guaranteed prices for farm produce for at least the next four years.

Flax

As well as food crops a vast increase in the area of flax was needed and a target of 4,000 acres was set. Regarding prices for flax in 1940, the Ministry of Agriculture announced that: *the price for the 1940 Northern Ireland flax crop has been fixed at 17s 6d to 22s 6d per stone with an average price of 20s per stone.* This represented a big advance on the 1939 prices, which ranged from 10s to 16s 6d per stone. Sir Basil Brooke encouraged farmers to grow flax stating: *As a cash crop, flax will be profitable. The government has procured the seed and farmers will get it at prices no greater than Pre-war days.*

A Flax Growing Committee was formed in Fermanagh to encourage production of the crop. The committee was under the chairmanship of Captain J. H. King, Land Steward on Sir Basil Brooke's estate at Colebrooke. He told members in February 1941 that in Fermanagh there was as good land for flax growing as could be found. Captain King said: *"with fixed prices for the crop, Fermanagh farmers had a great opportunity of prospering from flax growing."* Lord Glentoran, Sir Basil Brooke's successor as Minister of Agriculture early in 1941, encouraged farmers in flax production. He said: *"We need retted flax for plane production and I am certain every farmer will support the gallant airmen by dam-retting his crop."* Farmers were encouraged to construct new flax dams or reconstruct old ones – a grant of 75 per cent of labour costs, under the Land Improvement Scheme, was available. Flax factories were built in Lisnaskea and Irvinestown by the Government and 1,000 acres of dried green flax, under contract, were required for each factory.

The Ministry of Agriculture advertised in spring 1943 under the heading *'Grow Flax for Victory'.* Ten pounds per acre were offered for each acre harvested and a guaranteed market was assured. The Ministry would purchase the dam-retted fibre at 25 to 30 shillings per stone according to grade. Green flax was sold under contract. This request by the Ministry for more flax was accompanied by two special patriotic appeals: *Do Not Let the Services Down* and *The RAF looks to you this year to keep them supreme in the air.* The Ministry suggested that a farmer using his own family labour could make £50 per acre from flax.

Livestock

A Livestock Control Scheme was introduced on 15th January 1940. Under this scheme Northern Ireland farmers received the same fixed price for their fat cattle, sheep and pigs as their counterparts in Great Britain. The prices for cattle and sheep depended on the killing-out percentages. Home bred steers, heifers and cow-heifers attracted 64s 6d per cwt for Specials with lower prices for grades A to C ranging from 61s 6d to 41s 6d depending on killing out percentage. Specials were regarded as having at least a 60 per cent kill-out whereas a Grade C was 50 per cent. Fat sheep received an annual average price of 12d per lb estimated dressed carcase weight. Lambs received an additional 1½d per lb. Fat pigs were paid for at 103s 7d per cwt dead weight in the range 112 lb to 180 lb. Heavier pigs attracted a lower price. Prices were also fixed for eggs varying with the time of year. In early February the price paid to producers was 1s 4½d per dozen.

Under the Livestock and Meat Control Scheme, fat cattle and sheep were purchased at centres throughout the Province by the Ministry of Agriculture on behalf of the British Ministry of Food. In Enniskillen, purchasing was carried out on the second and fourth Wednesdays and commenced at 8am. Fivemiletown was on the first Friday, Irvinestown on the second Monday and Lisnaskea on the third Wednesday. The Ministry's Purchasing Officer determined the killing out percentage on a visual examination of the animals.

Prices in the 1940s

At Enniskillen Fair on 10th February 1940 calves made £6 6s 0d per head on average, store cattle were 33 to 39 shillings per cwt liveweight, springing cows and heifers averaged £18 and young pigs £1 12s 6d. By 1943, springing cows and heifers in Enniskillen Fair were making £26 or slightly more.

Ministry purchases all milk

At the outbreak of the Second World War the Northern Ireland Ministry of Agriculture, acting on behalf of the British Ministry of Food, undertook the reorganisation of the collection and usage of milk in Northern Ireland. The delivered price of milk in early 1940 varied from a minimum of 1s 5d to 1s 3d per gallon depending on Grade (A to C). Maximum collection charges were imposed. In November 1940, the Ministry became the purchaser of all milk off farms and was responsible for its subsequent use. Factories and milk depots were set up, redundant creameries closed down, and haulage and transport were reorganised so that all available milk could be best used in the national interest. By the winter of 1942/43 prices were up to 2s 6d per gallon for liquid quality milk, with manufacturing grade making 1s 11d. In response to the better prices, milk production

in Northern Ireland increased by 15 per cent during the period 1940 to 1942.

At this time, the Ministry was making a plea for higher levels of milk production. The appeal was couched in the following terms: *The Nation simply must have greater supplies of milk not only during the coming winter but also in succeeding winters to maintain the health of the community during this period of strain.* This was accompanied by a campaign to improve milk quality. In mid 1943 a White Paper detailed the measures which were implemented. The premium on grade A milk was increased. Heat treatment of other milk was required where facilities could be provided. Standards of inspection of dairy cows and cowsheds were brought into line with those pertaining in Great Britain. The inspection procedure was extended to all milk producing farms. In the year ending March 1944, 30,530,000 gallons were used for liquid consumption in Northern Ireland and in addition a further 2,360,000 gallons were sent to Scotland. Milk for human consumption needed to be of a good standard particularly due to the distances involved from where it was produced to the point of consumption. This led to the introduction of the Resazurin laboratory test for milk coming from farms. Only milk that passed this test was considered fit for human consumption. The use of milk for cream production was prohibited by the Food Order 1940. Cream was regarded as a peace-time luxury that had to be foregone during wartime. The demand then was for condensed and dried milk to meet national requirements.

Impact on Fermanagh creameries

The Ministry's reorganisation scheme entailed the roadside collection of milk from farms by lorry and consequently the small creameries and collection centres were not needed. The creameries serving County Fermanagh that survived were Derrygonnelly, Springfield, Erne, Irvinestown, Fivemiletown and Brookeborough and the Scottish Cooperative Wholesale Society (SCWS) in Enniskillen. In addition, the Ministry built a new creamery in Lisnaskea from which bulk milk was moved to other markets. The Lisnaskea creamery also had the capability of processing the milk. From July 1942, the Ministry arranged the collection of all milk in the Province to ensure supplies for liquid consumption without rationing. The surplus over local requirements was sent to Great Britain to help meet its needs for liquid milk. This liquid export trade continued for many years. In August 1948, for example, 50,000 gallons of milk were being flown daily from Nutt's Corner to England and in August 1951, 60,000 gallons were being shipped from Larne to Stranraer.

Diversification

There was an increasing economic need in the 1940s to diversify milk processing so that it would not depend totally on butter making. Creamery butter making had been a big advance in terms of consistency, quality and economic return to the farmer compared to that from the farm produced commodity. However, butter making only used the fat constituent of the milk and the skim milk was returned to the farm for calf rearing and pig feeding. The first processing project that utilised all the milk nutrients and affected the Fermanagh creameries was the Nestle factory in Omagh, which started operations in June 1942 producing canned evaporated milk. While most of the creameries adversely affected by this new factory were in

Wesley Campbell ploughing with a Fordson tractor at Makeny, Ballinamallard, in Spring 1939.

Tyrone, it led to the closure of the Ballinamallard and Lack creameries in Fermanagh. The Ministry's wartime policy, referred to as the 'Concentration Scheme', led to the closure of 22 milk processing establishments in Fermanagh.

Calf rearing concerns

Milk prices at the creameries during the war were very attractive and there was some concern that this could impact adversely on the standard of calf rearing. At a Fermanagh County Committee of Agriculture meeting in April 1945, Mr J. J. Coalter from Letterbreen raised concerns about the impact of creamery milk sales on calf rearing. He made two points. The first related to the extent to which holders of Grade C Licences sent most of their milk to the creameries because of the relatively high price of 2s 6d per gallon. He said that calves being reared on

Messrs Bob McFarland, Tommy Booth and William Armstrong from Ballinamallard harvesting oats at Breandrum, Enniskillen, for Mr H. A. Burke during wartime (Courtesy of Miss Dora Elliott).

Mr William Wilson, Ratoran, binding oats at Thomastown (Courtesy of Mr and Mrs Cecil Cooke).

farms were not getting enough milk. On the other hand, many producers had lost their licences because of the sub-standard condition of their byres. Because of this they lost their entitlement to the rationed feed associated with dairy cows and again calf rearing suffered. An appeal was made to the Ministry to have 'calf starter' included as part of the wartime livestock ration supplies.

Rationing

Feedingstuffs for livestock were rationed during 1940. From 1st October, the maximum daily ration for dairy cows was 7lb, breeding sows 5lb, fattening pigs 2lb and poultry 1oz. Farmers were issued with ration books. Maximum prices were fixed for practically all kinds of animal feedingstuffs under an Order dated 29th September 1939. For example, the price fixed for imported wheat was £5 10s 0d per ton and for barley £6 0s 0d per ton.

Challenges of 1942

Sir Basil Brooke, Minister of Agriculture, when addressing the County Committee of Agriculture in December 1940, warned Fermanagh farmers that the winter of 1941- 42 was going to be worse than the previous two years as there would be absolutely no feedingstuffs imported. It was decreed in the autumn of 1941 that all saleable potatoes must go for human consumption – they were regarded as the property of the nation. The army had been engaged in harvesting and 31,000 man-hours of work were carried out by soldiers on Fermanagh farms in the month of September.

In January 1942, Mr McClintock was advising farmers to get out their horses and start ploughing. In a press article, he wrote an article entitled: *Few tractors – get out the horses.* He said that many farmers were waiting for contractors with tractors to come and do the ploughing. He pointed out that the available tractors, at most, could plough one acre in every six that had to be ploughed.

An increase of seven per cent in the area of cropping was required for 1942. However, the definition of arable land in a County Fermanagh context was giving rise to problems, as was the scarcity of petrol and tractor vapourising oil (TVO). An article in the local paper by Mr McClintock publicised the Land Improvement Scheme under which a 75 per cent grant was available covering labour costs for farm improvement work. The Scheme included the construction of flax dams. A free soil analysis service was also available to farmers. Maximum contract rates for cultivations were suggested by the Ministry in spring 1942. Ploughing charges were: old lea 27s per acre, stubble 23s per acre, and harrowing with a disc 7s per hour. Farmers were asked to grow more barley and oats. The price of oats and barley was guaranteed from £26 5s 0d to £27 10s 0d per ton and potatoes were: 90s to 105s per ton depending on variety.

Livestock issues

During the early years of the war there were many concerns regarding livestock. These included the threat of smuggling cattle from Eire and the associated fear of bringing in Foot and Mouth disease. The Minister of Agriculture, Lord Glentoran, stated in May 1941 that the *'Defence of the Realm Act'* would be used against smugglers and that offenders would face jail rather than fines. Despite the concerns about Foot and Mouth disease members of the County Committee would have been keen to import breeding ewes from Eire. There was also a severe shortage of suitable feed for pigs.

Concern about the Tillage Order

In June 1942, a deputation from Springfield and Corryglass Branches of the Ulster Farmers' Union, led by James Flanagan of Letterbreen, was appealing through the County Committee of Agriculture for some relaxation in the operation of the Tillage Order. Farmers were compelled to plough 45 per cent of their arable area under the Order. Failure to comply with this requirement rendered offenders liable to a fine of £100. It was claimed that the land had

already been ploughed up to the limit and farmers had got to the end of the fields that were amenable to tillage. It was claimed that Fermanagh, as a milk-producing county, did not suit tillage and that first crop grass should count as tillage area in future years. The delegation claimed that the over-intensive tillage scheme of the Great War ruined the land and put it in rushes for many years. They said the same was going to happen to a greater extent unless there was some relaxation. The proposal from the Farmers' Union Branches did not receive the support of the Committee.

Earlier ploughing required

A new Tillage Order for 1943 required farmers to plant at least 45 per cent of their arable area in crops. It specified that at least one quarter of that area should be ploughed before the end of 1942. Machinery was becoming more plentiful by October 1942. Mr McClintock reported that there were 150 tractors and ploughs, 72 disc harrows and 88 binders as well as 46 mobile threshing mills in the county. He said that there were horses on practically every farm and that these should be working. In the autumn of 1943, there was concern about saving the harvest and an appeal was made to townsfolk to help. There was a *'Save the Harvest'* campaign public meeting held in the Enniskillen Townhall, under the chairmanship of Senator Whaley. The speakers included Major W. G. Nixon DL, Chairman of the County Committee of Agriculture. An appeal was made *for every townsman and woman and child to get into the harvest fields and work like super-men.* Despite the hardship suffered by farmers, the County Committee of Agriculture proposed a voluntary deduction of one penny in the pound from the value of sales to go to Red Cross funds. By September 1943, Fermanagh farmers had contributed £2,173 to these funds.

Concessions for Fermanagh

Concern was growing about the application of the Tillage Order under Co. Fermanagh conditions. It was realised that areas were being ploughed which were not suitable for cropping. In October 1943, Lisnaskea Branch of the Ulster Farmers' Union passed a resolution calling for an amendment of the Tillage Order to suit the soil and conditions in County Fermanagh. This resolution was accepted by the County Committee of Agriculture and forwarded to the Ministry. In 1944, some concessions were granted. The representations from the Farmers' Union with the support of the Ministry's staff in County Fermanagh bore fruit in that an amended Tillage Order was approved for Fermanagh for the 1944 season. In presenting the new Tillage Order to the County Committee of Agriculture, Mr McClintock stated that as a result of the cropping and the livestock produced during the war years, together with the inadequate supply and use of fertilisers, soil fertility had suffered. The plan for 1944 was to get better crops from a smaller area of land, improve grassland and make more silage.

Reduction in tillage area

The area of the arable land on each farm to be cultivated was reduced from 45 per cent to 30 per cent. However, phosphatic fertiliser in the form of 8 cwt of basic slag, 5 cwt of ground rock phosphate or 5 cwt semsol per acre had to be applied to one-sixth of the arable area and 6 cwt of special potato manure per acre had to be applied to the potato crop. The fertiliser specified for grassland qualified for a grant of 50 per cent under the Marginal Land Scheme where the arable area on the farm was less than 50 acres. Those farmers with more than 50 arable acres would get grant aid under the scheme if they could convince the Ministry that they were entitled to participate in it. This rate of grant also applied to the cost of grass seed and fertiliser used in sowing land out to grass. A grass seeds mixture comprised of at least 26 lb of Ryegrass, 6 lb Timothy, 2 lb of Alsike Clover and ½ lb Wild White Clover was a requirement under the scheme. Meantime, there was a shortage of Premium boars and a shortage of suitable food for pigs. A member of the County Committee commenting on the unsuitability of oats as a feed for pigs said: *"oats would put pigs on fire."*

Rev Robert Moore's visit

The Rev Robert Moore, the new Minister of Agriculture, visited Fermanagh County Committee of Agriculture in

Rev The Rt Hon Robert Moore MP PC, Northern Ireland Minister of Agriculture 1943 – 1960.

January 1944. In explaining the reduced tillage quota for Fermanagh, he stated that in an effort to get food at all costs land had been ploughed up in Fermanagh that should not have been ploughed. The Minister went on to explain that failure to get a good yield of crops was due to a lack of phosphates in the soil. He said that for that reason one of the conditions associated with the reduction in the tillage quota for County Fermanagh was that one-sixth of the arable area on each farm must have phosphatic fertiliser applied to it.

Meantime, meetings to promote the provisions of the new Tillage Order and the benefits of silage making were held at venues throughout the county. Silage feeding demonstrations at various venues were also organised.

During the year ending 31st March 1944, Fermanagh farmers received over £250,000 in direct payments from Government. The acreage payments in 1944 were £10 per acre for potatoes and flax and £4 for wheat and rye. The £2 per acre Ploughing Grant continued for grassland ploughed up after being out to grass for seven years.

The Rt Hon R. S. Hudson MP, British Minister of Agriculture 1940 -1945.

Mr J. E. J. Fawcett JP (Courtesy of Mr David Fawcett).

Fermanagh unsuited to tillage

Mr McClintock, accompanied by Mr J. E. J. Fawcett and Mr B. R. J. Barton, gave evidence to the Babington Committee in August 1944. He said: *"land in County Fermanagh is totally unsuited for tillage."* He also pointed out that only 98,000 acres out of 457,000 acres in the county could be classified as arable and that if proper standards were used the arable figure would only be 10,000 acres. He pointed out that 300 silos had been erected. He also said that there were no facilities for practical agricultural instruction and that there was a need for reasonable prices as farmers would be unable to compete with cheap imported food.

British Minister of Agriculture visits Fermanagh

The county was honoured by the visit in August 1944 of The Rt Hon R. S. Hudson, British Minister of Agriculture, who was in Northern Ireland to see something of the contribution of Ulster farmers to the agricultural war effort.

He visited Sir Basil Brooke's estate at Colebrooke, Lisnaskea Milk Depot, Mr James Falconer's farm at Tawneyreagh, and the farm of Mr R. J. Rutledge, Falls, Cornafanog. A very comprehensive report of the visits was given in the *'Fermanagh Times'*. The report read as follows: *The Minister spent three quarters of an hour on Mr Falconer's 180-acre farm and expressed pleasure at the efficient manner in which the place is being worked. He seemed to be under the impression that, as in England, the farmers of Northern Ireland are tenant farmers, and was surprised to learn that Northern farmers are owners of their holdings. Inspecting a field of grazing, he said it was as good a field of grass as he had ever seen. He expressed himself as agreeably surprised at the dryness of the fields generally, having apparently expecting to find the place sodden, but Mr Falconer explained that this had been the driest season for many years and the real trouble is that under a fertile depth of fertile soil lies solid blue clay subsoil which prevents soakage of the water into the ground, thus rendering the place sodden even after a short spell of rain. In November, for instance, one could only traverse the sodden fields in rubber boots. The Minister was greatly interested in this problem and thought ploughing to a depth of sixteen inches would solve it. He suggested ploughing to this depth this first year, thus turning up the subsoil and burying the*

Mr James Falconer
(Courtesy of Miss Rosaleen Falconer).

"fertility". Exposure to weather, he thought, would make the subsoil friable and when a second ploughing in the second year replaced the friable subsoil and turned up the "fertility" (now manure) the land would drain itself as efficiently as any and would be equally productive. Mr Falconer explained that the blue clay subsoil would not respond to weather treatment in the way the Minister thought, and besides there was no machinery in the North ploughing to a depth of sixteen inches. Mr Hudson thought a tractor plough would be effective, but having heard the Northern Ministry officials, seemed satisfied that Fermanagh's poor soil could not thus easily be improved.

Mr Hudson showed little interest in punched cattle, but evinced the keenest interest in cattle reared by Mr Falconer himself, and followed in detail Mr Falconer's detailing of his partial switch-over from beef cattle to milk production. He inspected the byre in course of construction and asked many questions about it. He was interested to hear Mr Falconer's view that there was no shortage of cattle in the Twenty-Six Counties.

Mr Hudson visited Mr Falconer's home and with him went into the accounts of the farm since 1937 in the greatest detail. Mr Falconer is one of the few who have all their accounts kept and audited by the Ministry in Belfast, so that the Ministry has a first-hand knowledge of the financial workings of a large Fermanagh farm.

Mr Falconer, who is vice-president of the Lisbellaw branch of the Farmers' Union, is one of Fermanagh's young progressive farmers. He is a nephew of the late Mr Patrick Falconer JP, previous owner of the farm, member of the County Committee of Agriculture, and Chairman of the local creamery.

The party next visited the farm of Mr R. J. Rutledge, Falls, Cornafanog, Lisbellaw, which is approached by a lane some one and a half miles long. "Welcome to Northern Ireland" was Mr Rutledge's greeting to the minister as he alighted from his car to be introduced to Mrs Rutledge and the family.

The Minister's attention was then attracted to flax harvesting operations on a neighbouring farm. "Not mine" said Mr Rutledge; "haven't time to work it," and the party proceeded past an apple orchard and a model duck pond to see some of Mr Rutledge's horses and cattle.

Mr R. J. Rutledge
(Courtesy of Mrs R. Rutledge).

Before leaving the farmyard, Mr Rutledge told his wife: "I'll be bringing Mr Hudson back in a minute or two to see an Ulster turf fire," and to the Minister – "Maybe you will have time to have a cup of tea before you go." But Mr Hudson's itinerary did not allow of a cup of tea at 12.30 so the party continued their tour. Mr Hudson wanted to know whether cattle diseases – particularly abortion – was common in the district. Mr Rutledge said he had never been troubled with it, but Dr Scott Robertson said abortion was still causing trouble in other parts of the country.

The Minister having seen some of Mr Rutledge's oats, the party returned to the farmyard, where he saw a sow and litter at close quarters, going inside the sty to see for himself. About the pork, Mr Rutledge had something to say:"Doesn't pay a farmer," he said, "to buy a pig and fatten it up with the price of pork here," and "we look to you of the British Ministry of Agriculture to see that our Canadian cousins don't 'do us out' in the English pork market after the War."

And Mr Rutledge had a complaint about the number of forms sent out by the Northern Ireland Ministry. "You would need to go to Portora to be a farmer nowadays," he said. The Minister then entered the 170-year-old farmhouse – it was built in 1774 – to see an Ulster turf fire, and Mr Rutledge explained to the Minister the functions of a "self-acting crook" by which pots can be easily managed above the fire.

Lady Brooke joined the party at this point and was also warmly welcomed by Mr Rutledge. "I didn't think I'd ever see Lady Brooke in our street: it's an honour past all talking about."

Mr Rutledge told the Minister that he and his two sons did everything about the farm – thatched, threshed, mended the shoes and harness. "The only thing we don't do is shoe the horses." And to substantiate his statement, he showed Mr Hudson a well-stocked store of tools, and a threshing machine.

Mr Hudson, who was subsequently raised to the peerage, died in 1957. In Viscount Hudson's obituary, *The Times* newspaper stated: *At the Ministry of Agriculture he* was that *rare phenomenon, a success.* The report continued: *During his time there the demands upon the agricultural industry were immense and kept increasing with formidable rapidity. As Minister he asserted all his rights of leadership, organizing, innovating, directing and encouraging. He spoke plainly, and was respected for it. He worked strenuously and others emulated him. Although the support he received, and was always ready to acknowledge, was great in quality and extent, there remained a measure of personal accomplishment, for which he richly deserved the gratitude of his fellow countrymen.*

Changes in cropping and livestock

Despite the difficulties of land and climate, the farmers of Fermanagh responded to the challenge of compulsory tillage in a very positive manner. Mr McClintock in his submission to the Babington Committee stated that not more than 98,000 acres could be regarded as arable and that if proper standards were applied only 10,000 acres would be classed as arable. Despite this limitation, the area under cultivation peaked at over 57,000 acres in 1943. The area under the plough increased by over 260 per cent from the base year of 1939 to its peak in 1943. The relaxation of the terms under the Compulsory Tillage Order for 1944 and thereafter was obviously welcomed by farmers who reduced their area under cultivation significantly. Prices for produce also influenced the area under the plough and the choice of crops to be grown. Quite obviously, the growing of flax was not so economically attractive in 1945 as in previous years.

With regard to livestock, cattle numbers increased by over 25 per cent from the beginning to the end of the war. Sheep numbers, which were relatively small to start with, declined slightly. Pig numbers declined very significantly and no doubt, this was due to a shortage of suitable feedingstuffs. Oats was the main cereal crop grown in the county but this was not a suitable feed for pigs due to its high fibre content. Oats and potatoes were very suitable feeds for poultry and consequently these, together with reasonable financial returns from the enterprise, resulted in a 70 per cent increase in numbers.

Table 8.1 Area of crops (acres) and numbers of livestock on County Fermanagh farms during the World War 2

	1939	1940	1941	1942	1943	1944	1945
Total Cattle	97,693	94,721	111,623	115,606	112,120	120,166	123,775
Total Sheep	17,527	18,142	17,401	15,600	14,656	13,369	13,742
Total Pigs	34,438	27,853	24,192	21,556	18,675	15,557	13,841
Total Poultry	946,533	885,893	1,351,703	1,445,149	1,504,216	1,597,817	1,610,014
Horses	8,917	8,869	9,029	9,012	8,435	8,387	8,153
Potatoes (acres)	7,877	11,130	12,958	15,394	16,094	15,140	13,597
Oats (acres)	11,711	24,284	32,198	35,030	34,830	25,489	22,362
Barley (acres)	13	477	445	295	264	127	59
Flax (acres)	15	277	2,279	1,511	2,390	2,562	994
Total crops (acres)	21,436	39,305	51,969	56,443	57,112	46,195	39,254

Source: Economics and Statistics Division, Department of Agriculture and Rural Development.

Despite the increase in the number of tractors during the period of the war, horses were still very important for ploughing, cultivating, harvesting and transport. Horse numbers during wartime declined by less than 10 per cent.

Comparison with production levels during the First World War

The area of crops grown in County Fermanagh during the First World War peaked in 1918, the final year of the conflict. Peak crop production during World War II occurred in 1943 and declined thereafter until the end of the war in 1945. The area under tillage at its peak during the Second War was almost 20 per cent higher than that in 1918. No doubt, the greater area under crops in the 1940s was due, at least in part, to compulsion being introduced right at the beginning of the war and to the availability of a limited number of tractors which made cultivation easier.

Cattle numbers increased steadily, year on year, during the Second War whereas numbers were more or less static from 1914 to 1917 with a significant drop in 1918. Cattle numbers at their peak during the Second War were 18 per cent higher than in 1939 and almost 12 per cent higher than in 1916, which was the peak year during the First War.

Pig numbers showed a similar pattern during both World Wars. They declined by 40 per cent during the Second War compared to a decline of over 34 per cent in the 1914/18 conflict. Poultry showed a very different pattern – increasing in number during the Second War by 70 per cent compared to a decrease of almost eight per cent during the earlier conflict. The decline in the pig population in both wars was, in large measure, due to shortage of suitable feed.

A Rhode Island Red hen (Courtesy of Mr V. Graham).

Post war prospects

In March 1945 Mr Churchill, Prime Minister of Great Britain, said: "*Nothing is more clear that when the war is over the world will face an acute shortage of food for several years.*" Meanwhile, a small Fermanagh poultry farm received widespread publicity for its productivity in 1945. Thomas Kernahan, Greenhill, Brookeborough, was making a comfortable living from 10 acres of medium to poor quality land. He kept one breed only, Rhode Island Reds. He claimed that this breed was hardy, produced good-sized eggs, fertility was high and the chicks were easily reared. The poultry were all run on free range. He specialised in selling hatching eggs from his Accredited Poultry Farm. In addition to the poultry, he grew potatoes and oats on two and a half acres each year.

References:

Files of *The Impartial Reporter* and *Fermanagh Herald* held in Enniskillen Library.

Ministry of Agriculture for Northern Ireland *Monthly Reports* held in Dundonald House Library.

Chambers, Dr George, *The Rise and Fall of an Indigenous Industry: Milk Processing by in County Fermanagh from the Seventeenth Century until the Present Day.* Fermanagh History and Society, edited by Eileen M. Murphy and William J. Roulston, published by Geography Publications, Dublin (2004).

MacLurg, Alastair, *Ulster Farmers' Union – The History of its First Seventy Years 1917-1987.*

Chapter 9
Horses to tractors

Until the twentieth century, agricultural production in County Fermanagh depended mainly on manual labour and that provided by equines for cultivation, harvesting and transport. For manual field work the spade was an important implement. Spades used in Fermanagh were designed for coping with the difficult soils. These implements were narrow, long and had a bend where the shaft ended within the metal. A spade works at Rosslea, owned by McMahons, supplied most of the spades used in Fermanagh during the twentieth century. These spades were ideal for general digging including drainage work. They were especially suited for making ridges for growing crops and for digging potatoes.

Messrs Joe and Bob Elliott with their sister Dora at Drumconnis, Ballinamallard (Courtesy of Miss Dora Elliott).

Potato ridge or lazybed remains from Famine times at Topped Mountain.

In 1899, there were 7,862 horses in County Fermanagh (200 more than in 1850) and around 4,000 mules and asses. Donkeys and mules were used largely on small and mountain farms for transport. Pardogs, a sort of saddle to which creels or other containers could be attached, were part of the donkey harness in most cases. Creels were used for transporting turf, potatoes, and any other commodity that could be placed in them.

Modified self-emptying creels, with bottoms that could be opened easily, were used widely for transporting manure from the farmyard to the fields. Creamery cans could be mounted on either side of the pardogs for taking milk to

Mr John McIntyre, Dogs Big, Derrygonnelly, with his donkey and pardogs bringing turf from the bog.

the creamery. Carts and traps, which were simply smaller versions of those made for horses, were commonly used with donkeys.

Mr William James Gormley of Cules, Killadeas, in the 1920s with his pair of horses preparing a seed bed for oats. Drag harrows with wooden frames and steel pins were used for preparing seedbeds.

Cultivations

Horses were used on the larger farms for transport, cultivation and harvesting. Ploughs pulled by horses were of two varieties, chill (with wheels) and swing (without wheels).

Disc harrows were occasionally used on the more advanced farms. Spring tine grubbers were the implements for preparing ploughed ground for root crops. Drill ploughs were used in preparation for planting potatoes and other root and vegetable crops.

Saddle-back harrows and inter-row grubbers prepared the drills for moulding up as a weed control measure. Backpack and hand operated horse cart-mounted sprayers were used for blight control operations in crops of potatoes.

Tumbling paddy in storage.

Hay

Mowing machines, either one or two-horse, were used for cutting hay. Hay was normally turned manually using rakes in order to speed the drying process.

On larger farms, mechanical hay turners or kickers replaced the need for hand turning. In difficult seasons it was sometimes necessary to lap the hay as an intermediate step in the drying process. Horse drawn hay rakes then rowed the hay. The rows were gathered in using a piece of equipment, called a tumbling paddy, in preparation for ruck or rick building in the field.

Messrs James and Richard Little cutting hay with a two-horse mower at Drumgallon in 1952.

Horse drawn spring tine grubber.

Ready for work. Mr Hugh Burke of Gortaree, Derrylin, and his son, Sean, preparing to do some carting. This is a farming scene typical of the first half of twentieth century. The loose hay in the shed is neatly stored and the cart has been tipped up when not in use.

A hay stack on a small farm

After the hay had totally dried out the rucks were transported on a ruck shifter to a hayshed in the farmyard or to a haggard beside the farmyard. The hay was then used as the main source of winter fodder for livestock.

Harvesting

Scythes were used for cutting hay and harvesting grain crops on small farms until they were replaced in time by horse drawn equipment.

Mr William James Gormley on his horse in a hay field at Cules, Killadeas, in 1920. A tumbling paddy is ready for gathering-in the hay.

Mr William Kerrigan mowing a good crop of oats in the townland of Camgart, Clabby, in the 1940s.

Hay rucks in West Fermanagh.

Modified mowing machines, on which a foot operated slatted wooden table was mounted behind the cutting bar, was used for harvesting grain crops. An additional seat was mounted over the right hand wheel of the mower on which the man sat who manipulated the foot operated slatted table. This operator was equipped with a tilting rake, which he used to direct the cut oats or other grain crop on to the slatted table which was raised at an angle.

Each sheaf was then tied in the middle with a band made from the harvested crop before stooking in the field. Four sheaves were leaned against each other and tied together near the top, with another band of straw, to form the stook.

Binders that were pulled by either two or three horses were in use on the largest farms, in the early twentieth century.

A restored horse-drawn binder havesting oats at Moynalty, County Meath.

Transport

A most important function of horses was farm transport. Carts were used for all types of transport. Slipes (wheel-less carts) were also used in the early years particularly under very wet ground conditions where wheeled carts would tend to become bogged down.

Mr Jack Campbell of Makeny with his horse and cart in the 1930s (Courtesy of Mrs Stella Campbell).

Harvesting oats on the Maguire farm at Tully, Aghadrumsee. A visitor, Mr J. McGrory from Scotland, tries his hand with a tilting rake. Others included (from left) are Rita Maguire, Pat Maguire and Sean Maguire. Mr Frank Maguire is holding the reins (Courtesy of Mr Frank Maguire).

A restored horse drawn mower with reaping attachment.

Mr Frank Maguire, Tully, and his son, Sean, stooking sheaves of oats (circa 1936) (Courtesy of Mr Frank Maguire).

Horses and carts alongside a Model T Ford lorry (IL 1140) in Scallon's quarry at Moysnaght, Clabby, in the early 1930s (Courtesy of Mr T. McCusker).

Mr William Foster in his forge at Lisbellaw (Courtesy of Mrs Lorna Prescott).

Traps were often used for family transport. These were lightly but soundly constructed and were well sprung and had rubber shod large diameter wheels.

Care of the horses

Generally horses were the best fed and cared for animals on the farm. It was essential that they were in good health and were fed on a diet which enabled them to sustain long periods of hard work particularly in the springtime and at harvest. The task of keeping the horses' feet in good shape rested with the local blacksmith. Keeping the hooves trimmed and well shod were essential.

The old and the new in the 1950s. Edward Kirkpatrick taking a load of turf for sale in Fivemiletown. Behind the horse and cart on Clabby village street is Brunt Brothers' Austin lorry. Brunts had a grocery and hardware shop in Fivemiletown. Their lorry did a weekly round in each district in the local countryside, visiting farms and other countryside dwellers. They delivered groceries, meal, coal etc and collected eggs from the farms.

Tractors

It was not until the outbreak of the Second World War that tractor power began to have a significant impact in County Fermanagh. When compulsory tillage was introduced tractors were becoming a much more practical proposition for farmers. This was due to improvements in design and more importantly the availability of sources of finance for tractor and machinery purchase. In March 1940, it was reported that there were 40 tractors in County Fermanagh and by the end of 1941, there were 127 tractors with ploughs and 40 disc harrows.

The early tractors

The first tractors to have a significant impact in the county were Fordsons. These tractors, model F, were first made in America in 1917 and in that year it was estimated that there were only 70 tractors in the whole of Ireland.

Manufacture of Fordsons commenced in Cork in 1919. Over the years, improvements were made to these tractors but the basic design remained the same. In the 1920s, Fordsons sold at around £156. In 1922, Fordson tractor production was switched by the Ford Motor Company from Cork to America.

Mr John West of Rossahilly beside his Model F Fordson tractor and binder in the 1920s. Mr David West, John's brother, is seated on the tractor (Courtesy of Mr and Mrs Jim West).

By 1928, manufacture of Fordsons had ceased in America and production was transferred back to Cork. From that time Cork became the only Ford tractor producing factory in the world. However, in 1932 production was transferred to the Ford Motor Company works at Dagenham in England. The Fordsons weighed around one and a half tons and had advantages over earlier makes in that they were generally lighter, much more manoeuvrable and, above all, cheaper to buy. The Fordsons were able to pull two furrow ploughs and were particularly good for threshing with adequate power at the pulley.

Mr Irvine Campbell (foreground) in 1938 with his Model N Fordson tractor (IL 3320) and binder. Other members of the Campbell family are on the tractor. Wesley is seated on the right hand mudguard, Leah is on the left hand mudguard and Thelma is standing behind (Courtesy of Mrs Stella Campbell).

Significant contribution

These Fordson tractors, for the next three decades, made a very significant contribution to agricultural development and Britain's ability to feed its population during two World Wars. However, for ploughing and other cultivations the early Fordsons were nothing more than a replacement for a team of horses in that the implements were independent of the tractor and were attached to the tractor drawbar. This meant that the combined length of the tractor and implement was quite long which presented difficulties particularly when working in small fields like those in Fermanagh.

Fordson and trailed plough.

A further drawback was that they were unsuitable for row crop work. In Fermanagh when Fordsons were used for ploughing and cultivating, drills for root crops such as potatoes were usually made using horse drawn drill ploughs. In 1945, the model N was replaced by the Fordson Major (model E27N). Whilst the Major was a considerable advance on the early Fordsons, it was relatively heavy and not suitable for use on most Fermanagh land. In addition, it was rather unwieldy and did not have an automatic in-built depth control mechanism for cultivation implements. Majors were exceptionally good for transport and pulley work such as threshing.

Harry Ferguson

It was not until an Ulsterman designed a compact economical small tractor, with hydraulic lift and 3-point linkage, that a major break-through was made in farm mechanisation. The contribution of Harry Ferguson, the son of a County Down farmer, to world agriculture was significant, and nowhere was this appreciated more than in County Fermanagh. Ferguson's programme of development took a number of decades before success was achieved. Many disappointments were encountered over the years. Ferguson's determination and genius, with major input from a number of skilled Ulster engineering staff,

resulted in 'the little grey Fergie' which was to become a world leader in tractor design.

Advertisement for the Overtime tractor that appeared in The Farmers' Journal in 1921.

Interest in ploughs

Ferguson established a garage business in Belfast in 1911 and as well as selling cars, he obtained an agency for the American-made Overtime tractors.

He was employed by the Irish Department of Agriculture to give ploughing demonstrations using this tractor in the spring of 1917. It was thought that this form of mechanisation would help to increase home food production that was so important due to the severely reduced food imports because of the war with Germany. During the demonstrations, Ferguson began to realise the shortcomings in the design of existing tractors and ploughs and this set him out on a mission, which eventually would lead to a revolution in tractor and plough design with a worldwide impact. It became known as 'The Ferguson System'.

His first effort was in designing a new plough. The newly designed implement, mounted on an Eros tractor (a modification of a Model T Ford car) was demonstrated by Ferguson in Counties Antrim and Londonderry in December 1917.

Potential of Fordsons

The production of the Fordson tractor in America in 1917 was a major development in tractor design. This new tractor therefore offered the prospect of widespread adoption by those engaged in food production.

Ferguson and his engineer, William Sands, set about designing a plough specifically to suit this tractor. The new Ferguson plough was attached to the rear of the tractor using a coupling device called a Duplex hitch. Efforts by Ferguson in 1920 to have the Ford Motor Company in America manufacture the plough failed. Ferguson realised that the best opportunity for selling the ploughs was in America and he persisted in his search and eventually succeeded in getting Roderick Lean in Ohio to undertake manufacture of the plough. The plough initially had a depth wheel attached and Ferguson realised in time

A 1919 Fordson.

Fordson tractor and Ferguson-Sherman plough showing floating skid (owned by Mr Geoffrey Livingstone, Loughgall).

that this was responsible for excessive wheel slip by the tractor under poor ground conditions. Ferguson set about overcoming this problem. This was achieved by fitting a floating skid, which ran in the furrow bottom. It was connected to the Duplex hitch by way of pivotal links. It operated in such a way that the original working depth of the plough was maintained irrespective of whether the rear wheels of the tractor were on a height or hollow in the field. The ploughs were well received by farmers and production continued until 1924 when the Lean company went out of business. Ferguson then succeeded in 1925 in getting Sherman Brothers, who were the Fordson dealers for New York State, to undertake manufacture of the plough, which was marketed by a new company called Ferguson-Sherman Incorporated.

Automatic depth control

Whilst the new plough performed satisfactorily, Ferguson saw the need for automatic depth control on a range of cultivation implements without having to use a depth wheel. Research and development work by Ferguson in Belfast led to a draft control system, which revolutionised the whole approach to tractor and implement design. The principle was based on the fact that in uniform soils the draft was proportional to the depth at which the implement was working. At constant depth the draft was constant. If the implement's working depth was reduced, the draft would be lighter and the converse was true if the implement was working at a greater depth. Ferguson found that the best way of raising and lowering implements in response to draft pressure was one based on hydraulics, using an oil pump fitted externally to a Fordson tractor. Discontinuation of manufacture of Fordson tractors in America by the Ford Motor Company (manufacturing transferred to Cork in 1928) led Ferguson to consider the design of a new tractor, which would incorporate an integrated implement and draft control system.

The Ferguson-Brown

A new tractor designed by Ferguson and manufactured by the David Brown Company was complete in 1933. After the prototypes, painted black, had been developed and tested adequately the new grey painted Ferguson-Brown tractors began to roll off the production line in 1936. The tractors, which were sold by the Harry Ferguson Ltd marketing company, cost the farmer £224 with specially designed implements costing £28 each. They outperformed all other tractors especially under difficult soil conditions. Production ended in early 1939 after 1,200 tractors had been manufactured. This was due to a disappointing volume of sales resulting from the poor economic state of farming and the relatively high price of the tractors and equipment due to high costs associated the low volume of production.

A restored Ferguson-Brown tractor and plough.

Need for mass production

Ferguson believed that if he was to realise his ambition of revolutionising world agricultural production through his invention mass production was the only way that costs could be kept down. The master of mass production at that time was Henry Ford and Ferguson decided that a link up with Ford offered the best prospect of achieving his ambition. Contact was made with Ford through the Sherman Brothers and arrangements were made for Ferguson to demonstrate

Ferguson-Brown tractor being demonstrated at Johnstown Castle, County Wexford, by Mr Harry Ferguson (Courtesy of Irish Agricultural Museum).

his tractor on Ford's Fairlane Estate in America. Ford was most impressed and a 'handshake' agreement between the two men was reached at the demonstration. Ford would manufacture the tractor and Ferguson would be responsible for design and engineering matters.

American launch of the Ford-Ferguson tractor in 1939 at Ford's Fairlane Estate. Mr Harry Ferguson is seated on the tractor with Mr Henry Ford and his son Mr Esdel Ford on his right hand side. (Photograph courtesy of the Ford Motor CompanyLtd).

Ford-Ferguson tractor

The new Ford-Ferguson tractor was launched in June 1939. The tractors were marketed in America by a company formed by Ferguson in partnership with the Sherman Brothers, known as the Ferguson-Sherman Corporation. Ferguson had hoped that the British Ford Motor Company, which was manufacturing Fordson tractors at the time, would also manufacture the Ford-Ferguson tractor. This did not happen, as the British Ford Motor Company would not permit Ferguson to become a director of that company. Ferguson was considered to be a difficult man due to his assertiveness and his intolerance of those who disagreed with him.

Sir Basil Brooke advocates mechanisation

Meantime, Sir Basil Brooke, Minister of Agriculture, was encouraging farmers to double their output through mechanisation. In March 1939, Sir Basil said: "*The machine has to a large extent superseded the man in almost every other industry. In agriculture it has gone a long way in the same direction. But in order to fully utilise its possibilities you must make the machine supersede the horse. Buy tractors to do the farm work and you will save both your labour and your pocket.*"

By November 1939, only 90 tractors and ploughs had been imported into Northern Ireland since the beginning of the War. Sir Basil Brooke at that time stated that 1,400 tractors and ploughs were needed to enable another 250,000 acres of crop to be grown.

Mr Harry Ferguson (hand on wheel) with Messrs Henry Ford and Ferguson's gifted staff members, (from left) draughtsman John Chambers and engineer and designer William Sands (Courtesy of The Impartial Reporter).

Sir Basil Brooke, Minister of Agriculture, at Greenmount Agricultural College examining a knotter on a binder (Courtesy of Mr Derek Alexander).

FERGUSON'S TRACTOR DEMONSTRATION

ON THE FARM OF MR. S. J. CROWE,

DRUMWHINNEY HOUSE, KESH.

ON THURSDAY, 9TH MARCH, COMMENCING AT 12 O'CLOCK.

ALL FARMERS ARE INVITED TO ATTEND THIS DEMONSTRATION & SEE THE FERGUSON MACHINERY IN OPERATION.

Ulster Distributors :

HARRY FERGUSON (MOTORS) LTD.,

DONEGALL SQUARE, — — BELFAST. 1034

One of the last demonstrations of the Feguson-Brown tractor and machinery was held at Kesh.

Demonstration at Greenmount

Harry Ferguson brought the newly developed and American made Ford-Ferguson tractor and implements to Britain in 1939. This machine, although featuring many of the advances incorporated in the earlier Ferguson-Brown tractor, represented a considerable advance. One of its first demonstrations was at Greenmount Agricultural College on 12th October 1939. The tractor could not have come at a better time as compulsory tillage had been introduced and tractors were in great demand. The Ford-Ferguson with its hydraulic lift and depth control mechanism was a major advance on anything else that was available at that time. Ninety per cent of the tractors in use in Britain then were Fordsons. The demonstration at Greenmount was attended by the Agriculture minister, Sir Basil Brooke.

The Greenmount event was followed by demonstrations throughout the United Kingdom at which the new tractor was very well received by the farming community.

Tractor demonstrations in Fermanagh

A demonstration of the Ferguson tractor and machinery was held on the farm of Mr S. J. Crowe, Drumwhinney House, Kesh, on Thursday 9th March 1939 by the Ulster distributors, Harry Ferguson (Motors) Ltd. This must have been one of the last public demonstrations of the Ferguson-Brown tractor.

Lister-Cockshutt ploughs, costing £32, were being advertised at this time. These were two-furrow trailed ploughs which were very suitable for Fordson tractors. Demonstrations, organised by the County Agricultural Executive Officer, of various makes of tractors at work were held in February 1940 at the farms of Mr F. West, Mullyduff, Newtownbutler; Mr B. Ferguson, Glenlevin, Derrygonnelly and Mr Lyons, Drumsillagh, Florencecourt.

'Horse must go'

Mr J. M. Thompson (of Harry Ferguson's garage in Belfast) gave evidence in 1943 to the Agricultural Enquiry Committee, held under Lord Justice Babington, that in the interests of economy and efficiency 'the horse must go'. This view was echoed in October 1948 when Mr Rhynehart, Chief Inspector of the Ministry of Agriculture, addressed the Fermanagh County Committee of Agriculture and questioned the future of the horse as the source of power on the farm.

In short supply

Throughout the Second World War American-built Ford-Fergusons were imported into the British Isles. In March 1944, these tractors were still in short supply and were only available on steel wheels. Rubber tyred wheels became available for Ford-Fergusons in January 1945 at a cost of £52 10s 0d. An advertisement by Harry Ferguson (Motors) Ltd of Donegal Square East, Belfast, published in the County Fermanagh Farming Society's Show Schedule of 1945, proudly claimed: *100 per cent Mechanisation is the solution to the farmer's difficulties. The most suitable machinery for this mechanisation is the Ford-Ferguson with hydraulically operated farm implements.* Few Fermanagh farmers at that time would have believed these prophetic words of Ferguson. His claim would soon come to be a reality.

British manufacture of Ferguson tractors

Despite Ferguson's failure to interest the British Ford Motor Company in the manufacture of his tractor, he continued his search for a manufacturer in the United Kingdom. An

Advertisement for the Ferguson tractor as it appeared in The Farmers' Journal in January 1952.

approach to the Northern Ireland Government in July 1945 about setting up a manufacturing plant in Ulster met with a Government response that a loan would be made available. Ferguson did not want this approach. He wanted a company to undertake the manufacture of the tractors, which his company would then market. Success came when he got agreement with the Standard Motor Company to undertake the manufacturing of the tractors. The first Coventry made Ferguson tractor, the TE 20, came off the production line at the end of 1946. These tractors were similar to the Ford-Ferguson but had four speed gearboxes. Initially, the tractors were fitted with American made Continental engines but after a short period, these were replaced by Standard engines similar in design to the engines used in the Standard Vanguard car.

The Ferguson TE 20

In 1946 the Fermanagh Farming Society's Show Schedule carried another advertisement from Harry Ferguson's Belfast garage – it read as follows: *We have pleasure in announcing that the new Ferguson tractor, made in Coventry, will be available soon. It will at last offer to the Ulster farmer a British-built tractor incorporating the Ferguson System. Its equipment, which has been on view at various agricultural shows in Northern Ireland, includes the following:- Ferguson 2/3 ton trailer, Ferguson potato spinner, Ferguson power driven saw, Ferguson scoop, Ferguson carrying box, Ferguson tractor jack.* The Ministry of Agriculture announced in September 1946 that applications for purchase would be accepted for the new Ferguson tractor manufactured by the Standard Motor Company in Coventry.

The TE 20 belonging to Mr Jack O'Brien, Garvary.

The three point linkage attached to the plough on Mr Jack O'Brien's tractor.

Ferguson's impact on Fermanagh

Nowhere throughout the world has Harry Ferguson had a greater impact on the farming community than in County Fermanagh. Prior to the introduction of the Ford-Ferguson, farmers in the county depended mainly on horses for cultivation and farm transport. The few tractors were mainly Fordsons. These were alright for transport and for powering threshing mills but they had severe limitations for cultivation. Ploughs were trailed which meant that the total length of the tractor and plough was substantial. The steering was such that there was a wide turning circle. This meant that headlands were necessarily wide and represented a considerable proportion of small fields. Traction under difficult conditions was also poor. The advent of the Ford-Ferguson, and its successor the TE20 Ferguson, overcame all the Fordson's shortcomings. The new tractors were lightweight with good traction. They had mounted cultivation implements, which meant shorter headlands. Turning circles were reduced because of the good lock on the steering assisted as necessary by independent rear wheel brakes. The hydraulic lift, with its three-point linkage, opened up a whole range of possibilities, which made the task of farming so much easier.

The carrying box or link-box, as it was called locally, was a great asset on farms for those small transport jobs. The buckrake was a fabulous advance for silage making. Previously, grass had to be manually loaded onto trailers or on the larger farms collected from the field using green crop loaders. Both methods involved heavy manual work. The Ferguson tractor and buckrake could gather grass from the field and transport it to the silo with minimum manual input.

Break with Ford

Ford was obviously concerned about the potential impact of the British made Ferguson on the market for Ford-Fergusons. Ford took action in November 1946 and made it clear that the Ford Motor Company wanted a controlling

interest in the American Ferguson company and that the name Ferguson would be dropped from the company name. Ferguson, of course, was not agreeable to this change. In July 1947, Ford produced his own tractor, known as the 8N, which incorporated most of the Ferguson features.

Ferguson launched a civil action against Ford in January 1948 claiming that Ford had copied the Ferguson system and had ceased producing Ford-Ferguson tractors. Settlement was reached in April 1952 with Ferguson receiving $9.25 million in compensation and Ford was debarred from continuing manufacture and sale of the 8N tractor. This case brought widespread publicity to Ferguson, his tractor and associated implements. In the meantime, the British made Ferguson tractor had gained a worldwide reputation for excellence as well as dominating the British market for tractors.

New era in tractor manufacture

Ferguson set the standard for other manufacturers. In time, when patent rights expired, most other manufacturers adopted modified versions of the Ferguson three-point linkage system with automatic depth control features.

Merger with Massey Ferguson

Ferguson was dissatisfied with the progress being made in revolutionising world agriculture and believed that if he could link-up with another farm machinery maker working in the global market greater progress could be made. After prolonged negotiations with the Canadian Massey Harris Company agreement was reached in 1953 that Ferguson would sell his company to Massey Harris, but present it to the public as an amalgamation, and that Ferguson would become the nominal chairman of the new Massey Ferguson Company. Ferguson received $16 million dollars, which was regarded as the value of his company at that time. Good relationships with Massey Harris management did not last long. Ferguson was critical of design work and the management of the company. At the time of the 'amalgamation' Ferguson engineers had a larger version of the TE 20 well advanced in development. The Massey Harris engineers treated the development of a more powerful version of the TE 20 as the greater priority. These differences led to Ferguson's rather acrimonious resignation from the company. Ferguson devoted a good part of the remainder of his life to the development of four-wheel drive cars. He died at his home, Abbotswood, Stow-on-the Wold, Gloucestershire, in October 1960.

Four wheel drive tractors

The next significant development in tractor design was the adoption of four-wheel-drive with low ground pressure tyres. This enabled much more powerful tractors to be developed to cope with the high output machinery designed for speedy operation and with a minimum labour requirement. The new breeds of tractor, although a great deal heavier than the original Ferguson, were able to cope equally well or better than the small tractors of the post-war era particularly on the difficult land in County Fermanagh. The Grassland Experimental Husbandry Farm, Castle Archdale, was to the forefront in testing the early four-wheel-drive tractors where they really proved their worth under the difficult soil conditions of County

Mr Mervyn Elliott, Drumconnis, Ballinamallard, and his sons, Hugh and Angus, in 2009 with their restored 1964 Fordson Super Dexta tractor.

The very popular Massey Ferguson 135 at work on Mr Mervyn Elliott's farm at Drumconnis.

The Ford 8N belonging to Mr John Wade, Donemana, County Tyrone, at a vintage display at Enniskillen Show. Mr Ronnie McIlwaine is in discussion with Mr Wade.

Femanagh. A wide range of very good tractors, including Massey Ferguson which continued to incorporate many of the design features pioneered by Harry Ferguson, were available to the farming community at the end of the twentieth century.

References:

Fraser, Colin, *Harry Ferguson.* Old Pond Publishing. Ipswich. (1972).

Neill-Watson, John, *A History of Farm Mechanisation in Ireland 1890 – 1900.* Farm Machinery and Trade Association. Dublin. (1993).

Files of *The Impartial Reporter* and *Fermanagh Herald* held in Enniskillen Library.

A Ford 7610 four-wheel drive tractor mowing grass for second cut silage at Drumconnis.

Chapter 10
The Castle Archdale Experimental Husbandry Farm

Pressure on the Ministry of Agriculture to establish a research farm in County Fermanagh came through the Fermanagh County Committee of Agriculture. Captain The Hon John W. Brooke, Chairman of the County Committee, who was farming at Colebrooke and also on Lord Erne's farm at Crom, was the main advocate for a research establishment in the county.

Captain The Hon John W. Brooke (Courtesy of Viscount Brookeborough).

At a County Committee meeting in January 1950, which Mr Harkness from the Ministry of Agriculture attended, Captain Brooke claimed that the Ministry needed to take a *completely new look* at Fermanagh. He said there were two problems – drainage and winter housing for livestock. He stated that an enormous area of land did not produce grass in May because it was poached during the winter. At another meeting of the committee, he complained about the lack of knowledge and the Ministry's failure to get modern farming methods across to farmers. He said that there was little difference in farming practice between the years 1920 and 1950. He believed that a research farm, which would concentrate on the problems faced by Fermanagh farmers, would bring immense benefit. At this time, the Ministry's advisory staff were conducting grassland experiments on farms in the county. Their success no doubt gave encouragement and justification for establishing a dedicated research centre in Fermanagh. The County Committee's campaign came to fruition when the Castle Archdale Experimental Husbandry Farm opened in spring 1955. Mr A. E. W. Steen of the Ministry of Agriculture, based at Stormont, was in charge of the farm and the first Director was Mr Charlie Porteus, a graduate in agriculture from Queen's University. The original plan at Castle Archdale was to compare the economy of a traditional type of small grassland farm with a similar farm where production had been intensified using fertiliser, controlled grazing and where the fodder was conserved as silage.

Castle Archdale office and laboratory.

Professor Cooper's views

Professor Cooper of Newcastle University, a noted authority on agriculture, in a report on the Castle Archdale Experimental Husbandry Farm in 1959, recommended that an effort should be made to improve drainage on the farm. He also suggested experiments using phosphatic fertiliser and liming to bring the pH to 6.5 and to over 7. In addition to these treatments, the value of oversowing and chemical ploughing was to be assessed. Further experiments in establishing clover in grass swards were also recommended.

With regard to the small farms in Fermanagh, Professor Cooper stated: *The milk that these small farms produce is not required nationally and it is also a heavy charge on the Farm Subsidies Account. The farms are too small for economic production of meat – either from cattle or sheep, for neither of these animals is sufficiently intensive. Forestry, on the other hand, seems to be a logical way of using this land, but progress to this end is slow.* He went on to state that it might be possible to speed up afforestation by offering owners an annual payment for each acre of land planted to the satisfaction of Forestry Division. He concluded his comments on afforestation by stating: *Furthermore, it would provide a long-term solution of what is a complete anachronism in modern agriculture, namely the existence of economic small farms on land of low inherent quality.*

Regarding Fermanagh generally, Professor Cooper emphasised the need for a county soil survey and the value of demonstration farms.

Early developments

Increasing the output from grassland was one of the early challenges at Castle Archdale. Reseeding and improvement of permanent swards were the techniques used. The experience of reseeding at Castle Archdale was recorded in May 1962. Attention was drawn to the need to get rid of surface water before ploughing and reseeding. The importance of ploughing when conditions were sufficiently dry and the weather settled was emphasised. Follow-up cultivations, liming, fertilising and sowing to grass all within four days was possible when the weather was favourable. Tall Fescue, as a grass species, was mentioned as being possibly suitable for establishing a permanent ley. Subsequently, techniques for reseeding without ploughing were evaluated. Housing for cattle in winter was another priority. In 1963 and 1964, the value of cubicles for bullocks was being highlighted. The difficulty of working with machinery on the heavy soils and the drumlin topography was another area addressed. The use of four-wheel drive tractors was a pioneering development at the farm.

A 1957 four wheel drive tractor based on a Fordson Major.

Castle Archdale farmyard in the 1960s.

Public demonstration

The first full-scale public demonstration to be held at Castle Archdale, was organised by Mr James Kerr MAgr, the Farm Director, in April 1967. The 350 farmers who attended the 'Open Day' were welcomed by The Rt Hon H. W. West MP PC, Minister of Agriculture, who said that the purpose of the Centre was to produce by experiment, measurement and observation the kind of practical information which is of real value to farmers on heavy wet land in Fermanagh or in any other part of Northern Ireland. Mr West said: "*Those who farm in such areas have to contend with all the usual problems of farming with the added difficulties arising from the type of soil. On your tour round the centre, you will see the many farming problems which are being faced, and on which information is being sought. Among these problems, there is the question of conservation of grass for winter feed. Hay making, as many of you know is unreliable in this area and silage making is often impracticable for the smaller farmer. It has been clearly shown at this centre, however, that it is not difficult to establish and maintain highly productive new pastures on these heavy, slow draining soils. It has been repeatedly demonstrated that this can be done either by ploughing, sod-seeding, or the use of modern herbicidal sprays. Perhaps equally important is the fact that it has been shown to be possible to improve most existing swards very considerably merely by good management. A little more than ten years ago, it was considered that high grassland outputs under these conditions were not practicable. This has already been shown not to be the case.*" Mr West pointed out that it was not enough merely to produce heavy yields of grass. He stated that farmers must also know how to turn the grass into profit. This applied whether the grass was grazed or was conserved as hay or silage for winter feeding.

Visitors at the 'Open Day' had the opportunity of seeing and discussing the experimental work in progress. This included: pasture renovation, grass variety trials, zero grazing, assessment of Tall Fescue swards, clover versus applied nitrogen plots, housing and management of a November calving suckler herd, feeding barley straw to suckler cows, conserving grass as haylage in a lined tower silo, feeding haylage to suckler cows and the use of slats in the housing of beef cattle.

Mr Harry West, Minister of Agriculture, addressing farmers at the 1967 'Open Day'. Mr James Kerr (left), Director, and Mr George Sherrard from the Ministry's headquarters are with the Minister (Courtesy of Mr James Kerr).

Feeding trials cattle shed.

Integration with Enniskillen Agricultural College

In 1971, the experimental farm at Castle Archdale, then entitled the Grassland Experimental Centre, Castle Archdale, became part of Enniskillen Agricultural College. The Castle Archdale farm extended to 115 hectares of which 95 were farming land. Although the farm was used for research and development work, it also was used for demonstrations and in giving practical experience for Enniskillen Agricultural College students. The farm at that time carried 120 suckler cows and their calves plus replacement stock. About 100 calves and 120 purchased lambs were fattened annually, with the remaining calves sold as stores. The suckler cows and their calves were divided into separate herds and kept on different farmlets with separate wintering facilities which allowed experimental work to be undertaken. The performance of suckler cows and calves of different breeds was also being compared in a recently erected fully-slatted house. As student numbers increased at Enniskillen Agricultural College, Castle Archdale played an increasing role in providing facilities for student practical work.

Friesian cross steers from the suckler herd.

Grassland Improvement

Over the years, the work at Castle Archdale was comprehensive and aimed at addressing the problems being faced by grassland farmers in areas of heavy wet land. Increasing grassland output and its profitable utilisation were priorities. Experiments, the results of which were reported in 1969, showed that the output from the natural sward could almost be trebled through rush control, liming and the application of moderate quantities of fertiliser. Reseeding boosted production by a further 30 per cent.

The technique of direct drilling was evaluated during the period from 1974 to 1978. Direct drilling involved the sowing of grass seed into land that had not been ploughed.

Grass species trial site.

Gabriel Murphy recording grass yields.

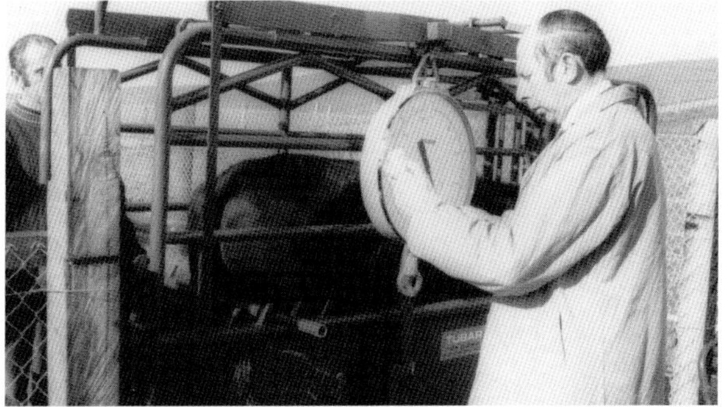

Nixon Armstrong and Des Maguire recording cattle weights.

Grass/clover sward being mixed grazed.

Four wheel drive tractor making an early application of fertiliser.

The green vegetation was killed off using a herbicide prior to the seed being drilled into the topsoil using a specially designed drill. The results showed that direct drilling was satisfactory where grass establishment was good and produced yields of grass as good as those from other methods of reseeding. However, it was pointed out that the risk of failure was greater unless strict attention was paid to the guidelines that were not always easy to achieve under County Fermanagh conditions.

A grass/clover sward proved to be very productive particularly in dry seasons. In 1987, the grass/clover sward had produced almost 1000kg per hectare of cattle and sheep liveweight gain by the month of September. Low cost techniques of rejuvenating Italian Ryegrass swards were developed and the benefits of using low ground pressure tractor, harvester and trailer systems for zero grazing were demonstrated.

Silage

The conservation of grass for quality winter fodder received detailed attention over the years. The benefits of silage making were extolled. A tower silo was an early development but the benefits of trench silos for farm conditions were soon demonstrated.

At the 'Open Days' and demonstrations the latest techniques in silage making were topics for discussion. In June 1971, a large-scale silage making demonstration was held. Two different types of forage harvester, flail and double chop, were in use.

Two silage making systems based on a one and a three man operation were demonstrated. The necessity for early cutting, use of additives, keeping the grass clean, quick

A four wheel drive tractor and specially designed trailer coped very effectively with forage harvesting under poor soil conditions.

filling and sealing with plastic sheeting was emphasised. At that time 1,750 tons of silage and 20 tons of hay were made at the Centre.

Drainage trials

Drainage trials comparing mole drains, gravel tunnels, piped trench drains and a control plot with no drainage commenced in the summer of 1974, with a more elaborate follow-up experiment in 1975 and subsequent years. The effectiveness of the drainage systems was assessed by measuring water tables, surface condition scoring, drainage outflows and grass yields. Early results indicated that grass yields could be increased by up to fourfold using the gravel tunnel system compared to no drainage. The gravel tunnels were appreciably more effective than the other systems on the heavy soils at Castle Archdale. Further details of the results from these trials are presented in Chapter 11 which deals specifically with drainage.

The Department of Agriculture held a major two-day demonstration on drainage techniques at Castle Archdale in June 1982 with over 1,800 farmers attending. The demonstration highlighted the role of secondary treatment including the merits of mole drains and gravel tunnels.

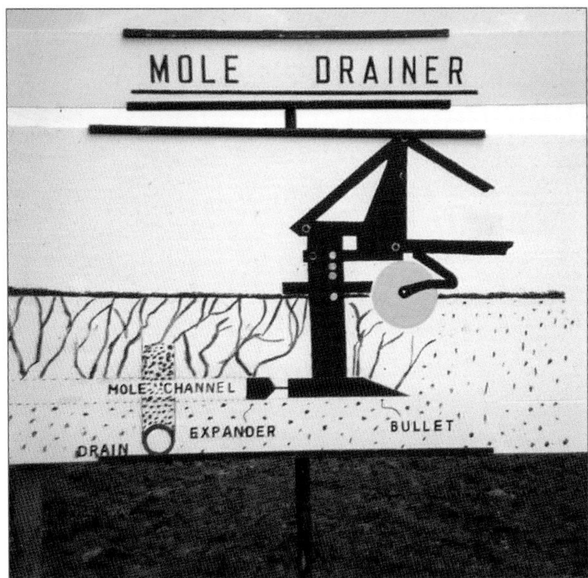

One of the many signs used at the drainage demonstration.

Slurry as a fertiliser

Dr Harry Gracey BAgr MSc PhD of Greenmount Agricultural College, in partnership with the Farm Director, Mr Donagh O'Neill BAgr, evaluated the role of slurry as a fertiliser for silage production over a number of years at Castle Archdale. These results were reported in June 1982. This work showed that slurry was an extremely valuable fertiliser. Best results were obtained if the slurry was applied early in the season before grass started growing. This enabled the nutrients to be well washed into the soil so that the plants could make use of them. Other work by the same partnership showed that returning all the slurry to cut swards supplied around 75 per cent of phosphate and potash requirements for sustained production. The importance of soil analysis to determine phosphate and potash levels was emphasised.

Suckler cows

Suckler cows were becoming an important farm enterprise in the west of Northern Ireland in the 1960s. Increasing output from the suckler herd was therefore a priority at the Centre. A breeding herd had been established in 1965 so that more information could be obtained on aspects of management and profitability. Issues investigated over the succeeding years included in-door calving, season of calving and housing requirements for suckler cows and calves. The economics of fattening single-suckled calves on various diets were also investigated.

By 1969, artificial insemination (A.I.) was being used with considerable success in the 100-cow suckler herd. From 1972 until 1975, trials were carried out on the effects of feeding concentrates on cow fertility. The trial showed that losses in body weight adversely affected conception rates and that this was particularly significant for cows that were being mated in the January to April period. Silage alone did not maintain body weight when cows were suckling. It was concluded that 1 to 1.5 cwt of concentrates per cow should commence 2 to 3 weeks before service and continue for four to six weeks until the majority of cows were served. The body scoring of suckler cows prior to mating was later proven to be a useful management tool.

Double suckling

During 1978 and 1979, a study was carried out to evaluate double suckling in the spring calving herd. This technique involved the purchase of calves with one being fostered onto each milky type suckler cow to complement the cow's own recently born calf. It was shown that by careful management and attention to detail and where there was successful fostering, calf sales approaching 500kg per cow at 8 to 9 months could be achieved. However, fostering was not always easy and in the 1979 trial, only 7 out of 13 fosterings that took place were completely successful. In the cases where bonding was poor, the dam's own calf showed a large advantage over the fostered partner.

Creep feeding

In December 1973, the benefit of creep feeding suckled calves was reported. An experiment which started on 25th February 1971 involving 40 autumn born calves,

averaging three months of age, showed that 1cwt of barley fed as creep gave an additional one quarter cwt of weight gain at weaning. Another experiment comparing rates of creep supplement showed that 2lb per calf per day was the maximum that gave a worthwhile response.

June calving herd

In 1973, a June calving 20-cow herd was established to complement the three autumn and one spring calving herds at the Centre. After three years' experience, it was concluded that the system had much to commend it for a wide range of farming conditions. The system was found to be flexible, management problems were reduced, good calf growth rates were achieved and maximum use was made of grass. It was considered that the system had the greatest application on farms where adequate housing existed and where sufficient quantities of good quality silage were made. An assessment of the financial merits over a number of years of spring, summer and autumn calving suckler herds was published in April 1980. This showed that the summer calving herd was the most profitable.

Reducing scour in Spring born calves

Calving cows indoors in the spring time was common on many farms in the west of Northern Ireland and often farmers experienced serious calf losses and reduced performance as a result of calf scour. In 1985 the Centre examined ways to reduce the scour risk through vaccination and methods of feeding colostrum. Assisting calves to suckle vaccinated cows gave the most promising result.

Herd replacements

Animals for rearing as replacements for the suckler herd at Castle Archdale in 1986 were mainly bought-in dairy bred 1 – 2 week old dropped calves. The purchased calves were generally Aberdeen Angus/Friesian crosses with some Limousin/Friesian crosses. In 1986, the cost of the bought-in Angus cross calves averaged £111 whereas the Limousin cross animals averaged £131. The aim was for these animals to calve down at two years of age. The pointers for successful batch rearing of these calves were: the purchase of healthy calves; the use of teats to encourage milk drinking; feeding to achieve a turnout weight of 110-120kg in January born calves; adopting a leader-follower system at grass; and making high quality silage for winter feeding.

Growth implants

Feeding trials on medium and heavy weight cattle were carried out during the winters of 1983/84 and 1984/85. The cattle were given a combined implant and the feed additive *Romensin* was included with the concentrates fed. The conclusions reached were that medium cattle, on this regime, required 4kg per day of concentrate on medium quality silage or 2kg per day on high quality silage. The comparable figures for heavy cattle were 6 – 8kg per day for medium silage and 4 – 6kg per day on high quality silage.

Ban on growth promoters

In January 1988, the EU banned the use of growth promoters in livestock production. Castle Archdale, in conjunction with Greenmount Agricultural College's farm at Loughgall, initiated trials to assess different treatments of male cattle in increasing beef output. Comparisons were made in relation to the performance of young bulls, vasectomised and immunized bulls, and with steers. This experiment was unique in the British Isles. Spring born bull calves were found to produce leaner carcases than steers and weighed 40kg heavier at 15 months of age. Later, the potential for once-bred heifers as a source of quality beef was assessed. The merits of Charolais, Simmental and Belgian Blue sires on the suckler herd were also evaluated at this time.

Mixed Grazing

Grass/clover swards were established and compared with improved permanent pasture. The grass/clover received 69kg and the permanent pasture 225kg N /ha each year and were grazed by different ratios of breeding ewes and spring calving cows at the same stocking rate. Liveweight produced per hectare was similar on both sward types and increasing the number of ewes along with each suckler cow from 1 to 3 increased liveweight gain per hectare by 18 per cent.

Mixed grazing of cattle and sheep.

Low cost housing

A new low cost housing unit to accommodate 30 May/June calving suckler cows and beef cattle from the Drumaran farm unit within the Centre was built in 1984/85. This

consisted of an open twin silo with a central reinforced concrete wall and clay banks on either side together with a slatted house (9 metres by 24 metres) – the greater part of which was not roofed. A 1981 survey had shown that about one third of the suckler herds in the Province were either not housed or did not have adequate housing. Research work in Scotland had shown that out-wintered cattle performed similarly to those indoors providing the former had somewhere dry to lie. The roofed part was primarily to provide for a creep area for the calves. These new facilities were aimed at producing winter housing for the suckler herd at low cost. At the time the facilities were provided the total cost was £25,100. On a commercial farm, the development would have qualified for a 37½ per cent grant.

Different types of low cost cattle housing were assessed over the years and the merits of each were discussed at 'Open Days'.

Farmlets

A 34-acre farmlet within the centre had been established in 1970 as a demonstration one-man commercial suckler cow unit. The 28 cows on the unit were Aberdeen Angus X Shorthorn which were regarded as an ideal type of cow for the conditions. The cows calved in November and were housed in cubicles with a creep area for the calves. Bulls used were Charolais, Hereford and British Friesian. Charolais bulls produced suckled calves that were on average 30lb heavier at sale. During the year 1968/69, the average weight at weaning (September) was 5cwt 1qr 2lb. Average daily liveweight gain, birth to weaning, was 1.74lb and on grass 2.0lb (May to October). The farmlet produced a total gross margin of £1,466 or £52 7s 0d per cow. After allowing for fixed costs, the farm income was calculated to be £1,124.

Dr William McLauchlan, Director, assessing the merits of a grass sward on the Overlaghy Farm.

Topless cubicles.

Cows 'easy feeding' at kennel yard.

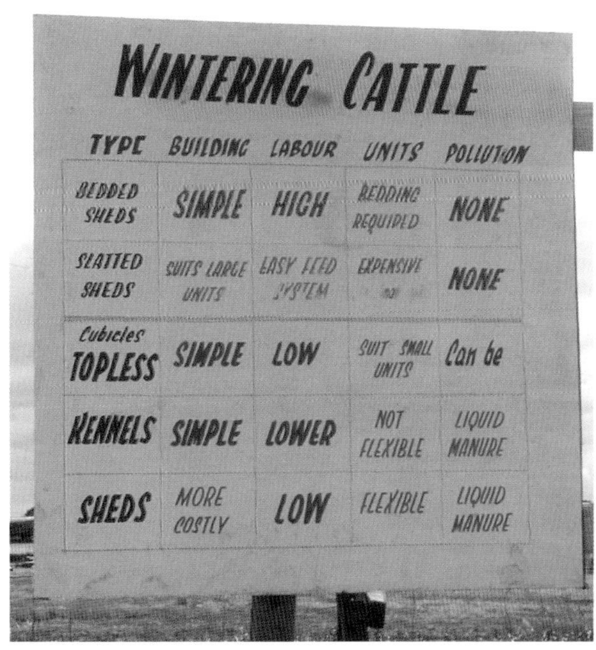

Cattle housing demonstration display board.

Angus X Friesian cross cows with calves from a Simmental bull.

Profitability of farmlets

The profitability of the two farmlets, Drumaran and Overlaghy, which had been established within the Centre for teaching purposes, had improved substantially in 1987/88. The 15-hectare Overlaghy unit, stocked with 20 May/June calving suckler cows with calves sold as forward stores in the spring and a March lambing sheep flock of mainly Greyface ewes, achieved a total Gross Margin of £8,744 or £583 per hectare. These results showed a 60 per cent increase on the previous year reflecting better suckled calf prices and reduced costs resulting from the better season.

The 20-hectare Drumaran farm, with its 30 May/June calving suckler cows, achieved a Gross Margin of £12,666 or £633 per hectare in 1987/88 which, for similar reasons to that applying to the Overlaghy unit, showed an increase of 100 per cent on the previous year. The steers from the unit were sold off grass at one year old at which stage they weighed 409kg and realised £490 per head.

Fodder shortage

In response to the poor summer in 1985 and the consequent fodder shortages, three 'Open Days', with 750 farmers attending, were held at the Centre in September. These events were held in partnership with the Department's County Fermanagh Advisory Staff. One topic highlighted was the feeding of low roughage diets to suckler cows. It had been shown earlier at the Centre that feeding straw supplemented with concentrates would provide a practical alternative to making sufficient hay or silage during summer to feed to stock during the winter. During the year a further 1,000 visitors attended Castle Archdale to see the work in progress.

Willows

Castle Archdale, in partnership with the Department's Horticultural Research Station at Loughgall, initiated trials in coppice willow for biomass energy production. Six hectares were grown in 1986 with the area increased to 13 hectares by 1991. Willows had the potential to produce energy equivalent to 7 - 8 tonnes of coal per hectare per

The Castle Archdale farmyard in 1991.

year. A combined heat and power unit had been installed at Enniskillen Agricultural College to utilise the willows grown at Castle Archdale. The willows were harvested every three years, air-dried and chipped. The gas produced by a gasification process powered an engine coupled to a generator, which had the potential to make the College self-sufficient in electricity. The unit at the College was an experimental prototype, which in practice, was unable in the long term to sustain the level of output necessary to supply the College's electricity needs. However, the information gained from its use proved valuable in the development of more advanced generation equipment.

Harvesting willows at Castle Archdale.

Finality

Castle Archdale took on the role of Beef Technology Centre for Northern Ireland in 1991 in recognition of the wide range of trial work being undertaken. The Centre continued to attract a large number of visitors with 1,300 attending an 'Open Week' in September 1991. However, the Centre's new role was to be short-lived. The Department of Agriculture and Rural Development's decision to withdraw from research and development meant an end to the work of the Castle Archdale Grassland Experimental Centre. Farming and other associated operations ceased at the Centre in February 1995. The Department retained the willow areas and the drainage demonstration plots for further assessment. Two of the workers at the Centre succeeded in gaining a lease on a substantial part of the property from the Department and they carried on commercial farming operations there for some time.

Castle Archdale Farm Directors

Mr Charles Porteus BAgr was appointed as the first officer in charge in 1955. On his return to the Agricultural Advisory Service, he was succeeded by Mr John Bailie BAgr who served until his appointment in November 1964 as a director of an ICI research farm in England. His successor, Mr James A. M. Kerr MAgr, was Farm Director until his promotion to Head of the Agricultural Department at Loughry Agricultural College in June 1967. Mr Kerr was succeeded by Mr Robert (Bob) E. Haycock BAgr. Mr Donagh O'Neill BAgr followed Mr Haycock who became Head of the Agricultural Department in Loughry College on promotion in 1972. Of all the Directors Mr Donagh O'Neill had the greatest involvement with Castle Archdale having been directly associated with it for over 17 years. After periods as an Agricultural Adviser and College

Mr Donagh O'Neill in discussion with Mr Charlie Corrigan at the drainage demonstration.

Lecturer/Farm Manager at Strabane Agricultural School, he was appointed to Castle Archdale where he served for 12 years.

He continued his direct association with Castle Archdale as Principal of Enniskillen College of Agriculture until his appointment as Deputy Chief Agricultural Officer in the autumn of 1989. Following Mr O'Neill's appointment to the post of Principal of Enniskillen Agricultural College, Dr William McLauchlan BAgr PhD became Director at Castle Archdale in 1984 and served until January 1993 when he was appointed Senior Beef Technologist at Greenmount Agricultural College.

Sadly missed

The *Fermanagh Herald* in its weekly feature entitled '*A View Across The Gate*' in October 1994 commented on the loss to Fermanagh arising from the closure of the Castle Archdale Grassland Experimental Centre. After briefly detailing its history and paying tribute to the excellence of the work carried out there relating to grassland improvement, drainage, farm business management and the environment, the feature's concluding two paragraphs were as follows.

The trials and the papers published on them will always stand the test of time in farming and those men pioneering the work will be remembered for some time. The farm will be sadly missed from the agriculture scene in the county as well as further afield as groups of farmers travelled from all over Ireland to benefit from the knowledge gained.

Objectives achieved

In 1950, when campaigning for the establishment of a research farm in County Fermanagh, Captain Brooke stated that there were two main problems facing farmers in the county namely drainage and lack of winter housing for stock. He also claimed that the Ministry of Agriculture was failing to get modern methods of farming adopted by farmers. From the time Castle Archdale Grassland Experimental Centre was opened in 1955 until its closure in 1995, it made a tremendous contribution to the development of agriculture in County Fermanagh. Methods of improving grassland output and its efficient utilisation by livestock were demonstrated. Work at the Centre contributed significantly to the fund of knowledge that was made available to the farming community not only in the west of the Province but much further afield. The work carried out at Castle Archdale was communicated to the farming community through demonstrations and 'Open Days' at the Centre and through press publicity. The results of the experimental work at the Centre have been recorded in detail in the Ministry/Department of Agriculture's Annual Scientific Reports. Successive Directors of Castle Archdale were always in demand at farmers' meetings to explain the results of the trials at the Centre. In addition, the Ministry of Agriculture's Advisory Service made full use of the information gained at the Centre in the course of their every-day work on farms. It can certainly be claimed that Castle Archdale achieved everything that Captain Brooke had wished for back in 1950.

References:

Cooper, Professor M. McG., *Report on Fermanagh agriculture.* Newcastle University. (1969).

Ministry/Department of Agriculture for Northern Ireland *Monthly Reports and Agriculture in Northern Ireland.*

Enniskillen Agricultural College Prize Days - *Principals' Reports.*

Files of *The Impartial Reporter* and *Fermanagh Herald* held in Enniskillen Library.

Chapter 11
Drainage

Farming in County Fermanagh has always been a challenging occupation due to topography, soil and climatic factors. The drumlin countryside, combined with heavy soils on the hills, waterlogged inter-drumlin hollows and a rainfall varying from 40 inches per year in the lowland area of the southern part of the county to over 70 inches on the hills, makes for difficult farming conditions. The fact that rain falls on two out of three days on average adds to the problems. The River Erne system, which drains the greater part of the county, also contributes to the difficulties. It is therefore not surprising that over the years drainage has been high on the priority list as far as agricultural improvement is concerned.

The Erne

The difficulties associated with Lough Erne and the River Erne are related to periods of heavy rainfall when the arterial drainage system is unable to discharge the volume of water quickly enough to avoid flooding of farm land, particularly in the Upper Lough Erne catchment. The problem arises because the Upper Lough Erne catchment extends to 1,050 square miles while the lough covers only 15 square miles or in a ratio of 70 to 1. This means that if an inch of rain falls in the catchment (over half the Erne catchment is in the Irish Republic) and it all ran directly to the lough it would raise the level of water in the Upper Lough by 70 inches. While this does not happen in practice for many obvious reasons it is of course clear that in periods of continuous wet weather, once the ground gets saturated, most of the rainfall will run off directly to streams and eventually to the Lough. This explains why flooding has been a problem around Upper Lough Erne. Upper Lough Erne is shallow and is surrounded in many parts by low lying land which floods when the lough water level rises.

The extent of the flooding under heavy rainfall conditions is therefore determined by the ability of the inter-lough channel and the River Erne to discharge flood waters from the Upper Lough into the Lower Lough and then into the Atlantic Ocean at Ballyshannon. Over the years, efforts have been made to increase the capacity of the inter-lough channel and the River Erne to enable them to cope better with flood waters.

Flooding in the Upper Erne as seen from the air in November 2009 (Courtesy of Mr John McVitty).

Problems associated with flooding include access difficulties to farms and other properties.

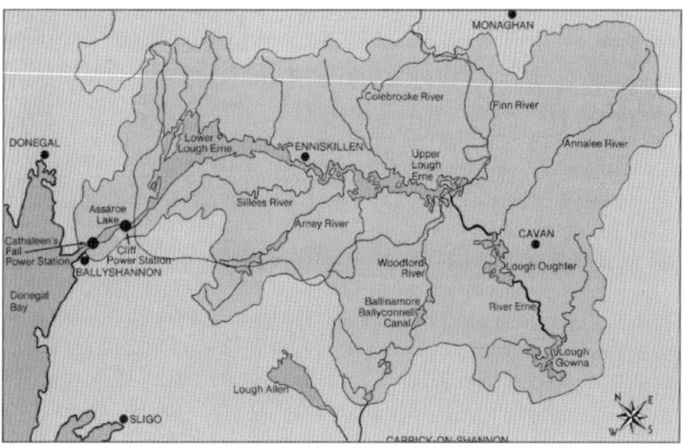

The Erne catchment
[Courtesy of Electricity Supply Board (ESB)].

Some work was carried out in connection with a navigation scheme under an 1842 Act. Under the Erne Lough and River Drainage Act of 1876, a Drainage and Navigation Board was established. This Board undertook extensive drainage work in the 1880s and statutory water levels were established for the two loughs. These were:

- **Lower Lough – 152.66 feet above sea level**
- **Upper Lough summer – 153 feet, winter – 155.5 feet above sea level**

Because of pressure from farmers the Board agreed to lower these levels for the Upper Lough by 1.5 feet in winter and 1 foot in summer. Local residents, who objected to the lowering of the lough, obtained an injunction against the Board in 1907. Responsibility for drainage work was transferred from drainage authorities to county councils under the 1925 Drainage Act. However, an exception was made in the case of the Erne Drainage and Navigation Board, which remained. This Board was empowered to formulate schemes for improvement but, because of conflicting navigation and farming interests, no scheme was ever proposed by the Board.

In 1927 the Northern Ireland Ministry of Finance and the Office of Public Works in Dublin undertook an examination of the problem of the drainage of the Erne basin jointly. One outcome of this was the purchase of the Belleek Pottery Company's water rights by the Northern Ireland Government and Fermanagh County Council in 1933. This permitted some experiments to be carried out with with the sluices at Belleek. Consequently, it was concluded that flooding in the Upper Erne catchment could not be controlled simply by lowering the level of the Loughs. When the Erne Drainage and Navigation Board regained control over the sluices at Belleek, after the completion of the experiments, they reduced the level of both loughs to about 3 feet below statutory level. This management regime continued until 1940 when a boat owner obtained compensation against the Board for damages because of the low level of the loughs. The outcome of this event was the resignation of the Board. The Ministry of Finance then took control of the levels of the lough that had to be kept up during the Second World War to facilitate the Royal Air Force, which used the Lower Lough at Castle Archdale as a flying boat base.

In the 1940s, agreement was reached between the Electricity Supply Board (ESB) in the Irish Republic and the Northern Ireland Ministry of Finance for a joint scheme which would facilitate the generation of electricity at Ballyshannon and exercise some control over the loughs in County Fermanagh. The work, which started in 1946, involved major deepening and widening of parts of the inter-lough channel and all of the River Erne leading from Rosscor to Ballyshannon. The agreement included provision for regulating water levels. The level of the Lower Lough would be controlled by the ESB and would not exceed 152 feet above sea level and would not be allowed to drop below 147 feet. The level of the Upper Lough would be controlled by the Ministry of Finance at the barrage and navigation lock gates constructed in the channel at Portora. Summer levels were not to exceed 154 feet if reasonably preventable. When the level of the Upper Lough reached 153 feet and was rising the Ministry of Finance engineer (later the Ministry of Agriculture engineer) at Enniskillen could ask the ESB engineer at Ballyshannon to reduce the Lower Lough level to 151.5 feet. The winter level was not to exceed 155 feet if reasonably preventable and there was the same arrangement for lowering the level of the Lower Lough when the water in the Upper Lough was rising. It was agreed that no valuable land would be affected if the water could be kept below 154 feet but if levels reached 156.5 feet, a considerable area would be flooded.

Aerial view of ESB Station at Ballyshannon
(Courtesy of ESB).

Aerial view of Cliff generating station (Courtesy of ESB).

Flooding in the Upper Erne basin was a serious problem prior to the drainage scheme of the 1940s. The Lisnaskea Young Farmers' Club had composed a song drawing attention to the problems faced by farmers due to the flooding. The song was based on Percy French's *The Mountains of Mourne* and sung to the same tune. The words were as follows:

Oh, Mary, Fermanagh's a wonderful sight
Our farmers are flooded by day and by night,
They can't grow potatoes or barley or wheat,
If the floods don't abate they'll be out on the street.
But now that I live here I find to my grief,
There's more scope for fishing than land to raise beef.
I have got to wear gum-boots when crossing the lea,
For the farmers of Fermanagh are being washed to the sea.

You remember our friend, Alan Tisdall, of course,
He went up to Stormont at the head of a force,
To talk to Sir Basil and strike on a plan
So that we in Fermanagh might have some dry land;
But in spite of their efforts the flood still rolls on,
But still we're neglected, are we once more to see
The crops of Fermanagh roll down to the sea.

Now we in Fermanagh are a hard working race,
But the way we're neglected is a blooming disgrace;
We can't save our harvest, the land it won't dry.
And we can't blame it all on the almighty on high.
The Government took charge when the Drainage Board ceased,
And by lacking in effort, the floods they increase,
If you should doubt me please come down and see,
How we in Fermanagh are being swept to the sea.

The root of our trouble, it lies at Belleek,
Where the flood-gates are closed seven days of the week;
But now that the seaplanes have left our Lough Shore,
The gates should be opened, to be closed never more.
If the channel were dredged at the West Bridge, Enniskillen
I am sure every farmer here would be willen;
The expenses to share for better than see
The crops of Fermanagh being washed to the sea.

Now Mary, I'll finish, and I hope that my song
Will focus attention on the watery wrong.
And show to you farmers living on dry land,
We no longer want Neptune down here as our God,
If those floods continue (and it is no lark)
The local young farmers must meet in an ark,
And now I must leave you, my good friend, Mary,
Where the crops of Fermanagh are being washed to the sea.

There is no doubt that the 1940s scheme brought very considerable benefits in terms of flood prevention and drainage in the Upper Erne catchment. In extended periods of exceptionally heavy rain flooding in the Upper Erne still occurred but one of the major benefits of the drainage scheme was that the flooding was for a relatively short time which would not have been the case previously. Despite the very considerable drainage benefits brought about by this scheme there were losses. A casualty was one of the best salmon fisheries in Europe and the loss of some prime wetlands in the Upper Erne basin. The prime salmon fishing was on the River Erne from Belleek to Ballyshannon. There were eight angling beats on this stretch of water which covered eight miles and nearly all of them could be waded. In addition, there was the Reserve water from Assaroe Falls and most of the beat to the bridge. Because of the potential benefits arising from the scheme, through relief from flooding and electricity generation, this angling paradise was sacrificed. In place of the miles of superb angling pools came a dreary channel, resulting from the excavation of 600,000 cubic metres of earth and rock from the river bed, and two dams or artificial lakes above the generating plants.

Drainage into the Loughs

Drainage from farmland, apart from that adjacent to the loughs, runs through a network of water channels including sheughs, minor water courses and rivers. To prevent flooding of farmland and to allow drainage from that land efforts have been made over the years to improve the water flow from these rivers and watercourses. Virtually all major watercourses in Northern Ireland have been subject to drainage works carried out by the Ministry of Agriculture or its successors under powers conferred on it by the Drainage Acts.

The two main Acts were the Drainage Act (Northern Ireland) 1947 and the Drainage Act (Northern Ireland) 1964. Under the 1947 Act, the Ministry carried out drainage schemes on designated main watercourses. Most of the rivers in County Fermanagh benefited from drainage works and subsequent maintenance under this Act.

The Salmon Leap at Ballyshannon before the drainage scheme was carried out (Courtesy of the National Library of Ireland).

Minor watercourses

Under the 1964 Act, schemes were carried out on minor watercourses. The minor watercourses were those streams that were so vital in connecting drainage schemes undertaken by farmers on their own land to the main rivers. Responsibility for designating the main and minor watercourses lay with the Drainage Council, which had been set up under the 1947 Act. The Drainage Council in designating watercourses had to consider agriculture, power production, inland navigation, fisheries and other interests. The Ministry's responsibility in relation to watercourses was not therefore confined to improvement of land although of course the main benefits did accrue to land. The work was undertaken based on the priority of need. The funding under the main watercourse scheme was on the basis of 50 per cent grant from the Exchequer and 50 per cent contribution from Rates. In the case of minor watercourses, funding was one third from the Rates and the balance from the Exchequer.

The Colebrooke River.

Works undertaken under these schemes were limited to those cases where solving the drainage problem was clearly beyond the financial and engineering capacity of the landowners. As was the case on the Erne, these works transformed natural meandering rivers into more efficient drainage channels that brought great benefits to the productive potential of farmland. However, in some cases this meant that natural wetland habitats were changed forever with a consequent loss of biodiversity.

A Minor Watercourse.

Drainage of farmland

Crops and grass thrive best on a free draining soil. If the soil is naturally free draining, the water is able to move through the subsoil into the deeper layers away from the root

zone of the growing plants. A rooting zone free of water logging is desirable during the growing season. Drainage may be required because of a high ground water table, an impervious subsoil or underground springs or seepage lines.

Field drainage, aimed at addressing these problems, has been at the forefront of agricultural improvement over the centuries. *The Impartial Reporter* in an article in February 1843 extolled the benefits of field drainage. The article began as follows: *We are so thoroughly convinced of the great utility of thorough draining in this wet hilly county of Fermanagh, for the sake of the landlords, farmers and cottiers, and to push forward the good Agriculture.* A *'Catechism on Draining'* appeared in *The Impartial Reporter* the following month, which, inter alia, showed the economic advantage of field drainage resulting from increased crop yields. The large estates were very conscious of the benefits resulting from drainage in the nineteenth century. For example, Lord Erne encouraged drainage on his estate. At Crom he built a plant for the production of drainage clay pipes. According to Crom estate records it took 3,500 tiles to drain one acre at a cost of £2 9s 0d. Lord Erne's agricultural advisers claimed that drained land would produce £2 per acre more in crop value per year. Lord Enniskillen's estate at Florencecourt also had a drainage clay pipe factory in operation in the 1850s. Many of these pipes have been dug up during drainage works in the twentieth century.

Professor Cooper of Newcastle University in a report on Fermanagh agriculture in 1959 summarised the challenge facing those trying to improve the output of the land through drainage when he stated: *the heavy Fermanagh soils are almost completely structureless and so permit of very little movement of water either horizontally or vertically. This is a characteristic feature of soils with a high silt and fine sand fraction, which are subject to heavy rainfall.*

The Land Improvement Scheme

The Land Improvement Scheme (introduced in 1929) was the first Government Scheme that offered grant aid for drainage work undertaken by farmers. This scheme was initially only available on farms where the Poor Law Valuation was under £75, but later on it applied to all farms. It offered grants of 85 per cent of labour costs in carrying out work such as drainage, stubbing of whins, fencing repairs, improvement of river embankments, construction of farm roads and reclamation work. The labour had to be employed and engaged through the Employment Exchange. In 1948, the sum of £18,000 was paid out in grant aid under this scheme in County Fermanagh.

Drainage undertaken at this time included sheugh clearance, the construction of open drains and under-drainage. The type of under-drainage involved the digging of channels and creating a cavity at the base in which water could flow freely. The cavity was formed by using carefully selected and placed stones, or by placing sods in a similar fashion or by using clay tiles (pipes). The work was undertaken by hand at that time.

The Land Improvement Scheme was succeeded by the Agricultural Development Scheme introduced under the Agricultural Act (Northern Ireland) 1949, which again offered grant aid for drainage improvement. The 1947 Agriculture Act passed at Westminster heralded a new era in farm improvement. Drainage was included as an eligible item in the Farm Improvement Scheme and offered grant aid at one-third of the cost of the work. In Northern Ireland, a one-sixth supplement was payable under the Agriculture Development Scheme in addition to the grant obtainable under the Westminster Scheme – this brought the grant available for items such as drainage up to 50 per cent. Mechanisation at this time was beginning to play a larger part in land improvement work, which enabled a greater volume of work to be undertaken.

Mole drainage scheme

In November 1947, mole drainage demonstrations, organised by the Ministry of Agriculture, were held at eight centres in County Fermanagh. The farms chosen for the demonstrations were those of Mr F. West, Mullyduff,

Cross section of a clay pipe drain.

Stone drain.

Newtownbutler; Mr F. Blake JP, Derrylin; Mr G. Watterson, Drumnarane; Mr R. J. Loane, Letterkeen, Kesh; Mr C. McPhillips, Crievehill; Mr G. Ferguson, Rooskey; Mr J. Kirkpatrick, Nutfield and Wing Commander Bullmore, Riversdale. These demonstrations preceded the introduction of a scheme whereby mole drainage work was carried out by the Ministry of Agriculture on County Fermanagh farms. Under the scheme an International crawler tractor, mole plough and operator were supplied by the Ministry, which commenced operations on 29th February 1948 and continued until 1950. The cost to the farmer, after a 50 per cent grant, on land which was previously assessed as being suitable for mole drains, was 30 shillings per acre. Two hundred applications were received under the scheme during 1948. Moles elsewhere proved to be an effective low cost means of drainage where soil conditions were suitable and where the standard of installation was good. However, much of the heavy land in County Fermanagh has a high silt content, which makes the subsoil rather unstable. Mole drains in this material tend to have a very short life. This drainage practice in Fermanagh was discontinued, as it was not considered to be a widespread success. No doubt, the absence of collector drains, spaced at appropriate intervals, which nowadays would be regarded as a prerequisite, also contributed greatly to the disappointing experience..

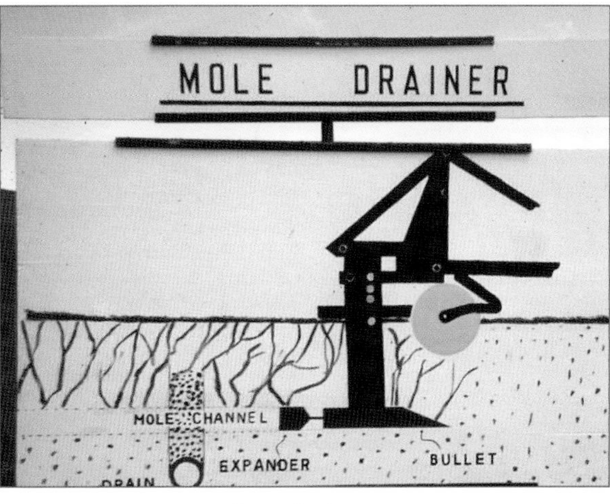

Layout of a mole drainage system

A mole plough shatters the soil and subsoil and permits water to drain more freely.

Mini trencher

The need to find a cost-effective solution for improving the surface condition of the land on Fermanagh farms was intensifying in the mid 1960s. Conventional piped field drains with permeable fill on top were very expensive particularly since they needed close spacing if they were to give the desired results. Mr Joe Pat Prunty, a drainage contractor from Newtownbutler, invented a machine called a mini-trencher. This machine cut a trench that was then automatically filled with gravel or broken stones from a top mounted hopper. The intention was that these 'stone' drains would run across the slope of the field into a collector drain. These drains were relatively cheap to make and therefore, economically, could be spaced more closely than conventional drains. This system of drainage was primarily aimed at remedying poor surface drainage by trapping water run off. They did not address the issue of poor soil and subsoil structures, which prevented the free percolation of water down through the layers of the soil. Furthermore, they were not deep enough to intercept springs or control spring line seepage.

Mr Joe Pat Prunty (right) discussing drainage issues with Captain John Brooke. Lord and Lady Brookeborough are in the background.

Mini trencher drainage machine.

Drainage developments

Plastic or PVC pipes replaced clay tiles as the common method of under-drainage from the mid 1960s. The use of plastic pipes for drainage was developed in Holland. Pipes made by *Wavin* were among the first plastic pipes to be used in Northern Ireland. Initially these pipes, which came in rigid lengths that socketed together, had the slits cut across the pipes but later longitudinal slits were found to be more satisfactory. Later, manufacturers developed corrugated coiled long lengths of piping which were much better suited to laying by the sophisticated machinery that was available for trenching and laying pipes. In addition the plastic pipes were cheaper than tiles and easier to lay. To have effective under-drainage the drains using clay pipes or the plastic equivalent need to be laid at a depth of 500 to 800mm. In heavy soils, it was found desirable to backfill these drains with gravel or broken stone to above the level of the subsoil.

Furthermore, in heavy land the drains need to be closely spaced for effective drainage. This was a very expensive system for land improvement and the cost effectiveness comes into question. Mole drains, on the other hand, do not use any materials in their construction and can be drawn through the soil at relatively close spacing by specialised machinery. To be most effective mole drains need to be drawn uphill. They need to discharge into properly constructed collector drains running across the slope at appropriate intervals. The distance apart of the collector drains, 20 to 30 metres, depends on the suitability of the soil for mole drains. For effective mole drainage a stable clay subsoil, containing few stones, gravel or sand veins, is required. Furthermore, the mole drainage operation needs to be carried out when ground conditions are suitable, normally between May and September. At mole drain depth, the subsoil should be plastic enough to form a stable channel. Above the mole drain it should be dry enough to crack and form fissures through which the water can flow downwards.

Backfilling pipe drains using broken stone.

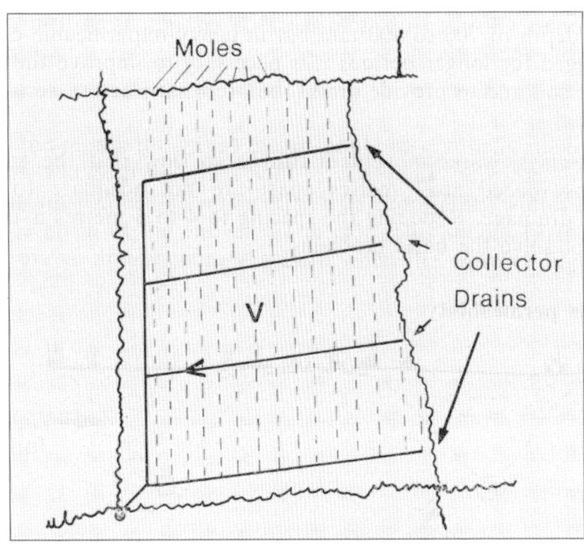

Mole drainage layout plan.

Gravel Tunnel Drainage

The results from the earlier experience of mole drainage in County Fermanagh were disappointing. Much of the heavy land in County Fermanagh has a high silt content, which is rather unstable. Mole drains in this material tend to have a very short life. The benefits of the mole drainage system, without the shortcomings, were realised when the gravel filled mole drainage system was developed. Mr John Mulqueen MAgric who was the Officer-in-Charge at the An Foras Talúntais Research Farm, Ballinamore, County Leitrim, invented the system. Mr Mulqueen worked in close co-operation with Mr Joe Pat Prunty, the drainage contractor from Lettergreen, Newtownbutler, in developing the new technique. Valuable financial support for this development came from the Northern Ireland Agricultural Trust. Specialised gravel tunnel machinery was manufactured by Mr Tommy Fisher MBE JP of Ballinamallard to a design developed by Mr John Mulqueen and Mr Joe Pat Prunty.

The first drainage in County Fermanagh using this system was carried out at the Grassland Experimental Centre,

Mr John Mulqueen.

Castle Archdale, in 1973 when Mr Donagh O'Neill was Director. Experimental plots were subsequently laid down in 1974 at Castle Archdale. In addition, fields on a number of farms in the western part of the Province were drained using the system for practical assessment. The gravel tunnel drainage work on farms, which extended to around 150 ha, was sponsored by the Northern Ireland Agricultural Trust and evaluated by the staff of the Department of Agriculture. The new drainage system proved successful and was approved for grant-aid in 1976.

The gravel tunnel drainage system was similar to the mole drainage technique except that the mole channel was filled with half to three quarter inch crushed stone or gravel. The filling of the channel meant that the drain would be stable and not subject to collapse. The gravel tunnel drains were drawn up and down the slope at around 1.5 metre spacings and 400 to 500mm deep over collector drains that ran across the slope. As in the case of mole drains, a successful gravel tunnel system depends on the effective cracking and restructuring of the soil and subsoil so that the water can reach the drains freely.

The gravel tunnel machine won the Silver Medal at the 1975 Royal Ulster Agricultural Society show at Balmoral. A profile of a gravel tunnel drain is beside the display board.

The general requirements for a successful gravel tunnel installation are summarised as having the following: a good outfall for the main drain; a well-designed collector drain system; proper spacing and depth of gravel tunnels with an adequate fall when the work is being carried out. Effectiveness also depends on dry soil conditions so as to ensure adequate cracking of the subsoil to allow drainage water to flow freely to the gravel tunnels. The layout for the system was similar to that used for successful mole drainage.

Gravel tunnel machine in action.

The conclusion of the experimental work at Castle Archdale and the experience at farm level showed that in the heavy soils of County Fermanagh secondary treatment, using moles or gravel tunnels, provided a much more effective under-drainage system than conventional drains. Gravel tunnel drains proved to be suited to a much wider range of soil conditions than mole drains.

Merits of gravel tunnels

In October 1980, a feature article in *Farm Week* stated that in Fermanagh, Department of Agriculture Advisers and farmers, young and old, saw land improvements as the top priority – even more important than machinery, stock and buildings. Mr John Courtney BAgr, Dip Ag Eng, of Prunty Contracts, pointed out in the article that farmers were becoming increasingly convinced of the merits of gravel tunneling. It was cheaper and much more effective than conventional drainage. It was pointed out that collector

drains were normally placed at 25 to 30 metres apart with gravel tunnels spaced at 1.5 metres. The cost of this system, including the collector drains, was around £550 per acre or £1,330 per hectare. The same article dealt with the experience of Mr Edgar Hogg of Maguiresbridge who had purchased an area of neglected land. The production in the summer of 1979 from the first 22 acres to be reclaimed was 1,500 bales of rushes. This area was in 13 fields before the reclamation started. After the reclamation and drainage programme all that remained of the divisions was one main hedge and trees left to provide shelter and a conservation area. The land had been drained using gravel tunnels. The reclaimed area, after ploughing, had been sown in oats as crop silage and undersown with Barlenna ryegrass. It produced an excellent crop of silage with a good strike of ryegrass.

Drainage Conference

The Department's Advisory Service held a major conference for drainage contractors from Tyrone and Fermanagh at Enniskillen College in February 1981. Mr Vincent Courtney BAgr, County Agricultural Executive Officer for Tyrone and Mr Sam Morrow BAgr, his counterpart in Fermanagh acted as joint chairmen.

Mr John Courtney.

Mr Moreland Ingram BAgr, head of the Department's Farm Buildings and Land Improvement Division in Belfast, stressed the need for cost effective systems of drainage.

The next speaker was Mr John Mulqueen, who was then head of the Marginal Land Division of the Department of Agriculture in the Irish Republic, and who pioneered the gravel tunnel system of drainage when working at the Research Farm in Ballinamore. Mr Mulqueen showed that drainage problems could be divided into four categories:

Mr Moreland Ingram (left) and Mr Joe Pat Prunty on a drainage site.

1. Tight slow draining soils and impervious layer problems,
2. High ground water problems in flat valleys and river basins,
3. Seepage problems arising from outside water getting into an area,
4. Drainage problems arising from a combination of these factors.

He emphasised the need for carrying out a thorough examination of the soil and the surrounding area to ascertain what was causing the problems before attempting a solution. He stressed the importance of studying the 6 inch and 25 inch maps of the area and marking significant features. Once a survey of the ground had been carried out by walking over the area test pits should be dug at appropriate locations to establish the sequence of soil layers and the nature of ground water flow. It was only when this had been done and the cause of the poor drainage established that an effective drainage system could be designed. Mr Mulqueen said that to drain slow draining and impervious soil layers effectively it was necessary to

Mr Donagh O'Neill

increase permeability by loosening with a sub-soiler or mole drainer or gravel tunneling.

Interceptor drains needed to be installed where the seeping of outside water into the area caused water logging. In cases where there was strong artesian seepage, the drain must be located in the aquifer carrying the water or at least connected to it. When these specific problems had been solved, heavy soils could be drained using gravel filled moles.

Castle Archdale experience

The final speaker was Mr Donagh O'Neill, Director of the Grassland Experimental Husbandry Farm, Castle Archdale, who described some of his experiments to compare the effectiveness of mole and gravel tunnel drainage with normal piped drains spaced apart at 6.5 metres. His conclusions, based on six years experience, were:

1. Traditional trench drains alone were not adequate for effective drainage of mineral soils of low permeability. They were also expensive. Rather than drain at 6 metres, these traditional drains should be spaced much more widely apart (30 to 40 metres) to act as collectors for a secondary treatment such as moles, gravel tunnels or even sub-soiling.
2. Mole drains and gravel tunnels gave similar results in a stable soil.
3. A mole drainage system may be installed for

The Florencecourt drainage site. Mr Alan Warnock BAgr, Agricultural Adviser, is conducting the demonstration.

little more than half the cost of a gravel tunnel system.

4. Mole drains should be used in situations where there was a reasonable life expectancy (six to ten years).

5. Gravel tunnels should be installed where the suitability of the soils for moling is in doubt or where a permanent drainage system is required.

The benefits of the new approach to drainage were realised by farmers who responded by undertaking large scale comprehensive schemes.

The development of the gravel tunnel system opened up a whole new approach to the drainage of heavy soils. Mr Prunty's contribution to this development was recognised when he was appointed MBE and awarded the Belfast Telegraph Cup in 1987 for his outstanding contribution to agriculture.

Drainage demonstrations

The development of the gravel tunnel drainage system coincided with the introduction of generous grant aid for land improvement works under the Northern Ireland Agriculture Development Programme. The Department of Agriculture's Advisory Service also undertook an intensive advisory programme. This programme included a large demonstration, held at Castle Archdale on 26th and 27th May 1982, which featured all aspects of drainage including under-drainage, mole drains, gravel tunnels and subsoiling. Press articles and public meetings also publicised the new approach to land drainage.

Demonstration sites at Lisnaskea, Florencecourt, Kesh and Garrison were also established by the Advisory Service, the cost of which was funded by the Vaughan Trust. These sites proved very valuable and demonstrated the superiority of gravel tunnel drainage in a wide range of soil conditions. Mole drainage was also very effective but on a more limited range of soil types. The sites at Kesh and Garrison proved to be totally unsuitable for mole drains whereas the Lisnaskea and Florencecourt sites were very suitable for this low cost drainage system.

Benefits of drainage

IIn 1983, it was recorded at Castle Archdale that effective drainage resulted in 42 extra days grazing. At the Lisnaskea site an additional 37 extra grazing days were possible and at Florencecourt, where the trial plots were on very heavy land, 50 extra grazing days per year were obtained. Not only was the grazing season extended but there was also an appreciable improvement in sward composition and in utilisation of the grass. In April 1984, it was estimated that £4 million was being spent per year on drainage in Fermanagh costing around £1,400 per hectare on average. The Agricultural Advisory Service was impressing on farmers that on difficult land effective drainage systems could be carried out at around £1,000 per hectare if farmers adopted the most cost effective systems. It was pointed out that once drainage has been carried out there was very considerable potential for further improvement through reseeding, increased fertiliser use, intensive grazing, multi silage cuts and reduced concentrate usage in stock feeding.

Mr Stanley Lytle.

Transformation

The generous grant aid and the intensive advisory programme encouraged farmers to undertake extensive drainage schemes. Of particular significance in relation to advisory work was a tape/slide presentation prepared by Mr Stanley Lytle BAgr, Deputy County Agricultural Executive Officer, which was shown at farmers' meetings in centres throughout the county.

This presentation dealt with every aspect of drainage in County Fermanagh. Aspects of drainage covered in the presentation included:

- indicators of the need for drainage
- the selection of the correct drainage solution to the particular problems
- the implementation of a cost effective drainage solution.

This together with the on-farm advice offered by the Department staff and the availability of well-equipped and skilled drainage contractors enabled farmers to undertake

Mr Michael McCreesh, Department of Agriculture's Area Officer in Lisnaskea, discussing progress on a drainage site with the contractor, Mr Martin McGrory, Lisnagole, Lisnaskea.

well-planned drainage schemes. As a result, there was a large uptake of drainage and other land improvement work.

The number of notifications under the various schemes for drainage averaged 1904 per year during period 1981/85. This represented an increase of 65 per cent over the base year 1980/81. During the 1982/83 year, farm drainage grant under the Agricultural Development Programme in County Fermanagh amounted to over £2.3 million. Consequently, during the period when attractive grants were available, large areas of County Fermanagh were transformed into highly productive grassland, a state that in large measure still pertained at the end of the century.

References:

Ministry/Department of Agriculture for Northern Ireland's *Monthly Reports* and *Agriculture in Northern Ireland.*

Records of the County Agricultural Executive Office.

Files of *The Impartial Reporter* and *Fermanagh Herald* held in Enniskillen Library.

Cooper, Professor M. McG; Newcastle University. Paper entitled: *Land use in County Fermanagh* (1959).

Highly productive grassland.

Chapter 12

Grass as a crop

Interest in increasing output from grassland was evident from the earliest days of the Fermanagh County Committee of Agriculture. In its first Annual Report in 1906, the results of experiments using fertiliser on grazing and meadows were reported. These experiments showed the positive cost benefit of applying fertiliser to grassland where management was good. In March 1920, the value of basic slag as a fertiliser was being extolled. An application of 10 cwt of slag to the statute acre had trebled the output of meat. On poor pasture, a dressing of 6 cwt basic slag per acre was profitable because cows in milk would repay the cost of the slag in the first season after application.

Nature's best food

In 1926, the merits of grass as food for dairy cows were being advanced. Mr Greacen, Inspector with the Ministry of Agriculture, when addressing a meeting of farmers in Fermanagh in November of that year stated: "*Grass is nature's best and cheapest food for the dairy cow.*" He said: "*Grass should form the staple food of the cow for six months of the year, and dried grass – hay we call it – with some turnips should form a considerable proportion of the diet for the next six months.*" He then went on to extol the merits of feeding meal according to yield.

Mr D. T. Ritchie, Agricultural Instructor, informed those present at the meeting that by manuring the pasture they would not only produce more grass but also a more nutritious quality of grass giving a saving of 30s to 40s in the purchase of a balanced ration.

Nitram's recommendations

The value of using dressings of sulphate of ammonia on grassland, which had been treated with lime, phosphates and potash, was being promoted as part of a new grassland management system by Nitram Ltd in 1927. Up to four dressings of sulphate of ammonia were applied during the season. This treatment was combined with a recommended rotational paddock grazing system. Six or seven paddocks were recommended for dairy cows and three for beef cattle. It was claimed that the adoption of the new system could double output from grassland. The Northern Ireland Minister of Agriculture, Mr Edward Archdale, who attended a demonstration of the new system on a farm near

"Grass is nature's best and cheapest food for the dairy cow."

Clogher, said that he was practising the system on his farm in Fermanagh. Several lectures were given in Fermanagh by Mr J. Irwin of Nitram Ltd. He emphasised the need for the use of complete fertilisers but that phosphate and potash could be applied during the winter months or in early spring with nitrogenous fertiliser being applied at intervals during the growing season. Using this method enabled early grazing in spring and late grazing in the autumn, which led to increased milk production and savings in the use of concentrates. Many farmers attended a follow-up demonstration of the system which was held on the farm of Mr Edgar Dickson, Donegall, Springfield, with many farmers attending. Mr J. Greacen of the Dairy Department and Mr T. C. Skelly, Agricultural Overseer, Rosslea, were also present.

The benefits of applying fertiliser are clearly seen.

Mr Edgar Dickson (Courtesy of Mr and Mrs W. Dickson).

Early grass

'Grow early grass' was the advice offered by the Ministry of Agriculture for Northern Ireland at the beginning of February 1929 as a method of overcoming a shortage of feeding stuffs. The recommendation was aimed at stimulating the early growth of forage crops and pastures by applying fertiliser. A mixture of 1 cwt of sulphate of ammonia, 2 cwt of superphosphate and 2 cwt of kainit was recommended for immediate application at the rate of 4 to 6 cwt per statute acre.

Grassland experiments in the late 1920s

A report in the local press of grassland experimental work appeared in August 1931. A process for improving output from grassland up to three-fold by using rush cutting, drainage, grassland renovation, fertiliser treatment and rotational grazing was described. A plough was used to make shallow drains across the impervious soils of the hills every 10 yards with the spoil being spread across the resulting land in between. The grassland was then thoroughly harrowed to tear off the mat of coarse grass and 'fog'. Fertilising consisted of an application of 4 cwt of *Semsol* (phosphatic fertiliser), 1 cwt of potash salts in February followed by 1½ cwt of sulphate of ammonia at the end of March. In the second year of treatment, it was found that stock could be turned out three weeks ahead of normal turn-out. Remaining rushes were cut in July and again in September. The experiment was carried out on three milk-producing farms. In 1928 the three farms, during the grazing months of May to October, sold 4,966 gallons of milk to the creamery from 25 milking cows. In 1929 the milk output from the farms during the grazing months was 11,231 gallons from 33 cows. In 1928 the area grazed on the three farms was 74 acres and in the following years, because of the increased productivity and better quality grass, only 42 acres were required. In 1928 (base year) the grazing stocking rate was three acres per cow. In the next two years, the rates were 1.3 and 1.2 acres per cow respectively. Milk output per acre increased from 84.66 gallons per acre in 1928 to 281.4 in 1930. When milk was priced at four pence per gallon (the 1930 ruling price), the application of the fertiliser and other improvement work was shown to be cost effective. The article concluded by stating that Mr Tierney, who farmed in a difficult district between Lisnaskea and Newtownbutler, had adopted the system and that a visit to his farm would convince any farmer of the great success that could be obtained.

Visit to Wales

In the late 1930s, interest was beginning to be taken in the potential of grass as a crop. Mr W. T. McClintock, County Agricultural Executive Officer, and Mr D. T. Ritchie,

Agricultural Instructor, visited Aberystwyth in Wales during the summer of 1938 to see the results of grassland improvement experiments. They were most impressed and on their return Mr McClintock stated at the Fermanagh County Committee of Agriculture: *"It is nearly impossible to exaggerate what has been done; it is absolutely marvelous."* At the same time Fermanagh farmers were being encouraged to apply lime to the land. Grants were then available for applying lime and basic slag at attractive rates.

Colebrooke demonstration

The Fermanagh County Committee of Agriculture visited Sir Basil Brooke's Colebrooke estate in August 1938 to see the improvement work on grassland being carried out there. It was stated that the Government's intention was to double the number of cattle in Northern Ireland. To do this it was claimed that two blades of grass would have to grow where one grew before. Professor Mercer of Queen's University gave a talk on increasing grassland output at the demonstration.

Selective weedkiller for grassland

Trials were carried out in Fermanagh, and in other parts of Northern Ireland, in 1945 on the effectiveness of a new selective weedkiller supplied by Imperial Chemical Industries Ltd (ICI). The new product was found to control a number of common weeds, including rushes, but it did not damage grasses. The spring of 1949 witnessed the first publicity for commercially produced selective weedkillers for use on grassland. A demonstration on the use of *'Agroxone'*, an ICI weed killer based on monochloro phenoxy acetic acid (MCPA), was held at Crom Castle estate at that time.

Appeal for self-sufficiency

In January 1950, the potential for increased agricultural production was fully discussed at the Fermanagh County Committee of Agriculture. Mr Harkness, of the Ministry of Agriculture, appealed to farmers to become as self-sufficient as possible. He considered that purchased feed prices would rise as a result of the removal of Government subsidy. He appealed for a 20 per cent increase in the Northern Ireland area of oats and wanted improvement of grassland and the better utilisation of that grassland for winter livestock feeding in the form of silage or dried grass. In response to the many questions, Mr Harkness said that milk had increased in price from sixpence halfpenny pre-war to three shillings and sixpence in 1950. He thought that in the future the emphasis on milk would not be as great as in the past. He believed that the right thing in Northern Ireland, particularly for the small farmer, was to concentrate on the class of livestock that would be dual purpose. He said that the Dairy Shorthorn in the past probably suffered from the fact that it sacrificed milk production for beef characteristics to some extent. This was the reason the Ministry had been importing a number of English Dairy Shorthorns with an adequate milk yield.

Demonstrations and experiments

Captain John Brooke had built a grass drying plant at Colebrooke in 1948 and was using high levels of nitrogen to boost grass growth. He claimed that he was getting an economic response when using 8 cwt of sulphate of ammonia per acre. A demonstration on growing grass and grass drying was held at Colebrooke in July 1950 when 200 farmers attended. Captain Brooke was anxious for the Ministry of Agriculture to intensify grassland research work. At the County Fermanagh Committee of Agriculture he complained about lack of knowledge and said that he had been advised that he 'might' get a response in production if he applied 1½ cwt of sulphate of ammonia, whereas he knew that 8 cwt per acre gave an economic response. He claimed that the Ministry had failed to get modern farming methods across to farmers and said that little difference was evident in farm practice between 1920 and 1950. One headline in the *Fermanagh Herald* in October 1950

Colebrooke Park
(Courtesy of Viscount Brookeborough).

An establishing reseed.

Professor Linehan.

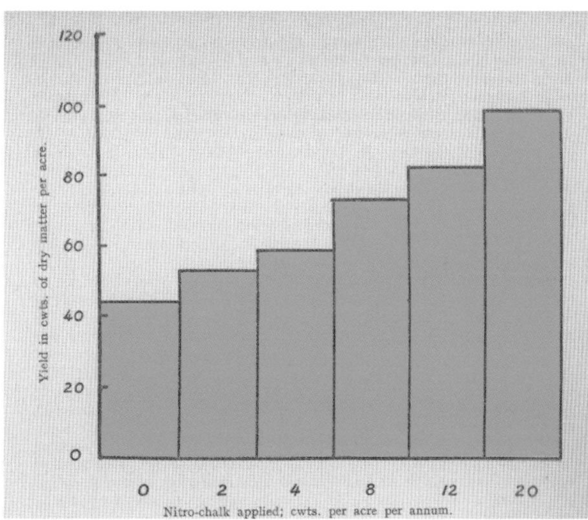

Effects of nitrogen fertiliser on grass yields (Crom experiment).

was: *Premier's son says Ministry of Agriculture is complete and absolute failure.* At this time, Captain Brooke was making the case to have a research farm located in County Fermanagh.

Open Day at Crom

An 'Open Day' was held at Crom Castle estate in August 1950, when visitors had the opportunity of seeing the productivity of grass from two different grass seeds mixtures under two different fertiliser treatments. Professor Linehan of the Faculty of Agriculture, Queen's University, who conducted the experiments, was the speaker.

He said that nitrogenous manures produced marked yield increases on swards composed entirely of grass. He pointed out that if other soil nutrients were not deficient the degree of yield increase appeared to be almost proportionate to the quantity of nitrogen applied even up to such heavy dressings as 20 cwt of nitro-chalk per acre. He pointed out that the contribution to the overall yield of the grass sward from clover declined rapidly as the rate of application of nitrogenous fertiliser increased.

A good grass/clover sward can be very productive and reduces the need for applied nitrogenous fertiliser.

Experiments at Tubrid and Riversdale

In 1950, Mr W. T. McClintock stated that experimental plots and demonstrations existed on about 100 farms in the county. He indicated that most farms had the potential to double production from grassland. It was suggested that the farms at Riversdale and the Vaughan Institute farm at Tubrid should be used for experimental and demonstration purposes. The work subsequently undertaken at these centres received great praise from the County Committee of Agriculture. Results of an experiment on permanent pasture carried out over the years 1951 to 1953, under the supervision of Mr Tom Moore MAgr, Deputy County Agricultural Executive Officer, at the Vaughan Institute farm at Tubrid, Kesh, showed that output from the experimental plots was 190 per cent higher than that of the control plots in terms of liveweight gain by grazing cattle. The fertiliser treatments, in addition to lime, used in the Tubrid experimental plots in 1951, 1952 and thereafter are

shown on the following chart. The control plots received no fertiliser or lime. Aberdeen Angus cattle were used to graze all plots rotationally.

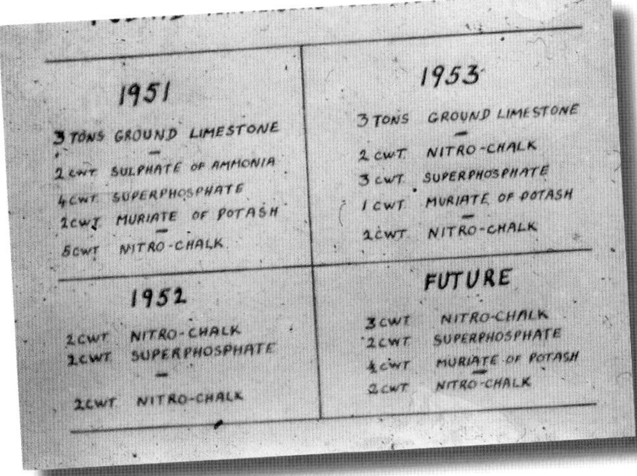

Details of the fertiliser treatment on the Tubrid plots from 1951.

The Tubrid trial area.

Meantime, the value of different grass seeds mixtures was being assessed. A demonstration of the virtues of Timothy/Meadow Fescue swards was held on Mr Jason Hassard's farm at Tully, Churchill.

Imperial Chemical Industries' (ICI) interest

Captain Brooke at Colebrooke was continuing his grassland improvement work and ICI through their local adviser, Mr Sam Agnew BAgr, organised a demonstration of the work for farmers in May 1953. The value of the gas *Cymag* was featured at the demonstration. It was claimed that its use had exterminated 2,000 rabbits at Colebrooke. Rabbits at that time were considered a serious pest and were described by Captain Brooke in 1954 as a menace. He said that when myxamatosis arrived in the country it was important to ensure that all rabbits were exterminated. In the meantime the County Committee of Agriculture was pressing the Ministry to introduce a rush destruction scheme.

Bellanaleck to the fore

The productivity of the farm of Mr Ben Loane, at Rushin, Bellanaleck, had increased very significantly through improved grassland measures. In 1954, ICI in co-operation with the local Ministry of Agriculture Advisory staff, organised a demonstration for farmers. The demonstration showed how permanent grassland productivity could be enhanced through liming, fertilising and controlled grazing using electric fences.

Mr Ben Loane (Courtesy of Mr I. Loane).

The Loane farm subsequently became an ICI grassland demonstration farm. On the 12th April 1957, there was a good turn out of farmers to see self-feeding of silage and the production of early grass. That year strip grazing during the day started on 1st April and by 7th April concentrate feeding to the 40 cow dairy herd had ceased. The cows were self-fed silage during the night. Several cows were yielding over four gallons per day on that regime. During the summer strip grazing, which had been in use on this farm from 1950, was practised.

It was claimed at the demonstration that the feeding of silage, which enabled less meal to be fed because of silage's superior feeding value compared to hay, could lead to a saving in feeding costs of over £25 per week in a 35-cow herd. Early grass combined with silage feeding could lead to a saving in feed costs of over £54 per week for a similar sized herd.

ICI's advice at that time regarding soil fertility in relation to grassland production was as follows: Generally 2 - 3 tons of lime should be applied to a quarter or third of the farm every year; 2 – 3 cwt of phosphatic fertiliser and 1 cwt of muriate of potash per acre together with up to 10 cwt sulphate of ammonia or its equivalent should be applied per acre. Where more than one cut of silage was taken an additional 1 cwt of muriate of potash was recommended.

Brookeborough farms

The Ministry's Advisory Staff in County Fermanagh, for demonstration purposes, used the small farm of Mr William Dunn at Munmurray, Brookeborough, very extensively. In April 1955, one hundred farmers attended an early grass demonstration, which was conducted by Mr George Pollock NDA, Agricultural Advisory Officer. The farm extended to 27 acres, two acres of which were in crop. The farm was carrying nine cows (normally eleven) at the time together with ten young stock. There were also two sows and 25 fattening pigs. One hundred and fifty chickens were reared annually on deep litter. Mr Dunn had built a silo which held 100 tons of silage three years previously. He hoped to start silage making in early June, using a Ferguson tractor, mower and buckrake. The importance of letting the temperature develop in the ensiled grass was emphasised. Mr Dunn used the Ministry's soil analysis service in order to establish the nutrient status of the soil on his farm.

Early grass

The number of farms used by the Ministry's Advisory Staff for early grass production demonstrations was extended in 1956 to include those of Messrs John Ferguson, Blaney; W. Hassard, Blaney; G. Breen, Stragowna; P. O'Brien, Knocknashangan, Kilcoo, Garrison and W. Little, Doon, Tempo. The advertisement which appeared on 17th and 20th April was headed *'Early Grass for Increased Profits'.* Mr George Pollock, Agricultural Adviser, and Mr Walter Keag BAgr, the newly appointed Deputy County Agricultural Officer, conducted the demonstrations. The Ministry's staff also held early grass demonstrations that year at Tubrid and at the Grassland Experimental Husbandry Farm at Castle Archdale.

In the same year ICI held an early grass demonstration on Mr Joseph Doonan's farm at Forthill, Brookeborough. The use of *Agroxone*, a selective weed killer that controlled rushes was featured at the Doonan demonstration. In the meantime, Mr Tom Moore, former Deputy County Agricultural Executive Officer for Fermanagh and at that time Deputy Chief Inspector of the Ministry, was addressing the Ulster Agricultural Organisation Society on grassland production. He claimed that on three out of four farms in Ulster grassland output could be doubled.

Demonstration at Dunn's farm in the early 1960s.

A demonstration of the value of MCPA based weedkiller in controlling rushes.

Farm trials

Increasing output from permanent grassland, which represented 95 per cent of the grassland in County Fermanagh, was an important issue in the early 1950s. Messrs George Pollock and Moreland Ingram, who were the Agricultural Advisers in Fermanagh, presented the results of fertiliser trials on this type of grassland in October 1958. The trials were carried out during the period 1953 to 1957. The farms on which the trials were held were those of Messrs W. Little, Doon, Tempo; J. Ferguson, Blaney, Enniskillen; M. Connolly, Mullaghbrady, Rosslea; G. Breen, Stragowna, Kinawley; P O'Brien, Knocknashangan, Garrison; and J. Aiken, Drumnarullagh, Kesh. The fertiliser treatments involved the application of either sulphate of ammonia or nitro-chalk combined with special potato manure or with superphosphate and muriate of potash. From 1955 all centres received 2 cwt superphosphate, 1 cwt muriate of potash and three bags of nitro-chalk per acre. The increase in production due to the fertiliser application (6 cwt per acre) over the five-year period averaged 78 per cent over the six sites. At this time, a grant of 50 per cent was available for fertiliser purchase under the Marginal Land Scheme and the application of this level of fertiliser gave a reasonable level of financial returns providing the grass was properly utilised.

Grassland competitions

The County Fermanagh Farming Society, whose main event during the year was the County Show in Enniskillen, took an interest in grassland improvement with further encouragement from Mr Walter Smyth MAgr the local ICI agricultural adviser. In 1957, the Society ran a Special Grassland Competition, which was confined to farmers with a valuation of under £50. This competition continued for a number of years until this aspect of the Society's role was taken over by Fermanagh Grassland Club. The comments of the judges, who were Messrs Sam Moore BAgr MSc (ICI), T. Hayes McElroy and William Hamill, following the 1962 Grassland Competition run by the Society are worth noting. Their report stated: *Having regard to the usually accepted and inherent disadvantage of climate, soil type and small farms under which the Fermanagh farmer works, it is quite amazing to see the high production, which is being obtained on some farms. This is as good as any and probably better than most of the production which is obtained anywhere else in Northern Ireland, and for that matter anywhere else in the world.* The open competition that year was won by Mr William Dunn, Munmurray, Brookeborough. A winner of another class was Mr Victor R. Graham, Drumgarrow, Ballinamallard. Both farms were open to visitors on a specific day.

William Dunn with the cup (Courtesy of Mr and Mrs W. Dunn).

Richardsons' interest

By 1960, fertilisers were being manufactured in a granular and more concentrated form. At that time, Mr Monty Kelly BAgr of Richardsons Fertilisers was extolling the virtues of Richardsons No 4 Grassland fertiliser and stating that one ton of the new product had the same nutrient value as one and a half tons of ordinary Grassland fertiliser. Richardsons' latest film, *'Farming in Ulster'*, was a feature of a fertiliser conference held in the Minor Townhall in Enniskillen in February 1964. Richardsons produced another educational film entitled *'Profitable Partnership'*, which was shown to farming audiences in Fermanagh in 1966.

Controlled grazing systems

The value of the electric fence as a means of strip grazing and maximising output from grassland was widely appreciated. It was the method used by intensive grassland farmers up to the early 1960s. It was claimed that a 25 per cent increase in output could be achieved with the proper use of an electric fence which enabled higher stocking rates. The use of a back fence was a further enhancement of the system.

Strip grazing increases efficiency of utilisation of grass.

Paddock grazing became popular in the 1960s, especially for dairy cows. Under this system, fresh grazing was provided every 24 hours. With a rest period of three weeks, 21 paddocks were required. With productive well-managed pastures summer grazing requirements should not exceed 0.5 acres per cow. In other words, a 40-cow herd required 20 acres for summer grazing divided into 21 equally sized paddocks. Semi-permanent electric fencing was used to form boundaries to the paddocks. Ideally, the paddocks were square in shape to minimise poaching and each had a water supply. A central access road was a requirement. This system of grazing brought great discipline to the farming system. Fertilising each grazed paddock was a daily or two-day requirement if the intensive grazing management system was to be sustained. For beef cattle, two-day or three-day paddocks were considered to be more practical.

The potential of grazing rye as an early bite for dairy cows was evaluated on Mr Bobbie Thornton's farm in the 1960s. Mr Sam McEwen BAgr, Agricultural Adviser, is discussing its production potential with Mr Thornton.

Zero grazing

Zero grazing involved cutting the grass and carting it to the animals. This system offered improved utilisation of grass by avoiding poaching and fouling and it meant that grass could be rationed to different classes of stock. The major disadvantages were increased labour and machinery costs, more bedding required for housed stock, and increased effluent and slurry disposal problems. The increased costs of fuel made this system very expensive. Zero grazing was used successfully at the Grassland Experimental Husbandry Farm at Castle Archdale and on Lord Erne's estate at Crom during 1963..

The Castle Archdale Experimental Husbandry Farm

The establishment of the Castle Archdale Centre in 1955 was a great boon. Experiments on increasing grassland output from permanent pasture and through reseeding brought a great fund of knowledge to advisers and farmers in the west of Northern Ireland. Research was not limited only to grassland output but also to its economic utilisation. Details of the extensive work undertaken at Castle Archdale are to be found chapter 10.

Zero grazing feeding arrangements at Castle Archdale.

References:

Ministry/Department of Agriculture for Northern Ireland's *Monthly Reports* and *Agriculture in Northern Ireland.*

Files of *The Impartial Reporter* and *Fermanagh Herald* held in Enniskillen Library.

Records of the County Agricultural Executive Office.

A.A.McGuckian A Memorial Volume, edited by A. E. Muskett. The McGuckian Memorial Committee, Bryson House, Belfast (1956).

Chapter 13
Silage

In the latter part of the twentieth century, silage was the accepted method of fodder conservation on practically all farms in County Fermanagh. It had almost totally replaced hay, which had been the main form of winter fodder at the beginning of the century. The transition to silage making was quite a slow process. Hay did not require sophisticated machinery in the making process or for transporting to the farmyard for winter feeding. It could be stored for winter use in a stack in the haggard or hayshed. Furthermore, it was suitable for feeding to out-lying and byre-housed stock. In the early years of the century, arable cropping was a feature on most farms. Oats was the main cereal, commonly referred to as 'corn', and was available to supplement hay as a winter fodder, either in the unthreshed sheaf or as straw. Hay making in County Fermanagh was difficult in most years because of the uncertainty of suitable weather for drying the grass crop. In addition, increased levels of production through the application of fertiliser to grassland made the task of saving the hay more challenging.

In 1931, Dr Henry Kennedy of the Irish Agricultural Organisation Society was making a strong case for silage. He said that lack of continuity of production is an outstanding feature of the agricultural economy. He quoted the dairying industry stating: "*Our dairying is seasonal, rising rapidly from the low winter level to a high peak in June, from which it again sinks rapidly to the winter level about the middle of November; eighty per cent of the output is produced from May to October.*" He said that the first essential of modern farming, as distinguished from primitive agriculture, was the conservation of adequate supplies of nutritious winter food for livestock. Dr Kennedy described haymaking in Ireland as a huge gamble, with the odds heavily against the occurrence of suitable weather in the few critical weeks of late June and early July.

Lapping was used when weather conditions for haymaking were poor.

He said that the poor condition of our cattle in spring was a chronic result of that gamble. In advocating silage, he said: "*We can take the guess work and the gamble out of our provision of winter fodder, and by using the new technique we can provide nutritious food for winter production, which should result in a real revolution in our farming methods.*"

Building a hay ruck.

Early initiatives

Reeves-Smyth when writing about the agricultural development work undertaken by the Third Earl of Erne stated that one of the Earl's last acts in 1884 was the building of a silo at Crom, which he stated was probably

Horse drawn ruck shifters were still being used in the 1950s.

the first in Ireland. The importance of silage as a means of conserving grass for winter feed took on a new significance in the early years of compulsory tillage during the Second Word War. Mr McClintock, County Agricultural Executive Officer, wrote articles in the local press about the benefits it could bring to farmers and the nation. He had recorded that there was one silage maker in Fermanagh in 1935. In August 1940, Mr McClintock stated that 20 portable silos had been purchased in Fermanagh during the previous two months. These small silos were circular, made of wire mesh or thin concrete slabs and lined with specially prepared paper to exclude air.

Small concrete proprietary silo.

In the summer of 1940, silage demonstrations for farmers were organised by the County Staff of the Ministry of Agriculture on the farms of Colonel Richardson at Rossfad and Chittick's of Boa Island. In 1941, further silage demonstrations were held on Mr J. J. Coalter's farm at Letterbreen on the same date as the June Fair Day in Enniskillen. During that summer, 80 Fermanagh farmers attended a silage making demonstration at the Agricultural Research Institute at Hillsborough. Mr McClintock stated that 55 farmers in Fermanagh had made silage in 1941 with a total quantity of 1,222 tons. Further silage demonstrations were held in 1942 at McCullagh's, Springfield and McHugh's of Tullyrosmearn. Mr McClintock continued to write articles on the benefits of silage stating that: *Fermanagh was a silage county.*

Mr James Leonard, Kinglass, Macken, bringing grass to his clamp silo in 1942.

The ladies of the Leonard household helped with the work including consolidation of the grass in the clamp and the application of molasses in 1942.

Mr William Swan, Drumany, making concrete blocks for his new silo in 1942.

In 1942, there were 97 silage makers in the county and this had increased to 272 in the following year. A Ministry of Agriculture film on silage making was shown at a number of centres that year in County Fermanagh. Two Fermanagh farmers were featured in that film, Mr James Leonard of Kinglass, Macken and Mr William Swan, Drumany, Thompson's Bridge. Stills taken from the film give an indication of the work involved.

The silo at Drumany under construction in 1942.

Grants for silos

In June 1942, the Fermanagh County Committee of Agriculture was pressing the Ministry of Agriculture to introduce a 50 per cent grant for the construction of silos. Its efforts were rewarded in March 1943 when grants were offered. The County Committee paid tribute to Mr McClintock for his contribution to the campaign. Mr McClintock described the new scheme as one of *the best schemes ever for this county* and *the most important development for a long time.* He claimed that the amount of imported meal pre-war could be reduced by half if farmers made silage. Grants were on a modest scale initially. Farms under 20 acres, with provision for 14 or 15 tons of silage, attracted a grant of £8. Farms of 20 to 35 acres were entitled to a silo for 25 tons with a grant of £12. A grant of £20 was available for a silo of 40 tons on a 35 to 60 acre farm. For farms over 60 acres the grant was £30.

The campaign to make more silage in 1943 was helped when the experience of Mr J. E. Collum, HML, of Bellevue, a member of the County Committee of Agriculture, was made public. Mr Collum had been making silage since 1911 and claimed that grass silage was the cheapest, most satisfactory and foremost food for all classes of livestock. He appreciated the value of early cutting of grass for silage and had 40 tons ensiled in the third week of May 1943.

Mr J. E. Collum in the uniform of His Majesty's Lieutenant for County Fermanagh (Courtesy of Mrs Maureen West).

Tillage concessions

Tillage concessions were offered to Fermanagh farmers in the 1944 season if they had made silage in 1943. Providing the full quota required under the Tillage Order was cultivated in 1943 a reduction in tillage area, related to the amount of silage made in 1943, was granted. Mr Tom Moore, who had been appointed Deputy County Agricultural Officer for Fermanagh, was an enthusiast for silage making and addressed many meetings and demonstrations throughout the county from March 1943. Mr Moore, on his transfer from Fermanagh, served in the Ministry of Agriculture's headquarters in Stormont and was subsequently promoted to become Chief Inspector of the Ministry.

Mr Charles Keys, Drumkeen, Culkey, consolidating grass with his horse in his new trench silo in the summer of 1948 (Courtesy of *The Impartial Reporter*).

Silage making at Crocknacrieve, Ballinamallard, on Mr Warren Loane's farm in the early 1950s. From top left: Mr Reginald Loane of The Waterfoot, Mr Warren Loane with his son, Charles, and Bob Boyle. Below left: Roger Montgomery and Pat McCarney (Courtesy of Mrs Anne Loane).

Mr Warren Loane JP DL in the 1980s with the original silo (Courtesy of Mrs Anne Loane).

Mr Tom Moore MAgr.

Grade A milk from silage

A feature in the local papers in February 1944 described the farming activity on the farm of Mr Bryan Pulvertaft at Gortatole, Florencecourt. The article was headed *'Fermanagh Farm Experiment – Grade A Milk from Silage'.* It was stated that Mr Pulvertaft made a large quantity of silage (120 tons). He fertilised his grassland well, kept 43 cows yielding 600 gallons each and he had a milking machine.

The cylindrical silo, on Loanes's farm (pictured opposite) constructed using curved concrete blocks, was approximately 15 feet in diameter and 18 feet deep including 6 feet below ground level, and held approximately 75 tons of silage.

Silage at Coranny

The farm of Mr Hugh McMahon, Drumswords, Coranny, was featured in the Ministry's *Monthly Report* of June 1946. Mr McMahon was described as being an enthusiastic silage maker. His silo, built into a bank, was fourteen feet square by twelve feet high with concrete walls tapered from about 14 inches at the base to eight inches at the top with the inside corners neatly rounded off. The silo held from 40 to 50 tons of silage. A sliding roof was regarded as being a notable feature. A three-acre field produced two crops of grass during the season for the silo. Fertiliser treatment consisted of a dressing of farmyard manure and 2 to 3 cwt per acre of superphosphate in early spring, followed in April by at least 1cwt of sulphate of ammonia per acre. Mr McMahon fed the silage to his 14-cow dairy herd and to 20 fattening bullocks with excellent results. The article concluded with Mr McMahon's commentary on the silage: *"Silage is the last crop I would consider giving up."*

Silage campaign

The campaign for silage making intensified in 1950, with silage demonstrations held at Mr Alan Tisdall's farm at Farnaconaghy, Lisnaskea, and Mr George Cathcart's farm at Arney, Bellanaleck.

Details for construction of a silo were contained in the Ministry of Agriculture's Advisory Leaflet 101. Notices appeared in the press warning farmers not to discharge silage effluent into watercourses. The development of the trench silo together with the introduction of the Ferguson TE20 tractor gave silage making a great boost. The invention of the buckrake that was mounted on the tractor's three-point linkage revolutionised silage making for the small farmer.

The grass intended for silage was cut with a mower. It was then lifted from the swathe and transported to the trench silo, where the material was unloaded simply by releasing the trip handle and driving forward. Shaking out the material in the pit to avoid air pockets was quite a demanding job for a man particularly if the loads were arriving in quick succession. In April 1951 the Ministry's Advisory Staff held a demonstration at Mr James Armstrong's, Keeranbeg, Donagh, where silage (both grass and crop) was being fed from a trench silo. In 1952 among the many agricultural advisory activities undertaken was a *'Silage Making'* lecture illustrated with lantern slides given by Mr Tom Moore, Deputy County Agricultural Executive Officer, in Drumarkey School, Lisnarick.

Silage only diet

In 1953, the Agricultural Research Institute at Hillsborough was promoting the merits of silage as a feed for fattening cattle. Trials there showed that Shorthorn store bullocks (2½ to 3 years old when purchased) could be fattened over the winter on silage only. Liveweight gains varying from 2.3 to 2.8 lb per day over the winters of 1948-1953 had been obtained from a silage only diet.

Filling the silo

A grant of 50 per cent of the cost of building a silo was available in 1953 under the Agricultural Development Scheme. With regard to filling the silo, the Ministry's

Mr George Cathcart's silo at Arney being filled using a Ferguson tractor and buckrake in the late 1940s. The tractor is being driven by Mr Tommy Patterson. Tommy's daughter, Nuala, is standing on the wall. Mr Pat Cooney is lighting his pipe before spreading the grass in the silo. Mr John Aiken BAgr, Agricultural Advisory Officer, is observing progress (Courtesy of Mrs Marion Maxwell).

advice was that if over 100 tons of silage were being made a green-crop loader was justified. For smaller quantities, a tractor and buckrake were considered satisfactory. Forage harvesters were mentioned as a possibility where silage making was extensively practised by neighbouring farmers who could share the machinery.

Silage Subsidy

A Silage Subsidy amounting to fifteen shillings per ton was available in 1955. In 1956, Mr McClintock reported that 400 farmers had made 30,000 tons of silage and that it was expected that 600 farmers would make silage in 1957.

In 1956, a United Kingdom Scheme was introduced which offered grants of 50 per cent on the construction of silos subject to a maximum payment of £250. The silo construction was costed on a standard cost basis. A trench silo 45 feet long by 20 feet wide by nine feet deep qualified for the maximum grant at that time. Furthermore, whilst the grant was officially 50 per cent of the cost, the actual cost was considerably less than the standard costs (based on English prices) applied by the Ministry. Therefore, the out-of-pocket expenditure by the farmer was quite small.

An early trench silo on McGowan's farm at Blaney.

In addition to the generous grant for building a silo, a Silage Payments Scheme that provided for the payment of 15 shillings per ton of silage made, offered a further incentive for farmers to make silage.

Silage feeding

The feeding of silage to stock was a new topic for demonstration in March 1957. Demonstrations were held by the Ministry's County Staff on the following farms: Messrs T. Maguire, Sheetrim, Derrylin; T. S. Fleming, Annaghgrane, Cornafanog, Lisbellaw; R. Hamilton, Moysnaght, Clabby; E. Courtney, Tattynageeragh, Coranny and R. Bell, Mullaghgare, Newtownbutler. The demonstrations were conducted by the Agricultural Advisers, Messrs George Pollock and Moreland Ingram. Mr McClintock or his Deputy, Mr Walter Keag, attended each demonstration. It was reported that almost 400 farmers attended these demonstrations.

Self-feeding and loose housing

The concept of self-feeding of silage was gaining pace at this time. A demonstration, again in the month of March 1957, of this system together with the loose housing of cows in a cattle court was organised by the County Advisory Staff on the farm of Mr Geoffrey Rogers at Churchill. The cows were bedded on straw and it was claimed that, under this system, it required one ton of straw per cow per season. A similar demonstration was held on the farm of Mr George Cathcart at Arney where bullocks were self-feeding and where they were straw-bedded in an adjoining cattle court.

Imperial Chemical Industries (ICI) staff in the same month held a self-feeding and early grass demonstration on the farm of Mr Ben Loane of Rushin, Bellanaleck. Mr Wilfred Thompson of ICI conducted the demonstration. He pointed out that Mr Loane's 40 cows had been fed on silage and cake at a cost of £40 per week, whereas if they had been fed on hay and cake the weekly feed cost would have been £65. In addition to the saving in feed costs, it was claimed that the self-feeding and loose housing saved 30 man-hours per week. Mr Loane's herd started strip grazing on 29th March that year and several cows were yielding four and a half gallons per day.

Dairy cows self feeding silage.

The County Advisory Staff of the Ministry held a grassland and silage making demonstration on Mr William Dunn's farm on 31st May 1957. It was stated in August that year that 40,000 tons of silage would be made during the year

in County Fermanagh. This compared with 13,400 made in 1950.

Massive increase

Silage making received further encouragement in that the Ministry of Agriculture offered silage makers 20 shillings per ton for the first 100 tons and twelve shillings and sixpence for the next 400 tons in 1958. Meetings were held by the County Advisory Staff during November 1958 in Crieve, Derrylin, Brollagh, Derrygonnelly and Corryglass. Mr McClintock reported at that time that the tonnage of silage made in Fermanagh was approaching 100,000 tons.

Large public meeting

January 1959 witnessed one of the largest meetings of farmers ever held in County Fermanagh when 500 attended in the Gymnasium of Enniskillen Technical College under the chairmanship of Mr H. W. West MP. The special speaker was Professor James Morrison, of the Agricultural Research Institute, Hillsborough. His topic was *'My experiences in making and feeding quality silage'*. For the discussion period he was joined on the platform by Mr Tom Moore, Deputy Chief Inspector of the Ministry; Mr James Young, Principal of Loughry Agricultural College and two Fermanagh farmers Messrs James (Jim) Falconer and George Cathcart. The meeting was well advertised by the County Staff in advance – the press report read as follows: *Altogether, this should provide one of the most entertaining meetings for farmers everywhere who, nowadays, are rapidly developing, making and feeding grass silage. No farmer interested in the subject should miss this meeting.*

Professor Morrison informed those present that if poor grass was put in the silo poor silage would result. He said young grass, 12 to 18 inches long that had not shot, from either reseeded land or permanent pasture, was what was required. Wilting was desirable and the silo needed to be covered. Professsor Morrison stated that at Hillsborough cross-bred stores were putting on 2.5 to 3lb per day liveweight on silage alone. He said this was equivalent in performance to what could be obtained from summer grass. During the question period, one farmer asked if butchers were shy of silage fed beef cattle. Professor Morrison said that he did not experience any problems in that respect. However, Mr Falconer believed that there was a potential problem but said amidst laughter from the audience, "*a shake of seed sweepings over the animal's back will solve that problem!*"

Bright future

In November 1959, at a meeting in Ballagh School, under the chairmanship of Mr Edward Courtney, Mr McClintock told the 100 strong audience that approaching 100,000 tons of silage were made in County Fermanagh that year by 900 farmers. He said developments had been rapid from 1950 when just over 13,000 tons had been made. He pointed out that 3,000 farmers in the county should be making silage and that 500,000 tons could be made each year. Mr McClintock stated that with generous grants for silos and fertilisers and potentially good grassland, silage making had a bright future and their livestock would be of higher quality and less costly to produce.

Professor James Morrison OBE BSc NDA.

Mr William Dunn, pioneer grassland farmer (Courtesy of Mr and Mrs W. Dunn).

Silage making demonstrations by the Ministry continued during May 1959. Farms used were those of Mr William Dunn at Brookeborough and Mr Charles Armstrong of Manoo, Kesh.

In 1960, the Ministry's advice on silage making can be summarised as follows:

1. Aim for 25 per cent dry matter (wilting as necessary);
2. Best silage made from herbage cut and lacerated by a forage harvester (although most silage is still made using a buckrake);
3. Temperature should be allowed to rise to between 80 and 100 degrees Fahrenheit where grass is reaching the shooting stage for the first two fillings, and then continuous filling and consolidation thereafter;
4. In the case of young clovery or sappy grass the temperature should be allowed to reach 120 degrees Fahrenheit in each layer before thorough consolidation begins;
5. Lacerated material does not require molasses as an additive, otherwise add molasses at a rate of up to 2 gallons per ton;
6. Sealing could take the form of a six-inch layer of soil or damp waste herbage or farm yard manure.

Meantime, the intensity of stocking was steadily increasing on Fermanagh farms and this was well illustrated on Mr William Dunn's farm at Brookeborough. On 29th May 1962 two hundred farmers attended a silage making demonstration when it was shown that Mr Dunn's 25 acre farm supported 21 dairy cows, 4 heifers and 4 calves giving a stocking rate of one cow equivalent per acre. Mr Dunn had built a trench silo with 250 tons capacity.

Mr Edward Courtney, Chairman at the Ballagh meeting.

Additives and plastic sheeting

In 1966 a new additive, *Kylage* (a mixture consisting mainly of calcium formate and sodium nitrite), was being assessed and compared in effectiveness with molasses. In the same year, the weighted down plastic sheeting was being recommended as a seal for silos. The use of plastic sheeting proved a very worthwhile development. If it was properly put on and weighed down it almost eliminated top surface waste on the silo.

The effectiveness of a well weighted plastic cover can be seen on Mr George Moore's silage clamp at Tiraroe, Derrylin.

By 1970, formic acid had been shown to be a satisfactory additive. In 1987, recommendations regarding silage additives from Greenmount Agricultural College included the use of formic acid, sulphuric acid and mixtures of

Additive applicator.

the two acids with or without formalin. Additives were recommended for all three-cut systems and in dull showery weather on two-cut systems. Bacterial inoculants and enzyme-based additives superseded the acid based materials in terms of performance of both dairy and beef cattle.

Silage making machinery

Cutting grass in the early days of silage making involved the reciprocating knife mower. These wheel driven machines were pulled by either one or two horses depending on the width of the finger bar. Later, many of these machines were modified to be drawn by a tractor. Machines specifically designed for tractor use were also manufactured.

The development of the hydraulic lift and the power-take-off shaft, which came originally with the Ferguson Tractor System, was a major break through. This enabled the development of the power-take-off (PTO) driven mounted cutting bar which was a major advance. The tractor and cutting bar were easily manoeuvred in small fields. The machine was also easily transported from one field to another.

The development of live drive power-take-off was a further advance in that the cutting blade could be in motion before forward movement of the tractor and this minimised blockage of the cutting bar. The blades required regular sharpening to maintain cutting efficiency.

Mr Jack Veitch of Drumlone, Lisbellaw, had one of the first green crop loaders in Fermanagh (Courtesy of Mrs M. Veitch).

Mr Jack Veitch driving his Fordson tractor, IL 3476, with a load of grass which had been filled using the green crop loader. Mr Hugh Downey is standing on the tractor rear axle (Courtesy of Mrs M. Veitch).

An advertisement for the Ferguson TE 20 tractor and cutting bar in May 1951.

George Cathcart, Bellanaleck, with his Ford-Ferguson tractor and trailed mower. His son, Arthur, is seated on the mower (Courtesy of Mrs Marion Maxwell).

In the early days, transporting the grass to the silo was a labour intensive and back-breaking job. On most farms, the mown grass was forked onto trailers drawn by horse or by tractor and transported from the field to the silo. On some larger farms a green-crop loader was used that was a much faster and less labour intensive operation.

The buckrake

The invention of the buckrake by Mr Rex Patterson, a pioneer grassland farmer in Hampshire, together with the development of the Ferguson hydraulic three-point linkage system, revolutionsed silage making on small farms. A Ferguson tractor and buckrake could lift a substantial load of grass by simply reversing along two swathes cut by a mower. When loaded the buckrake was lifted by hydraulics and the load was transferred untouched by hand to the silo. This development combined with the trench silo was the first major break through in silage making in County Fermanagh.

The Patterson buckrake (mounted on a McCormick International B250 tractor). Winner of Silver medal at Royal Agricultural Society's Forage Harvesting Competition in 1950. (Courtesy of Hampshire County Council Museums and Archive Service).

Mower developments

The flail mower was the next significant development. With this machine, the grass was cut by free-swinging flails on a horizontal shaft, which rotated against the direction of travel. These machines were a considerable advance over the cutting bar in that they could cope easily with very heavy young crops of grass but had a higher power requirement. The disc mower was the next advance. This machine had pairs of contra rotating vertical cylinders with small blades on the bottom of each cylinder. These machines had a smaller power requirement than flail type machines and were capable of much faster cutting rates. Variations of this machine remained the most popular mowing appliance to the end of the century. All three of the above mowers were operating on farms in 1969.

A rotary mower and conditioner.

Forage harvesters

The first forage harvester in use in the United Kingdom from about the early 1950s was a machine called a *Silorator*. This machine had contra rotating drum mowers which fed the cut material into a chopping and blowing mechanism and hence via a chute to the trailer. An advertisement in *The Farmers' Journal* in August 1951 detailed the merits of the *International Silorator*. The complete machine, sold by T. and J. McErvel in Belfast, cost £85. These machines were a major advance in mechanised silage making.

Silorator advertisement in 1954.

Silage making at Bellanaleck

Silage had been made on the farm of Messrs Ben and Ivan Loane at Rushin from the late 1940s. The early silos, still in existence, were either round or square towers constructed with advice from Mr Tom Moore of the Ministry's County Fermanagh Advisory Service. These were followed by

constructing earth pits and finally roofed concrete walled trench silos. The amount of silage made on the farm increased year by year and in 1959 over 500 tons were made. A *Silorator* forage harvester had been used on the farm from 1956. Prior to this, a green-crop loader had been used for lifting and loading the grass in the field and a buckrake on a Fordson Major had been used prior to that.

The development of the flail-type forage harvesters was regarded as a big advance over the *Silorator*. A forage harvester demonstration held at Loughry Agricultural College in 1958 demonstrated a wide range of these machines.

The demonstration of forage harvesters at Loughry Agricultural College attracted large attendances.

At Loughry this harvester was powered by a Massey Ferguson 35 and the silage trailer was drawn by a Ferguson TE20.

Mr Ivan Loane, who had been using a *Silorator,* attended this demonstration. He was so impressed with the simplicity and speed of operation of the David Brown *Hurricane* flail-type harvester that he bought one to replace the *Silorator*.

Demonstration at Bellanaleck

The Ulster Farmers' Union and the Ministry of Agriculture organised a forage harvester demonstration on Mr Ivan Loane's farm on 4th June 1959. Most of the forage harvesters on the market at that time, mainly flail-type, were demonstrated and the machinery agents did very good trade. The flail machines were variable in size and simple in design. Hinged flails on a rotor moving at high speed against the direction of travel propelled the cut and chopped grass up the chute into a trailer. Trailed in-line, trailed off-set and side-mounted machines were available in a wide range of makes. The side-mounted machine with the trailer attached directly to the back of a small tractor, like a Ferguson 35, was very popular on the small farms in County Fermanagh. Forage harvesters not only provided a fast and efficient method of harvesting the grass but also lacerated the material leading to better quality silage. Research work at the Agricultural Research Institute, Hillsborough, was showing that lacerated or chopped grass gave quicker lactic acid fermentation than unchopped material. It was suggested that molasses, which had previously been recommended as an additive to assist with fermentation, was not necessary when the grass being ensiled was lacerated. Laceration of grass was now possible with the introduction of forage harvesters.

The demonstration at Mr Loane's farm was well attended. Mr Ivan Loane (in short-sleeved shirt) is behind his cousins Warren (right) and Reginald. On the extreme right is Mr Mervyn Hadden of Richardsons Fertilisers in conversation with Mr Sam Campbell of the Ministry of Agriculture's mechanisation division. Mr Cecil Haddick is driving the tractor (Courtesy of *The Impartial Reporter*).

Mr Michael McGirr, Breagho, cutting grass with a side-mounted harvester in 1975. These were very popular machines on Fermanagh farms.

Precision-chop harvesters enabled high outputs to be obtained.

Early model of a self propelled harvester working on Colebrooke Estate in 1968.

A self propelled harvester working at Clareview, Kesh, in the 1980s.

However, as time passed machines developed and became more sophisticated. Double-chop and precision-chop harvesters with more powerful tractors achieved much greater outputs. The double-chop machines used flails to cut the crop or reels to pick it up from a windrow. The material was then augured into a chopper-blower which discharged it through the chute into the trailer. The precision-chop was similar in action to the double-chop machine but had a special adjustable chopping mechanism, which cut the material into short lengths before it was blown into the specially designed trailer. By 1970, the flail-type harvester was still the most common harvester in Fermanagh. The bigger machines were to be found on the larger farms and in use by contractors. Later, contractors who made large quantities of silage relied on self propelled harvesters.

Silage at Crom

Farming activity at Crom Castle was in full swing in 1969 and a photograph in the local press featured silage making in progress. It was stated that 2,500 tons of silage were being made on the Crom Estate at that time to feed to the 200-cow dairy herd and followers.

Lord Erne and his farm manager, Mr John Bingham, in conversation with the tractor driver, Mr William Graham, at silage harvesting operations using a flail-type forage harvester in mid June 1969
(Courtesy of *The Impartial Reporter*).

'More from Fodder' Campaign

The Minister of Agriculture, The Rt Hon Phelim O'Neill MP, launched a major Province wide silage making campaign at Greenmount Agricultural College in January 1971. It was pointed out that in Northern Ireland only 6,000 farmers out of a total of 19,000 were making silage. The campaign revolved around a series of meetings held at centres throughout the Province followed by a major demonstration on silage making at Greenmount Agricultural College in May when all the latest silage

making machinery was on view and farmers were be able to see modern methods of conserving grass.

The Minister stated that vast changes in the industry were taking place at that time particularly with reference to the rising costs of feeding stuffs. He said the cost of feeding stuffs would rise irrespective of whether we entered the Common Market or not. The Minister continued: *"The whole question of high cost of feeding stuffs is a very serious matter for us. Therefore, we have to fall back on our natural resources. In this country I think it is true to say we can probably grow as good grass as anywhere in Europe, and as good as anywhere in the world, with the possible exception of New Zealand. I think it is the duty of the Ministry of Agriculture and myself to impress upon farmers that we must simply make the best use of our natural resources."* He concluded by stating that by proper conservation of grass farmers could benefit the profitability of their enterprises whether dairying or beef.

The *'More from Fodder'* meetings in Fermanagh were held during February 1971 at the following centres: Enniskillen Agricultural College, Stragowna, Tempo, Brollagh, Kesh, Teemore, Maguiresbridge and Newtownbutler. The speakers at Enniskillen College were Mr T. A. Larmour BAgr, Deputy Chief Agricultural Officer and Mr R. E. (Bob) Haycock BAgr, Farm Director of the Grassland Experimental Centre, Castle Archdale.

Mr Thomas A. Larmour.

Mr Larmour stressed the importance of quality silage stating that up to 6 lb more meal per day may be required to maintain a desired liveweight gain in fattening cattle when poor quality silage is made. He said this could mean additional costs of £10 or even £15 that would mean the difference between profit and loss. Mr Haycock, who made over 1,000 tons of silage at Castle Archdale, stated that the essentials for quality silage were: cut early, fill quickly, use an additive and seal well. The Agricultural Advisers in County Fermanagh addressed the meetings at the other centres. Over 1,000 farmers attended the meetings in the county. The dangers of silage effluent as a potential pollutant of watercourses were also being highlighted at this time.

Grass at the right stage for making quality silage. Mr Frank Tisdall, Agricultural Adviser, is discussing grass yield with Mr Eric Bruce, The Grove, Killymitten, Ballinamallard, in 1994.

Silage demonstrations

A silage making demonstration at Greenmount Agricultural College in May 1971 was attended by 5,000 people, including a number from Fermanagh. Fermanagh had its own silage making demonstration at Castle Archdale on Wednesday 2nd June 1971. Points of interest at Castle Archdale were: stage of cutting, use of additives, speed of filling, sealing the silo and systems of silage making. A one-man operated flail mower system and a three-man operated double chop harvester system were demonstrated.

Further encouragement of silage making was given under the Silage Payment Scheme, which came into operation in 1973 and was then extended to 1976. It applied to farmers who were making silage for the first time. The rate of payment was £1 per ton for the first 100 tons and 50 pence per ton for for the next 400 tons. Making better quality silage was a continuing feature of the Department's advisory activity in County Fermanagh in the early winter of 1977. Meetings were held at the Castle Archdale Experimental Husbandry Farm, Enniskillen Agricultural College, Tempo, Lisnaskea and Derrylin. An average of 90 farmers attended each meeting. The importance of early cutting was emphasised. Savings of £29 per head in beef production and £38 per head in milk production could be achieved by advancing the date of cutting the silage from 14th June to 25th May.

Importance of hay in the 1970s

Despite the progress made in silage making, Mr Sam Morrow, County Agricultural Executive Officer, stated that in 1979 almost half of the fodder made in County Fermanagh was still conserved as hay. However, rapid progress was made in the following years. For example, it was estimated that just over 250,000 tons of silage had been made in Fermanagh in 1971. By 1980, the tonnage made had reached over 500,000. By the end of 1982, it was estimated that hay accounted for 30 per cent of the fodder requirements on Fermanagh farms. In an attempt to improve the efficiency of farm production 25 co-operative forage groups (mainly silage) were established in County Fermanagh during 1985. In 1991, over 857,000 tons of silage were made in the county and hay represented around 15 per cent of the fodder.

Easy fed silage for beef cattle.

Easy feeding

With the increasing size of herds and flocks, together with the greater use of slatted floors, easy feeding of silage has displaced self feeding on many farms. Shorter chop lengths of grass and improved mechanisation has made stock feeding a fast and labour efficient operation. Feeder wagons which enable complete diets to be fed in a single operation are now common on the larger farms.

Trough fed silage for sheep.

A modern silo with feeder wagon. Mr Rodney Elliott and Mr Nicholas Coyle are discussing silage effluent management.

Mr Connor Maguire, Agricultural Adviser, and Mr William Rutledge, Guiltaugh, Cornafanog, discussing the use of a mixer wagon in a winter feeding programme.

Early model of a big baler.

Big bale silage

Big balers had been used at Greenmount Agricultural College successfully for silage making in the early 1980s. On a visit to the College in May 1986, by the Fermanagh Grassland Club, Dr Sam Kennedy demonstrated a new technique for sealing big bales in plastic wrapping. He said that the *'Silawrap'* machine, which had only been at the College since March, was the first machine patented in the world that employed a wrap-around technique for sealing big bales. Prior to this introduction, large plastic bags, which had to be tied individually on each bale, were used.

Bagged and tied big bales.

A public meeting to publicise this new system was held in Dungannon in March 1988. At this meeting, the new stretch film called *'Silawrap'* was promoted as *'a revolution in silage production'*. The system was featured at a silage

Modern baler and wrapper in action.

making demonstration at Greenmount in June 1988. It had been shown at Greenmount that bagging or wrapping the bales with stretch film was equally successful. Mr Sam Morrow stated in 1989 that big baling of silage was slow to take off in Fermanagh. However, from the early 1990s, contractors got involved and the technique became an acceptable form of silage making in the county. The direct costs of big baling are much greater than for conventional methods of silage making. However, it is very suitable for those small farmers who do not have silos. Furthermore, it has indeed proved very useful on farms as a secondary system where large quantities of silage are made by conventional methods. For example, big baling can be employed in circumstances where existing pits cannot accommodate all the grass or where small areas of grass surplus to grazing requirements would otherwise be wasted. Big bale silage has proved to be the solution to fodder conservation on many of Fermanagh's small farms.

Hay making is a cheaper way of conserving fodder than big bale silage. However, it is very weather dependent and consequently is only now practised on small farms in those years when there is very good summer weather or where ground conditions are unsuitable for balers.

References:

Ministry/Department of Agriculture for Northern Ireland's *Monthly Reports* and *Agriculture in Northern Ireland.*

Files of *The Impartial Reporter, Fermanagh Herald* and *The Fermanagh Times* held in Enniskillen Library.

Records of the County Agricultural Executive Office.

Livingstone, Peader, *The Fermanagh Story.* Watergate Press, Enniskillen (1977).

Messrs Din and Sean Gallagher building a hay ruck at Leitrim, Boho.

Hay was still being fed by Mr Stephen Irwin, Boho, at the end of the century to complement big bale silage, which constituted the major part of his winter fodder supply. Stephen is standing beside his Massey Ferguson 165 that he bought new in 1971.

Chapter 14
Livestock improvement policies

The first Irish Parliament grant aimed at improving cattle in Ireland was given in 1885. The scheme was administered by the Royal Dublin Society which adopted the system of subsidising bulls. Right from the establishment of the Fermanagh County Committee of Agriculture, at the beginning of the twentieth century, livestock improvement was a top priority. The County Committee, like those in other counties, operated Premium Bull and Boar Schemes and a Horse Breeding Scheme on behalf of the Department of Agriculture. These were a continuation and development of the original schemes initiated by the Royal Dublin Society. The Premium animals were superior sires which had been identified by Department of Agriculture inspectors at special livestock shows and sales usually held in the spring and late autumn. Those animals that were regarded as being of suitable quality were designated as being eligible for Premiums. The intention of the County Committee of Agriculture was to award Premiums to farmers strategically located throughout the county so that every farmer would have access to a good stallion, bull or boar within a reasonable distance of his holding. Livestock breeders could then bring their female stock for mating with the Premium sire as appropriate.

Selection of good sires, which attracted Premiums, was the means whereby livestock genetic improvement could be made. A farmer who had been approved for keeping a Premium sire would visit the approved sales and purchase the Premium animal of his choice. Frequently, farmers would ask the County Agricultural Organiser (later to become the County Agricultural Executive Officer) to select and purchase animals at the sale on their behalf. Those farmers selected to keep the Premium animals received financial support by way of an annual payment or Premium from the County Committee of Agriculture.

Horses

Horses were very important farm animals until tractors replaced them as the main source of power on farms. This transition gained particular momentum during and after the end of the Second World War. Of course, horses continued to have an important role for sporting and recreational purposes. The Department's schemes for improvement of horses followed a similar pattern to that for cattle and pigs. There were seven registered stallions in County Fermanagh in 1905. Superior stallions were identified by the Department inspectors and there were financial incentives to encourage their acquisition and use. Mares, suitable for breeding, were also identified at special shows for the purpose.

In 1922, the Fermanagh County Committee of Agriculture expressed its preference for Irish Draught and Shire breeds rather than Clydesdales, which were favoured by the Department. However, in 1937 of the five subsidised stallions in Fermanagh, three were Clydesdales, one a Halfbred and one a Thoroughbred. The increasing use of motor cars at that time was not welcomed by one member of the County Committee of Agriculture who said: "*the young fellows nowadays only drive these stinking machines over the roads of this county*".

Premiums for horses were still current in 1971 when Thoroughbreds attracted £120. Clydesdales, Irish Draughts and Connemaras received £50.

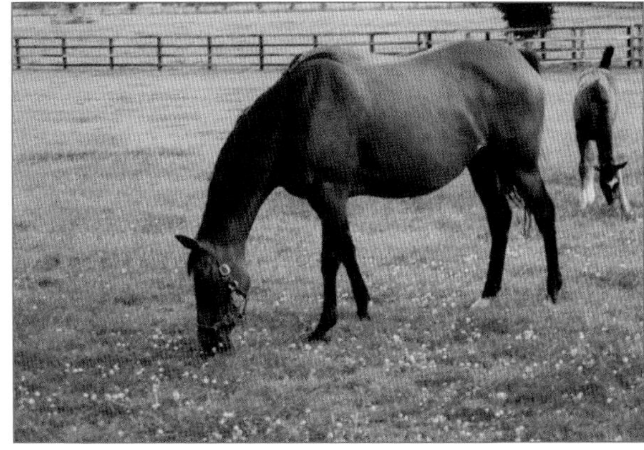

Thoroughbred mare and foal.

Premium Schemes

In 1906, Premiums for bulls were £15 per year and the only eligible breeds were Shorthorn and Aberdeen Angus. From 1922 onwards Dairy Shorthorns, Beef Shorthorns and Aberdeen Angus became eligible breeds. The Northern Ireland Ministry of Agriculture increased the funding available to the County Committee of Agriculture for the 1927/28 season. The sum of £1,050 was earmarked for

SIRES.

STALLIONS FOR 1908.

THOROUGH-BRED STALLION. 'Ravenscroft.' Registered under Department of Agriculture. Sire of winner Champion Cup, Sligo, 1907 (one of his first produce).
CLYDESDALE STALLION 'Height o' Fashion.' Registered under Department of Agriculture. Sire of best foal at Enniskillen, '04, '06 and '07, also of 1st and 2nd in three year olds, two year olds, and foals in '07.
HACKNEY STALLION, 'Terrington Conjuror' by Lord Drewton 2nd, first London, in '99, dam 9075 Lady Crompton, winner of over nine firsts at leading English shows.
For particulars apply
E. M. ARCHDALE,
9451 Riversdale, Ballinamallard.

HACKNEY STALLIONS.

IRISH IVY

The finest Mover ever Seen in Fermanagh.

Stud Fee	...	£2 2s 0d.
Groom's Fee	...	£0 3s 0d.

AND

BARON BONELLI

(For Pony Mares).

Stud Fee	...	£1 1s 0d.
Groom's Fee	...	£0 2s 6d.

Further particulars from owner
J. DAWSON, M.R.C.V.S.
9530 Enniskillen.

Advertisement for Premium stallions in 1908.

Fermanagh for the provision of an additional 46 Premium bulls to add to the 40 already in the county. Nineteen of these bulls were placed in the poor mountainous areas where there had never been a Premium animal before. This scheme, known as the Special Term Bull Scheme, represented a modification of the Premium Bull Scheme to suit the needs of the poorer areas of the county. The main difference in the two schemes was that the approximate amount of money normally available as Premiums over a bull's active life was contributed at the initial purchase of the animal in the case of the Special Term Bull Scheme thus easing the financial burden on the purchaser of the bull. The owners of the Special Term Bulls were asked to contribute £5 on delivery, £5 in October and another £5 in the following October.

Concern was expressed at that time about the suitability of highly-bred animals being placed on poor land. In a letter to the *Belfast News Letter* in January 1928 Mr W. Copeland Trimble, owner of *The Impartial Reporter,* appealed to the Ministry of Agriculture to make available bulls that were better suited to mountain pasture than than the pure bred Shorthorn. He said that an application for a *Roscommon Bull* was over-ruled by the Fermanagh County Committee of Agriculture on the recommendation of the Ministry's official.

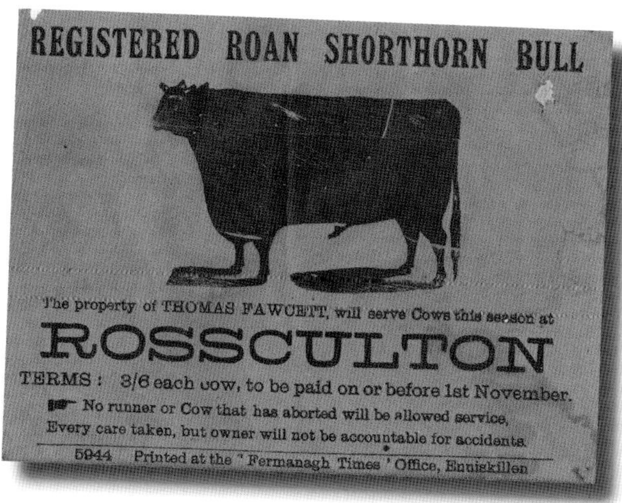

Thomas Fawcett's advertisement for his Premium bull in 1928 (Courtesy of Mr Basil Fawcett).

In 1935, purebred Dairy Shorthorns attracted a Premium of £19 whereas a bull where the dam only was registered received £16. The Premiums for other Shorthorns, Aberdeen Angus and Herefords amounted to £14. Premiums for boars were £8. Subsidised bulls did not always give the results expected and at the County Committee of Agriculture at that time there were complaints that 'badly coloured calves' were being produced.

Kenneth Veitch with his father's champion Aberdeen Angus bull in the 1960s (Courtesy of Mrs M. Veitch).

Too many Aberdeen Angus

Concern was expressed by the Ministry of Agriculture in 1937 about the number of Aberdeen Angus bulls in use in County Fermanagh. Fifty-five of the 107 subsidised bulls in the county were Aberdeen Angus. The Ministry

indicated at that time that the number of Angus would have to be reduced to 25 per cent of the total. No doubt, this was prompted by the need for an increased emphasis on milk production.

In 1939, there were 91 Premium bulls and 21 Special Term bulls in Fermanagh. In 1943, there was division among Fermanagh Committee members over a resolution forwarded by the Armagh County Committee as to the advisability of having Premiums for Ayrshire and Friesian bulls. In 1941, a shortage of Premium boars was noted.

Increased Premiums

The value of Premiums for bulls had been increased by the end of 1944. Rates were as follows: Double Dairy Shorthorn (dam and sire's dam milk recorded – 750 gallons) £30 (increased from £20 in 1941). Where the yield of the dam was 650 gallons the Premium was reduced to £22. Non-pedigree Dairy Shorthorns attracted a Premium of £16. Single Dairy Shorthorns (dam only recorded) received £18 and Aberdeen Angus £15. Premiums were first awarded for Herefords in 1947. In 1963, the breeds of bulls being used in Fermanagh under the Premium Schemes were 25 Dairy Shorthorn, 34 Aberdeen Angus and 21 Hereford.

The value of Premiums increased slightly over the years and by 1971, they were worth £30 for Shorthorn, Aberdeen Angus and Hereford. Special Term Bulls attracted a higher Premium of £95. Premium boars earned £25 and £15 according to class. These rates remained at a similar level until the termination of the schemes.

Premium bulls in a minority

On a visit to the Fermanagh County Committee of Agriculture in 1953, Mr J. G. Rhynehart, Deputy Chief Inspector of the Ministry of Agriculture, stated that of 359 bulls standing for service in the county only 89 were in receipt of Premiums.

In order to qualify for the Premium, bull owners were expected to make their animals available for the use in other herds and each bull was required to serve at least 40 cows in the season. With the introduction of brucellosis-free status herds three such herd owners could share Premium or Special Term bulls. By 1975, the number of Premium or Special Term bulls in Fermanagh had dropped to 47. Of the 29 Premium bulls, three were Dairy Shorthorn and the others were Hereford. There were 18 Special Term bulls, 14 of which were Dairy Shorthorns and four were Aberdeen Angus.

Performance Tested Premium bulls

In 1970, Beef Cattle Performance testing was underway at the Ministry's Livestock Husbandry Farm at Loughgall in County Armagh. During the period 1977 to 1987 about 200 young bulls each year were tested at Loughgall. The bulls, which were carefully selected from recorded herds, under the Beef Recording Scheme, arrived at the Loughgall Livestock Husbandry Farm at around six months of age. For the next six months their growth rates and food conversion rates were recorded. A potential purchaser was then able to see the performance of the different bulls in the published test reports. Premiums to the value of £100 per bull per year for a two-year period were made available. These applied to suckler herd owners whose herds did not exceed 40 cows and who had purchased approved recorded or performance tested bulls. Fermanagh farmers were able to purchase these bulls with generous financial support from the Vaughan Trust.

Mr J. G. Rhynehart (Courtesy of Department of Agriculture and Rural Development).

Milk Recording

A Milk Recording Scheme was initiated by the Irish Department of Agriculture in 1906 as an aid to cattle improvement. The Department encouraged the formation of Cow Testing Associations by arranging for the attendance of a lecturer at meetings of dairy farmers to explain the objects and advantages of these associations. It also supplied, free of charge, byre record sheets and a book for recording the results of each member's cows. The sum of one penny per cow was contributed for each monthly test carried out by the secretary of the association. A Department inspection was carried out with a view to the registration of all cows which were found to have produced not less than 210 lbs butterfat with at least an average butterfat of not less than three per cent and with a milk yield of not less than 6,000 lbs within a milking period of 45 weeks. A milk sampling kit was supplied at low cost by the Department. The first Cow Testing Association in Fermanagh was formed in 1909.

Inspections

Under the scheme pedigree cows were inspected and those that were of a good type and conformation were milk recorded. In 1914, the scheme was divided into two parts. One dealt with purebred cattle, supervised by the Department, and the other for the testing of non-pedigree cows through the medium of Cow Testing Associations, which were indirectly supervised by the Department. There were a number of Cow Testing Associations in Fermanagh at that time. Meetings under the auspices of the Irvinestown and Ballinamallard Association were held in Killadeas in December 1924. The Association consisted of 29 members with 230 cows under test. The Supervisor stated in his report: *a considerable number of very good cows were already in members' herds and only now have these been identified with certainty.* The report also stated that there was a considerable number of exceedingly poor producing cows identified by the records; these, in many cases, came as a surprise to the unsuspecting owners. Reference was made to the number of promising heifers bred from the two Dairy Shorthorn bulls introduced through the foresight of the Irvinestown Co-Operative Dairy Society. The six best cows recorded were 32 weeks in milk and averaged 7,836 lbs of milk with 277 lbs of fat worth £145. The six worst cows milked for 19 weeks and averaged 1,826 lbs of milk with 66 lbs fat only worth £34 11s.

Improved yields

In April 1927, Mr Greacen of the Ministry of Agriculture described a meeting of the Monea and Springfield Cow Testing Association as one of the best meetings he had ever attended.

During the year, 152 cows were under test. Those that had completed their lactations averaged 612 gallons per cow, which was an increase from 429 gallons per cow in 1925. The 10 best cows had an average milk yield of 931 gallons and the 10 worst averaged 402 gallons of milk. Prizes of £4, £3, £2 and £1 were awarded by the Ministry for the top four cows. The prizewinners were: 1st and 2nd Mr J. Connor, 3rd Mr James Lucy, and 4th Rev E. G. Seale MA. The Portora Silver Medal for the best heifer in the Association was awarded to a representative of the late Mr F. Meehan. The Association held its annual meeting for members at the end of March 1935. The best herd was owned by Mr H. M. Irwin JP, Derrygore, Enniskillen, which averaged 1,079 gallons per cow. The best cow, which yielded 1,238 gallons, was owned by Rev E. G. Seale MA, Portora, Enniskillen.

Mr R. Greacen, Ministry of Agriculture Instructor (centre front row) and Cow-testing Association supervisors in March 1922. From left: Mr Robert White, Victora Bridge; Mr William Connolly of the Erne Association. Mr Francis J. Meehan of the Derrygonnelly Association is on Mr Greacen's left and Mr William J. Noble of the Belleisle Association is seated on the right in the front row.

Associations in South Fermanagh

In March 1932, the fourth annual meeting of the Drumlone Milk Recording Association was held in Tiraffey Public Elementary School. The Supervisor commented that the year under review was one of the worst for a very long time owing to the very wet season. There were 52 members with 351 cows under test. The ten best cows gave an average yield of 902 gallons with 3.84 per cent butterfat. The ten worst cows averaged 401 gallons. The best cow, the property of the Earl of Erne gave, in 45 weeks, 1,063 gallons. Mr James Armstrong of Keeranbeg House had four young cows that yielded almost 900 gallons each.

Rev E. G. Seale MA, Headmaster of Portora Royal School (1917-1936).

One of Mr James Armstrong's Shorthorn cows in 1928.

In Northern Ireland, the Cow Testing Associations were disbanded in 1939 and the recording of non-pedigree or grading-up cows was incorporated into what was originally the Purebred Scheme. The purpose of the Purebred Scheme was to select cows for the breeding of purebred bulls, which would earn Premiums in the hands of farmers who would make the bulls available to their neighbours at a reasonable service fee.

The Portora Silver medal (Courtesy of Mr J. Meehan).

Minister's update on support for the livestock industry

The Minister of Agriculture, the Rt Hon Edward Archdale MP, informed Parliament in April 1927 that his Ministry was doing all that was possible for improvement of cattle with the funds at its disposal by:

1. Placing Premium bulls and boars in each county under the County Committee Schemes. Assisting Milk Recording Associations by grant aiding pedigree bulls to the extent of two-thirds of the cost subject, to a maximum contribution of £73.
2. Helping breeders of purebred Shorthorns to procure high-class pedigree sires through contributing two-thirds of the cost, subject to a maximum contribution of £333. At least three

Mr James Armstrong (Courtesy of Miss Jayne Armstrong).

breeders needed to co-operate and retain the bull for a minimum of five years.

3. In poor mountainous districts assisting County Committees to subsidise the purchase of bulls, so that the farmer had to make a relatively small contribution. For example, pay £12 over three years for a bull costing £36.

With regard to horses, the Minister stated that since 1922 the Ministry had secured two or three high-class Thoroughbred stallions. These had been sold to farmers selected by the County Committees at one-third of the cost price. A loan was available to the purchasing farmer to be repaid over five years. Clydesdales were the only heavy breed of horse encouraged and subsidised by the Ministry.

The Minister, in September 1932, extolled the virtues of the Shorthorn breed. He stated: "*The Shorthorn is an admirable dual purpose animal well suited to the requirements of the home and export trade crosses*".

A Shorthorn cow on Philip McDonagh's farm at Leam, Tempo, in early 1970s.

Bull Licensing

Bull licensing was introduced by the Northern Ireland Ministry of Agriculture in 1922 under the Livestock Breeding Act. The purpose of this Act was to rid the country of 'scrub' or poor quality bulls. To qualify for a licence a bull had to be above a certain standard of merit. Good body conformation was the sole criterion used by the inspectors at that time. In the early 1930s, the regulations under the Act were amended to restrict eligibility for a licence to pedigree bulls of all breeds and non-pedigree Shorthorn bulls of good Shorthorn type and character. In 1931, the Shorthorn was by far the most popular breed accounting for over 85 per cent of licences. Hereford and Aberdeen Angus accounted for over 13 per cent. Friesian and Ayrshire, together, represented less than one per cent. Measuring performance took on a particular significance when the Livestock Breeding Act was amended in 1949 to exclude the licensing of pedigree bulls of the dairy breeds whose dams and dams of sires had not produced minimum yields of milk and butterfat. After the introduction of Artificial Insemination (AI) in 1946, the number of non-pedigree bulls presented for licensing fell rapidly.

Another development was the Subsidy Bull Scheme. This scheme was aimed at assisting groups of three or four pedigree breeders to purchase top quality bulls which they would then share. A two-thirds grant was payable towards the cost of the bull. In 1960, there were 26 subsidised bulls in Northern Ireland shared by 78 breeders.

Higher standards

The standards for bull licensing were raised in 1965. From 1st January that year, non-pedigree Shorthorn bulls were only considered for licence if their dams had been milk recorded and had reached the required standards in respect of yield and butterfat. The Ministry was concerned in 1966 about the use of unlicensed bulls and boars and introduced measures in an attempt to stamp out the practice. It stated that the use of unlicensed bulls and boars, which were of inferior quality, was bound to have a lowering effect on the standard of livestock in the country. The Ministry sought the co-operation of all livestock yards and slaughterhouse authorities to help identify offenders. The maximum fine for offenders was £40. New rules regarding breeds eligible for bull licensing were introduced with effect from 1st November 1970. The new breeds eligible were South Devon, Whitebred Shorthorns and 7/8 bred Charolais. This was the first time that a non-purebred animal (apart from Shorthorns) was considered for a licence. This came about because of the very favourable impact on beef production that resulted from the introduction of the Charolais breed. Adequate numbers of purebred Charolais bulls were not available and the new rules represented a degree of expediency.

In the meantime, the Ministry was offering subsidies towards the purchase of high-class bulls of the Ayrshire, British Friesian, Dairy Shorthorn, Aberdeen Angus, Galloway, Hereford and Beef Shorthorn breeds in established purebred herds of high merit.

A 1970s Charolais calf from Charolais X Friesian cow.

End of bull licensing

The Department announced that statutory bull licensing would end on 31st December 1977. The discontinuation of bull licensing was coupled with the introduction of a Beef Recording Scheme, which was aimed at aiding the selection of beef breeding stock by breeders and prospective purchasers. This aimed at ensuring supplies of good breeding females and superior beef bulls for natural service.

A Simmental calf from a Shorthorn cow.

The Department also made clear in the announcement that on most farms artificial insemination offered by far the best choice of proven bulls at lower cost than keeping a bull for natural service.

Artificial Insemination

Artificial insemination (AI) for cattle was introduced into Northern Ireland by the Ministry of Agriculture in 1946. One of the drawbacks of the Premium and Special Term Bull Schemes operated by the County Committees of Agriculture was the potential to spread disease. Under these schemes, neighbouring farmers brought their cows to the farm where the Premium or Special Term bull stood for service. Diseases that may have existed in an area were easily spread through this practice. In an article in the Ministry of Agriculture's *Monthly Report* of May 1946, it was pointed out that the venereal disease Trichomoniasis was widespread in the country. Cows returning for service three, four, five or more times and cows not proving in calf were symptoms of the disease. A bull that served infected cows was a sure way of spreading the disease in an area. It was primarily for this reason that the Ministry of Agriculture established an Artificial Insemination Centre at Desertcreat, Cookstown, for research purposes. Two healthy clean bulls had been procured for the Centre. The AI experience at Cookstown was very positive and in May 1947, it was decided to develop the service as a Livestock Improvement Scheme. The development of the AI Service overcame the disease spreading potential of the natural method of service. Furthermore, a stud bull kept for the AI service had the potential to sire many more calves than in natural service. In natural service, one bull would have less than 100 matings per year whereas with AI one bull could provide semen, in practice, for around 15,000 services.

Hereford cows under hill conditions.

In natural service it takes some time before a bull is proven fertile and because of the relatively small numbers of his offspring some considerable time to assess his breeding value.

Artificial Insemination makes the most of top class bulls.

The use of AI proved to be more challenging in suckler herds because of difficulties in heat detection and the inconvenience of having to bring cows in for insemination. These difficulties do not arise in the dairy herd where observation is much easier as they are housed for milking at least twice daily and cows in heat are easily detected. The breeding value of a bull used in AI can be speedily assessed because of the large number of his offspring that are available for assessment. For the first three years of the AI Service, all inseminations were of the Shorthorn breed.

Need for AI Centre in Fermanagh

At the Fermanagh County Committee of Agriculture in January 1950, one of the members, Mr Thornton, complained about the Ministry's livestock policy. He said the cattle were deteriorating rather than improving. Mr J. E. J. Fawcett called for the setting up of an AI centre in the county. Many of the bulls being used in the county at that time were not of Premium standard. Success was achieved when a bull stud was established at Riversdale in 1951 to complement those at Ballycraigy and Cookstown. In 1953, there were 26 bulls at the centres comprising 18 English Dairy Shorthorns, 3 Ayrshire, 3 British Friesian and 2 Aberdeen Angus. By December 1960 there were 52 bulls, of which 18 were Dairy Shorthorns, 11 British Friesian, 6 Ayrshire, 10 Aberdeen Angus and 7 Hereford. From 1950 there was a steady decline in the use of Shorthorn in favour of Ayrshire initially and then British Friesian. In 1960, the inseminations in relation to breeds were 43 per cent Shorthorn, 27 per cent Friesian, 5 per cent Ayrshire, 15 per cent Aberdeen Angus and 9 per cent Hereford. In 1972 inseminations from Riversdale were 33,873 (273,000 was the Northern Ireland total) and in 1974 there were 34,565 from the centre.

An AI Shorthorn bull being shown to visiting Winter Agricultural Class students at Riversdale in 1950.

Milk Recording and Progeny Testing Scheme

In 1953 a new Milk Recording and Progeny Testing Scheme came into operation in Northern Ireland. A feature of the new scheme was the progeny testing of bulls. It had been shown in England that only seven per cent of bulls leave daughters with a milk yield greater than the breed average. The only way to test the value of a bull is by determining the merits or productivity of his offspring. Bulls entering the service were used for a limited period to provide an adequate number of daughters for testing. They were then used lightly until their progeny test results were available. The value of the dairy heifers was assessed on milk yield, percentage butterfat and solids-not-fat and conformation. Only those bulls whose daughters were satisfactory in those respects were retained for service.

This scheme applied to pedigree dairy cows and those non-pedigree dairy animals that were on the Supplementary or Grading Register of their breed. A satisfactory bull in the AI service was defined as one that had a positive progeny test based on a large number of daughters in many herds. The test had to show that the bull was increasing milk yield and that the conformation and milk quality of his daughters were satisfactory. In 1969 a 'nominated' service was available at a fee of £2 against £1 10s 0d for the ordinary service. The 'nominated' service meant that the farmer could specify the bull that he wished to use.

Change of AI policy

The AI Service made a big impact on cattle breeding over the years. By 1966, AI was responsible for the breeding in over 60 per cent of the cow population in Northern Ireland. A major change in policy in relation to animal breeding and the AI Service was announced by the Northern Ireland Department of Agriculture in early 1976. One of the reasons for this change was the low number of herds that were milk recording in Northern Ireland. This made it difficult to progeny test dairy bulls. The Department reduced the size of its bull stud and put greater reliance on semen from proven dairy and beef bulls standing at other AI Centres in the British Isles such as those of the Milk Marketing Board in England and Wales and the privately owned Cattle Breeders' Services Limited. Cattle breeders in Northern Ireland were therefore able to access a much wider range of bulls that had been extensively tested and proven in Great Britain. Later, outstanding bulls from much further afield would become available to breeders in Northern Ireland through the AI Service.

At the introduction of the new service, two categories of bulls were available: *'Bull–of–the–Day'* or *'Elite'*. The former were top class bulls suitable for most commercial dairy herds and the *'Elite'* category bulls were among the very best which were capable of making definite improvements in both type and production traits in herds where their semen was used.

The promotion of artificial insemination as a livestock improvement measure was a continuing feature of the Agricultural Advisory Service's programme for farmers during the 1980s. Meetings organised annually in Fermanagh by the County Advisory Service and addressed by Messrs John Wilson and James Hoy of the Department of Agriculture's Livestock Division, were very well attended by farmers.

Mr John Wilson, BAgr MS, Department of Agriculture's Chief Livestock Officer.

Increased usage of AI resulted. For example, during 1983/84 there were 34,000 inseminations in Fermanagh. The following year this had increased to 37,200. During the same period, *'Premium Bull-of–the-Day'* increased from

Bilsrow Mario. A Friesian bull whose semen was available in the 'Bull of the Day' category in 1981.

74 per cent to 85 per cent. The meetings were accompanied by follow-up training courses at Enniskillen Agricultural College on associated topics of heat detection and foot care.

In the 1985/86 year, the number of inseminations in Fermanagh had increased to 71,250. Seventy-eight percent of these were from beef bulls. Simmental represented 39 per cent, Limousin 21 per cent and Hereford 14 per cent of the total. The categories of semen used were: five percent *'Bull-of-the-day'*, 85 per cent *'Premium Bull-of-the-Day'* and 10 per cent nominated. In 1987 inseminations of superior AI sires in both dairy and beef herds were available at a subsidised rate of £4 per insemination.

Avoncroft Aster – a Premium Bull-of-the-Day Simmental which was available in 1984. He was one of the leading bulls of the breed used in Northern Ireland.

Privatisation

The Northern Ireland AI Service was established in 1946 and was operated by the Ministry of Agriculture until it was privatised and taken over on 1st October 1988 by AI Service (Northern Ireland) Society 1988 Ltd. The new organisation continued to obtain semen from extensively tested and proven sources. The introduction of 'Do-it-yourself' AI and the entry of commercial firms that supplied semen from a very wide range of bulls also made a major contribution to the development of cattle breeding.

In County Fermanagh, Mr Bill Armstrong of Lisnaskea, was involved in training operatives in the early stages of 'Do-it-yourself' AI. He then established Western Farm Enterprises at Lisnaskea and became one of the leading suppliers of top class animal semen to livestock breeders throughout Northern Ireland. Following his untimely death the business is carried on by his son, Alan.

Mr Bill Armstrong (left) handing over a sponsorship cheque to Miss Jill Roulston, a student at Enniskillen College of Agriculture. Mr Kenneth Johnston, Senior Lecturer, looks on.

Pig breeding

A Swine Breeding Scheme was introduced by the Department of Agriculture and Technical Instruction in 1901. Like other classes of livestock, pig breeding was regarded as important by the County Committee of Agriculture. In 1906 there were eight Premium boars standing for service in Fermanagh. The owners were William Wilson, Ashfield, Lisbellaw; William Wilson, Depot, Enniskillen; William R. Thompson, Keeran, Irvinestown; Thomas Bussell, Toolin, Maguiresbridge; John W. Swindells, Mullaghsillogagh, Fivemiletown; Sir A. D. Brooke, Bart, Colebrooke, Brookeborough; Samuel Coulson, Bellmount, Magheraveely; and John Deering, Cloghan, Derrylin. The Premiums were worth £5 each. Rev John Hall, Chairman of the County Committee of Agriculture, in September 1909 said: *"It was strange that pig breeding had not been pushed forward more, and that Ireland had not taken more advantage from it. Look at the millions they paid annually to Denmark for pork. They now should have a say in the matter and they would agree with him in trying to induce the Department to give more. A miserable £5 per annum was no good"*. The Secretary, Mr W. H. West, said there was a good deal of money to be made out of pig breeding at the present time. One reason that pig feeding had fallen off was that the girls of the county would not now feed pigs – they were instead making a lot of money out of crochet. Rev Father McKenna thought there was nothing to prevent them from doing both. The Committee resolved to call on the Ministry to increase the Premium from £5 to £7.

The Large White Ulster pig

The Large White Ulster was the main pig breed in Northern

Ireland until the 1930s. The traditional cure practised in Ulster required a pig with well-developed hams. The Large White Ulster breed met this requirement and was very popular with the roll bacon and ham curers. The sows of the breed were good mothers, prolific and produced good thriving litters, which matured early.

Large White Ulster sow.

However, in 1926 the suitability of the Ulster pig for the London pork trade was being questioned. It was claimed that with the increasing emphasis on Wiltshire curing and the exporting of live pigs to England the Large White York pig was more suitable for this trade. Pressure increased on the unsuitability of the Ulster breed for the export trade. In December 1931 the English judge at the Christmas sale of fat pigs held at the premises of Messrs John Robson Ltd in Belfast said: "*The method of cutting pigs in England demands a pig which carries more flesh than the White Ulsters. You must have a pig which does not carry too much fat on the back. Another point against the Large White Ulster is, in the case of gilts, that you almost invariably get a cushion of fat round the inside of the ham. This is not found in the York to such an extent. The great point about White Ulsters as far as shipping is concerned, is that they suffer badly in transit. Take 100 pigs out of the market, 50 Yorks and 50 White Ulsters, and by the time they get to their destination you will find out of the consignment of Ulsters only about four or five pigs are free from scratches, bites etc. In the case of York pigs they do not suffer to this extent*".

Demise of the Large White Ulster pig

In December 1926 of the 16 applicants in Fermanagh for Premium boars 11 wanted White Ulster. The Large White Ulster pig was generally fatter than the Large White (York). The use of Large White Ulster Premium boars declined rapidly from the 1930s. In Fermanagh Large White York and Large White Ulster boars were still eligible breeds for Premiums until the 1940s. In March 1944, the Ministry of Agriculture informed the County Committee that it would not any longer agree to Large White Ulster Boars being eligible for Premiums.

Large White York boar.

A Landrace boar.

The Large White York was then joined by Landrace as the two main commercial breeds of pigs. Leanness of the carcase was taking on a greater significance at this time.

Licensing

Under the Livestock Order of 1933 all boars for service had to be licensed and the Premium available was £9. The demand for Premiums boars in Fermanagh showed a modest increase in the 1940s when the County Committee of Agriculture budgeted for 22. The value of Premiums at that time had risen to £12 and in the 1950s it had increased to £15.

Demand remained reasonably steady in the 1960s. In 1963 in Fermanagh there were 18 Premium boars in service, 14 of which were Landrace and the others were Large White. By 1975, despite an increase in the value of the Premium (£25 and £15), the number of Premium boars had dropped to six, four of which were Landrace. At that time there were 100 licensed boars in Fermanagh.

Progeny testing

Progeny testing of pigs took on a particular significance when the Pig Litter Testing Station opened at Greenmount, Muckamore, in April 1954. The emphasis then was on the production of lean bacon which commanded a higher price

and on efficiency of feed conversion. The Testing Station concentrated on the progeny testing of pedigree boars. The aim was to provide reliable information to help the breeder who submitted progeny of boars for testing to identify boars and sows which transmit good qualities to their offspring. Furthermore, breeders using the information from the station could identify other stock possessing the qualities they wished to introduce to their own herds.

Accredited Pig Herds' Scheme

In 1958, the Ministry initiated the Accredited Pig Herds Scheme, the purpose being to provide facilities for breeders for recording and progeny testing their pig herds. Commercial pig producers could then obtain breeding stock of good quality from these Elite herds. From that time the award of Premiums was restricted to boars from Accredited Herds. Boars from herds which had attained satisfactory results in pig recording were eligible for a £15 premium while the higher premium of £25 was payable on sons of progeny tested sires. A new Pig Testing Scheme was introduced on 1st October 1966. Under the new scheme there were two types of Accredited Herds – Elite and Multiplying. The Elite Herds produced top quality breeding stock by intensive methods of selection and the Multiplying Herds would then increase the number of such stock for sale to commercial pig keepers. Financial incentives were offered to herd owners participating in the scheme.

Artificial Insemination for Pigs

The introduction of a pilot (AI) *"Do It Yourself"* AI Scheme, which came into operation on 1st January 1972, was a topic for discussion at a meeting for pig producers in Enniskillen Agricultural College. The semen came from progeny and performance tested boars kept at the Ballycraigy AI Centre. The semen was dispatched to the pig breeder's nearest bus station. Participating farmers were offered a demonstration of the technique by a Ministry inseminator.

Pig Production Development Committee

A major change in policy came in 1993 when the Department of Agriculture and Rural Development (DARD) withdrew from the provision of breeding services to the industry. Under the Pig Production Development Act (Northern Ireland) 1964, the Department established the Pig Production Development Committee (PPDC) as a statutory body. Its primary function was to provide services and facilities intended to benefit persons engaged in the production of pigs in Northern Ireland. Services included the on-farm recording of pedigree herds and the central performance testing of boars from these herds. These services were supplied to the Committee by Pig Industry Genetics Ltd, a private company established by the PPDC for this purpose in 1993 following DARD's disengagement from such services. The PPDC's activities were funded from the Pig Production Development Fund which was also set up under the 1964 Act. The Fund was wholly financed by a levy payable on pigs slaughtered in or exported from Northern Ireland with the exception of those imported for immediate slaughter.

Sheep breeding

Throughout the most of Northern Ireland the Scottish Blackface has been the main hill breed down through the years. The Greyface or cross-bred, that is a cross between the Border Leicester ram, an early maturing breed, and a Blackface ewe has been the common commercial ewe for breeding purposes on the lowlands. When this ewe is crossed with a Down type ram, such as Suffolk, it produces lambs of excellent conformation and meat quality. Texels were later to become a popular crossing ram. A Premium Scheme similar to those for other classes of livestock was operated by the Ministry for Blackface rams.

In Fermanagh in October 1929 when there was concern that the demand for Premium bulls would not reach the number allocated (120), Mr W. H. West, Secretary of the County Committee, suggested the adoption of a Lowland Sheep Scheme. He stated the proposed scheme would be similar to that for Premium bulls and boars and its purpose would be to aid the small sheep breeder. A scheme for Premium rams of the Border Leicester breed was provisionally adopted. Premiums valued at £5 were available in 1937. Due to unpopularity the scheme was discontinued in 1950.

Grants

Grants for the purchase of approved rams of the Border Leicester, Blackface, and Suffolk breeds for use in pedigree flocks were available from 1953. The grants varied between £10 and £24 depending on the breed of ram and the breed of the ewe flock.

Under the Sheep Improvement Scheme, introduced in 1987, grants amounting to a maximum of £24 towards the purchase of approved rams were available for Border Leicester, Blackface and Suffolk breeds for use in pedigree flocks. A condition for the Border Leicester and Suffolk breeds was that the applicants needed to be recording under the Sheep Improvement Scheme. The purpose of the scheme was to improve the carcase producing abilities of the rams produced by pedigree breeders for wider use in commercial flocks. Rams that had been performance tested at Loughgall had an Elite Ram Card whereas those performance tested on the breeders' farms had Top Index Cards. These rams with their certification were made available at special sales.

Privatisation

As was the case for beef cattle, recording of pedigree sheep was transferred from the Department of Agriculture to 'AI Service (Northern Ireland) Society 1988 Ltd' in autumn 1993. For the first two years, a Blue Star designation was used to identify the best rams but after that the nationally based Signet Sheep Breeding System was adopted.

References:

Ministry/Department of Agriculture's *Monthly Reports* and *Agriculture in Northern Ireland.*

Records of the County Agricultural Executive Office.

Files of *The Impartial Reporter* and *Fermanagh Herald* held in Enniskillen Library.

Files of *The Belfast Newsletter* for 1928.

Mr Stuart Johnston, Managing Director of the Ulster Farmers' Livestock and Auction Centre, and Miss Roberta McMullan of the Suffolk Sheep Society with a fine Suffolk ram.

Chapter 15
Livestock breeds and breeders

A significant development in 1947 was the publication in June of the Agricultural Enquiry Report, generally known as the Babington Report. Its recommendations had a considerable influence on the future development of agriculture in Northern Ireland. A large section of the report was devoted to livestock production because of its economic importance in Northern Ireland. The report dealt at length with livestock breeding. It concluded that the Ministry of Agriculture's policy should concentrate on developing and improving a breed of cattle, which would be economical as producers of both beef and milk. The Babington Committee members were satisfied that the Dairy Shorthorn, as it had been developed in England, was such a breed. Their recommendation was as follows: *But whether it be difficult or not, we recommend that the efforts of the Ministry of Agriculture be directed to producing and establishing a dual purpose animal based on the English Dairy Shorthorn with milk as the first objective, but suitably balanced with beef characteristics.*

A fine specimen of an English Dairy Shorthorn cow.

The Committee blamed the crossing of Beef Shorthorns with Dairy Shorthorn cows as leading to the deterioration of the breed as dual purpose animals. They went further and recommended that Beef Shorthorns should not be eligible for Premiums under the County Committee of Agriculture scheme and that about 15 English-bred Dairy Shorthorns should be imported each year to form a new strain of Dairy Shorthorns. The Committee also suggested that these bulls should be placed with selected applicants who would act as agents for groups of cow owners wishing to have their cows served by the bull. It was agreed that a group of between three and five, with at least 40 cows in total, would be eligible for one of these imported bulls. The Minister accepted the recommendations and asked each County Committee to select suitable persons who would be prepared to attend the annual November sale of Dairy Shorthorns in Reading and purchase bulls for Premium purposes. There was a good response from Premium holders and 14 bulls were purchased at the first sale with the bulls bought averaging 200 guineas. The Ministry of Agriculture purchased two bulls for their AI Service – one of which cost 500 guineas. Premiums for Beef Shorthorns were discontinued in 1950 because of the new policy in relation to safeguarding the breeding of Dairy Shorthorns.

A Beef Shorthorn cow and calf
(Courtesy of Shona Calder, Grand Tully Brae Shorthorns).

Friesians' potential

In 1923, reference was made in *The Impartial Reporter* to the potential of the Friesian breed. The report referred to their appearance at the Royal Dublin Society Spring Show a few years ago. It stated that they had been bred for milk on the Continent for half a century and that the breed had more beef claims than most dairy breeds. The breed had gained popularity in England and cows and heifers were commanding high prices. The report stated that at a recent sale at Slough, limited to the sons and daughters of 1,000 gallon cows and 800 gallon heifers, 60 Friesians made an average of £123 2s 7d. It also stated that according to a recent census there were 357 Friesians in Ireland. In February 1930 when the suitability of Friesians was raised at a Milk Recording Association luncheon in Belfast, the Minister of Agriculture, Sir Edward Archdale, said that Friesians were very useful cows but that they had to remember that the store cattle trade was better than the milk trade. The latter comment was challenged by some farmers present. The Minister continued stating that Friesians would give more milk, but the country wanted good store cattle. He said that they must remember that the cow that would give from 800 to 1,000 gallons of milk was a good cow. They got that in many Shorthorns and at the same time good calves and separated milk for pigs and poultry, the things that counted amongst the small farmers.

Farleton Nancy 4th – a fine Friesian.

The Ministry of Agriculture did not encourage the breed and this was reinforced in the Babington Report. In spite of this lack of encouragement, the breed increased through the importation of bulls from Great Britain by private breeders and by 1936 Friesians were beginning to have an impact on both milk and beef production in Northern Ireland. Despite the emphasis placed on the value of the English Shorthorn in the Babington Report, the Ministry in 1948 offered subsidies to groups of pedigree breeders (at least three in a group) for assistance with the purchase of high class stock bulls of other breeds as well as Shorthorns. Breeds eligible for the subsidy were: English Dairy Shorthorn, British Friesian, Ayrshire, Aberdeen Angus and Galloway.

As more dairy farmers switched from the Shorthorn to the Friesian breed during the 1960s, the number of Friesian bulls available through the AI Service increased. In 1960, the Earl of Erne purchased a young Friesian bull for a record price of 350 guineas at the Royal Ulster Agricultural Society autumn bull sales.

Transition

The Friesian breed at that time was largely based on the Dutch type of the breed. They were very popular cattle and the transition from Shorthorn to Friesian in the dairy herd was largely complete by the early 1970s. The British Friesian had greater beefing potential than the Holstein strain developed in North America. Despite this, there was a steady increase in the use of the Holstein strain during the 1980s through the use of imported semen. By the end of the century, the Holstein had become the dominant breed in the dairy herd. Beef breeds were used on part of the Holstein herds to provide animals for beef production.

Mr Seamus Gunn's Champion Holstein cow in 2003 at Enniskillen Show. From left: Messrs Mervyn Edgar, judge; William Watterson, Fivemiletown and Brookeborough Co-Operative Society, sponsors of the class; Seamus Gunn and daughter Lauren; Mr Richard Johnston, handler.

Change from British to Continental Beef breeds

In 1964 the beef breeds, Hereford and Aberdeen Angus, comprised 46 per cent of total inseminations. During the period from 1982/83 to 1986/87, there were significant changes in the demand for the different breeds of beef bulls in the AI Service. Aberdeen Angus had declined slightly in popularity from 10.5 per cent to 8.3 per cent. Hereford had shown a very substantial decline from 24.7 per cent of total beef inseminations to 6.1 per cent. Shorthorn usage had halved from a low figure of 2.5 per cent. Blonde d'Aquitaine, which had just been introduced in 1983, had grown to 7.4 per cent. Charolais had declined from 15.6 per cent to 10.4 per cent while Limousin had more than doubled from 11.3 to 28.5 per cent. Simmental, which was most popular, had shown a slight increase from 35.1 to 39.1 per cent. During the period of just over a quarter of a century, there had been a major change from British to Continental beef breeds. In 1960, all beef inseminations were either Hereford or Aberdeen Angus and by 1986/87, eighty-four per cent of beef breed inseminations were from Continental bulls.

Charolais importations

Towards the end of 1961, approval was given to import a number of Charolais bulls into Britain. Twenty-seven of these bulls were made available through the AI services. The progeny from 1964 onwards were compared with crosses from the British beef breeds. The outcome of the progeny tests was that the Charolais had advantages in birth weight, in growth rate and food conversion compared to the other crosses. However, preliminary tests by taste panels showed that the Charolais crosses had less flavour and were less tender and less juicy than the British beef crosses. In Northern Ireland, semen was obtained from five Charolais bulls in January 1963 and used on Friesian, Shorthorn, and Ayrshire

cows. Comprehensive testing of the 139 progeny was carried out at the Ministry of Agriculture's Livestock Husbandry Farm at Loughgall in County Armagh. The outcome of the testing programme showed that Charolais cross calves were heavier at birth, had higher daily live weight gain, higher killing out percentages and larger eye muscles.

The Ministry of Agriculture's Loughgall Charolais cattle in 1972.

Continental breeds' potential

By 1964, the Ministry of Agriculture had a major beef cattle progeny testing and feeding trial centre at the Livestock Husbandry Farm at Loughgall. Farmers were invited to attend a demonstration in March of that year when 480 cattle were on show. The breeds on display were Friesian and Dairy Shorthorn steers, Hereford and Angus crosses from Dairy Shorthorn and Friesian cows, Charolais crosses from Dairy Shorthorn, Friesian and Ayrshire cows. The conclusion reached was that the Charolais breed had a future place in beef production in Northern Ireland. Six Charolais bulls and 13 Charolais females were imported into Northern Ireland in January 1966 as the first step in establishing Charolais as a pure breed in the Province. Charolais semen, followed by that of Simmental, became available through AI from that time. During the 1965/66 year there were 172 first inseminations using Charolais semen. Importations of other European Continental genetics were to follow the Charolais and Simmental. In 1979, Limousin was available in the AI service followed closely by Blonde d'Aquitaine and then Belgian Blue in the 1980s.

Beef performance testing

Comprehensive performance testing of the main breeds of beef cattle was underway at Loughgall Livestock Husbandry Farm in 1970. The breeds at that time were Aberdeen Angus, Hereford, Shorthorn, Simmental and Charolais. Several of the top bulls tested at the centre entered the AI service. Others were available at breed club sales. During the period 1977 to 1987, about 200 young bulls were tested each year at Loughgall. The bulls which were carefully selected from recorded herds, under the Beef Recording Scheme, arrived at the Loughgall Livestock Husbandry Farm at around six months of age. During the next six months their growth rates and food conversion rates were recorded. A potential purchaser was then able to see the performance of the different bulls in the published test report. Premiums to the value of £100 per bull per year for a two-year period were made available. These Premiums applied to suckler herd owners whose herds did not exceed 40 cows and who purchased approved recorded or performance tested bulls.

Privatisation

In the autumn of 1993, the recording of beef and sheep, for livestock improvement purposes, was transferred to AI Service (Northern Ireland) Society Ltd as a continuation of the privatisation policy by the Department of Agriculture. Under the new arrangements for pedigree breeders, a nationally based Signet Beef Breeding System was adopted and BLUP (Best Linear Unbiased Predictor) figures became available for each tested bull. These figures enabled purchasers to identify the best bulls.

Need for better suckler cows

The Ministry of Agriculture's Beef Herds Replacement Scheme came into operation on 1st November 1972. Under that scheme, free artificial inseminations using dual purpose Dairy Shorthorns and Simmental bulls were available for beef type cows in Northern Ireland. The aim of the scheme was to help maintain employment by encouraging the production of more cows for the suckler herds with sufficient milk to rear a good calf for the beef finisher. In 1972 inseminations from Riversdale were 33,873 (273,000 was the NI total) and in 1974 there were 34,565 from the centre.

Breeds in Fermanagh suckler herds

A survey carried out in 1977 by the Department's County Staff in relation to the suckler herds in County Fermanagh showed that Shorthorn type cows were predominant at 28 per cent. Angus and Angus Friesian crosses represented 22 per cent and Hereford types at 20 per cent were next in popularity.

Simmental types represented 4 per cent. Hereford was the predominant crossing bull representing 43 per cent of the sample. Charolais and Simmental were having an impact representing 24 per cent and 16 per cent respectively of the bulls.

Replacements for the herd showed Hereford and Hereford cross Friesian types as being most common at 29 per cent of the total. Shorthorn at 21 per cent was next. Aberdeen Angus Friesian crosses were relatively popular at 14 per cent. Simmental was beginning to have an impact at 11 per cent of the total replacements.

Fermanagh cattle breeders

County Fermanagh, over the century, has depended heavily on livestock as a source of farm income. Cattle in particular have contributed very significantly. It is therefore not surprising that Fermanagh farmers should be well represented over the decades among the leading stockmen and cattle breeders in Northern Ireland.

At the Balmoral Spring Show and Sale in February 1948 Lisbellaw farmers did well. Seven cattle entered secured two championships, two reserve championships, four first prizes, one second prize and one third prize. Six of the animals were awarded Premiums under the Ministry of Agriculture's Livestock Scheme. The farmers concerned were: Messrs C. E. Veitch and Sons, Drumlone; T. R. Noble, Drummee; J. Dunlop, Lisbellaw; and W. Magee, Foydragh.

Good prices for Fermanagh-bred bulls

Fermanagh farmers were getting good prices for their bulls at the Royal Ulster Agricultural Society (RUAS) Sales in February 1951. Messrs C. E. Veitch and Sons, Lisbellaw, received the highest price for an Aberdeen Angus at 115 guineas. It was sold to Mr M. Knox-Browne, Fivemiletown. Mr T. Hurst of Ballinamallard sold two bulls at 90 guineas and Hugh Maguire of Lisbellaw sold a bull for 80 guineas. Two South Fermanagh farmers paid high prices for Shorthorn bulls namely Mr W. R. Egerton, Rosslea, (180 guineas) and Mr W. A. Little, Newtownbutler, (150 guineas). At the Balmoral Spring Show of 1965, 'Rathkeeland Dairy-Master' owned by Mr J. H. Crawford of Rathkeeland won the 'Daily Mail Cup' for the best Dairy Shorthorn bull. Mr Jack Veitch was scoring successes from the 1960s at shows throughout Ireland.

Brothers Loftus (Beechmount, Enniskillen) and Albert Lucy (Cullen, Monea) did very well with Herefords and Charolais cattle in the 1970s. At the Balmoral Sales in October 1972 Loftus had the champion Hereford bull which sold for 560 guineas. Loftus received 680 guineas at the Balmoral Sales in February 1975 for a Charolais bull.

Towards the end of the century Fermanagh breeders produced some of the very best dairy and beef pedigree cattle. This was demonstrated by their success in winning championships in the leading shows throughout Northern Ireland and further afield. Beef breeders from the county have been particularly successful at the Perth shows and sales and feature in the prize winners and top prices received on a very regular basis. Perth attracts the best cattle from throughout the British Isles.

The county has also produced some of the finest horses in the country. Mr Jim Hurst of Lisbellaw has consistently bred fine animals. Towards the end of the century his Half Bred mare won the Royal Dublin Society Horse Show championship on no less than seven occasions.

Mr Jack Veitch and his champion Aberdeen Angus bull at the Royal Dublin Society Spring Show in 1964 (Courtesy of Mrs M. Veitch).

Hereford Friesian cross cow and calf.

Aberdeen Angus cross cow with Charolais calf.

References:

Ministry/Department of Agriculture *Monthly Reports* and *Agriculture in Northern Ireland.*

Files of *The Impartial reporter* and *Fermanagh Herald* held in Enniskillen Library.

Reports of the the County Fermanagh Agricultural Executive Office.

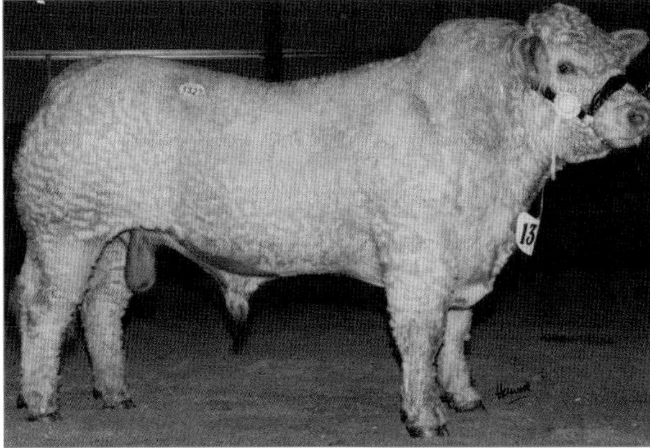

Killadeas Jack, owned and bred by Mr Stuart Bothwell, St Angelo House, Killadeas, made 14,000 guineas at the Perth Sales in 1995 (Courtesy of Mr S. Bothwell).

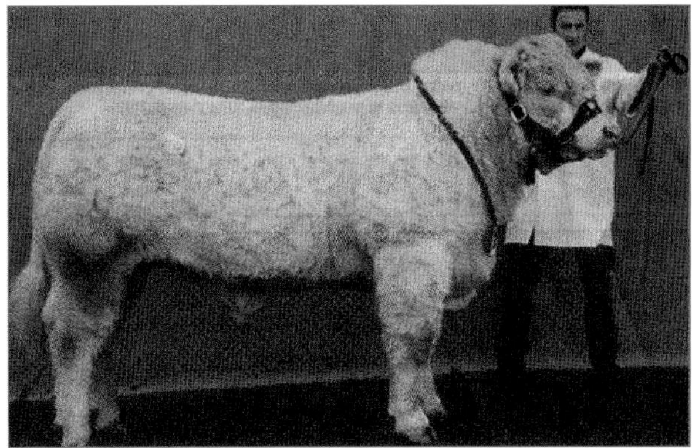

Killadeas Original, led by Mr David Bothwell was the top priced bull at 17,000 guineas at the Perth sales in the year 2000 (Courtesy of Mr S. Bothwell).

Mr Jim Hurst at the Royal Dublin Society Horse Show with his champion Half Bred mare 'My Irish Bride' (Courtesy of Mr and Mrs A. Hurst).

Mr J. H. Crawford and prize winning Shorthorn bull in the late 1950s(Courtesy of Mr W. Crawford).

Mr Arthur Crawford with Rathkeeland Dairyman's cups won during 1959 (Courtesy of Mr W. Crawford).

Messrs Loftus and Albert Lucy with their prize winning Hereford bull at the Royal Dublin Society bull sales in February 1962 (Courtesy of Mrs E. Dickson).

Chapter 16
Development of agricultural education in County Fermanagh

The first agricultural educational establishment in Fermanagh, apart from the Vaughan Charter School at Tubrid, Kesh, was the 'Carrick Agricultural College and National School' at Derryhoney, Lisbellaw. In his book, *Lisbellaw " The Hard Rocks"*, the author, Mr Joe Crawford, stated that the College was built between 1838 and 1840 and opened on 28th May 1840. It was built on the Rev J. G. Porter's land and it was his intention to appoint a Scotsman to teach agriculture. The first master was Mr William Smith who, according to Mr Crawford, was a practical agriculturist and horticulturist trained in Scotland. The curriculum included *outdoor work, literary and moral education in turn during a school day, and read the Holy Scriptures where it was desired by the parents.*

Carrick inscription.

Farming Society's interest

The County Fermanagh Farming Society also appreciated the value of agricultural education in the early years. The members of the Society agreed to hold a public meeting in Ennishillen Townhall on 24th September 1839. According to a report in *The Impartial Reporter* the purpose of the meeting was – *to consider the propriety of soliciting subscriptions and donations to carry out into practical working an Agricultural School, for instruction of the sons*

Carrick National School
(Courtesy of Mr and Mrs R. Trimble).

of the tenantry of this County in the science of farming. The report continued: *We believe the idea of the intended school originated with Miss Hall, who has proposed to bestow the very liberal sum of £1,000 as a foundation: Colonel Crichton, and the Rev J. G. Porter, have also made very liberal offers of assistance, and there is no doubt but that the gentry and farmers of the county will generally, if not universally, give their aid to so patriotic an undertaking.*

This proposal had taken further root by September 1841, when definite plans were made to establish a Fermanagh Agricultural School. The report in *The Impartial Reporter* of 9th September 1841, reads as follows: *The decided spirit of improvement that has been pretty generally shown by the Landlords of this and adjoining counties, in employing Scotch Stewards, not only for the introduction of a better system of Cultivation upon the lands in their occupation, but also for the instruction of their Tenants, affords a good presumption of the great advantage would be of to the country generally, if instead of employing strangers at great wages, the respectable Farmers' sons of this country could receive at a local School such an education as to qualify them for such situations. And when out, many would return to their fathers' farms to practise with youthful energy what they learned from their own experience to be a more profitable system of Cultivation, the effect would probably be far greater than from any casual instruction from a Visiting Agriculturist.*

To this purpose it is proposed to raise a Capital of £3,000, by £20 shares, including a donation from Miss Hall of £1,500, and that – The Most Noble The Marquis of Ely, The Right Hon. Earl of Enniskillen, The Right Hon. Earl of Belmore, Sir Arthur Brooke, Bart., M.P., Mervyn Archdall Esq., M.P., John Crichton Esq., Richard Hall, Esq., be appointed Trustees to the Establishment.

That the sums subscribed be forthwith lodged in the Provincial Bank to the credit of the Trustees. That a Committee of Management be appointed to meet at least once a month, for the purpose of conducting the business of the Establishment; to consist of the following persons, if Shareholders, of which five to form a Quorum, viz.:- John Crichton, Esq., Hon. John Cole, Hon. and Rev J. C. Maude, William D'Arcy, Esq., Edward Archdall, Esq., Rev J. G. Porter, Lieut. Col. H. W. Barton, Henry M. Richardson, Esq., Richard Hall Esq., George Brooke Esq., Simon Armstrong, Esq., Hollymount, William Archdall, Esq., James Lendrum Esq., F. W. Barton Esq., Wm. Hassard Esq., Robert Graham Esq., Francis Graham Esq., John G. V. Porter Esq., Rev John Richardson, Rev Loftus Reade, Rev Wm W. Deering, Hamilton Haire Esq., Henry Gresson Esq., Charles Fausset Esq., Robert Archdall Esq., George Wood Esq., Thomas Irwin Esq., Thomas Kernaghan Esq., Dr Hugh Collum, Mr William Frith, Mr William Graham, Mr Richard Bracken, Mr John Halliday and Mr John Wood.

Wm. Hassard Esq., Henry M. Richardson Esq. and Lieut. Col. Hugh William Barton were appointed as a committee to select a proper site for the School – enter into treaty, ascertain terms etc and then report to a general meeting.

The course for Education for this Establishment be principally directed to the object of preparing the pupils to become useful practical farmers, according to the improved system of agriculture. The Establishment to consist of 50 boys, to be increased should the funds admit of it. That a Master be procured capable of instructing the pupils in reading, writing, arithmetic, book-keeping, agricultural and commercial accounts, and land surveying. That an agriculturist be procured conversant with the most approved system of agriculture. The annual sum to be paid by the pupils not to exceed ten pounds. No pupil was to be admitted under the age of fourteen. Pupils must be able to read and write and the period of his stay not to exceed four years.

Those taking ten or more shares, including Miss Hall and her successors, to have the nomination of three pupils; every holder of one share to be entitled to nominate one pupil, in succession.

No further progress appears to have been made with this proposal.

Miss Hall's contribution

One of the individuals credited with the idea of the agricultural school in 1841 and offering generous funding for that purpose was Miss Anne Hall. Miss Hall lived in North Gloucester Street, Dublin. She owned extensive property in Dublin and had land interests in County Fermanagh including Derryinch and the islands of *Inishmore, Innisgrenra, Iniskeen and Innisgaura.* She also had strong associations with County Londonderry through the Clarkes of Maghera. Miss Hall died in 1841 and in her will, among many bequests, left money for the building of the agricultural school in County Fermanagh. The administration of the funds she bequeathed for agricultural education eventually fell to the Educational Endowments Commission. An Order in Council of the Royal Dublin Society, dated 10th February 1892, approved a scheme, framed by the Commission, for the management of an endowment founded by the late Miss Anne Hall. The scheme provided that the annual proceeds of a fund amounting to £3,628 14s 11d, Government Stock, should be administered by the Royal Dublin Society for the promotion of agricultural education in the counties of Fermanagh and Londonderry. The annual income was used in the early years of the scheme for funding lectures and demonstrations in milk production and butter making. In 1934, one scholarship to attend Greenmount Agricultural College, worth £65, available under the Anne Hall Endowment Scheme, for competition among candidates from Counties Fermanagh and Londonderry. In later years, the funds were used at the discretion of the County Agricultural Executive Officers in Fermanagh and Londonderry to fund or part-fund transport in connection with educational outings for students attending classes or other agricultural training and educational programmes.

New era begins

Education was regarded by the County Committee of Agriculture as a prerequisite for successful agricultural development right from the start. The early work of the instructors involved lectures, experimental work and advice. In 1906, a statement from the County Committee read as follows: *we consider there is a great necessity for practical teaching in agricultural subjects; the time when any further benefit can be derived from pioneer lectures has come to an end and should give place to courses of instruction of a practical nature in convenient centres.* This established the concept of Winter Agricultural Classes – a feature of agricultural education that would remain as a very important element for decades to come.

Winter Agricultural Classes

In September 1908, Winter Agricultural Classes were discussed at the Fermanagh County Committee of Agriculture. In response to a letter from the Ministry of Agriculture, members discussed the desirability of holding winter classes. Rev Father McKenna stated: "W*e want something new to attract people, as they are getting tired of lectures."* It was agreed that regular classes would be more effective than occasional lectures.

Mr Smyth, Agricultural Instructor, reported at a meeting of the County Committee of Agriculture on progress with the classes in January 1909. He said: "*The classes were going on splendidly, and the boys who were attending were getting on very well, but there was a small attendance. There were eight pupils on the rolls in Lisnaskea and eight in Irvinestown. The Lisnaskea boys were attending very badly, but the Irvinestown boys attended regularly."* The 1909/10 classes were held in Brookeborough and Springfield. For these classes, travelling expenses could be claimed *to cover the cost of third class railway fare, or a road allowance of 1d per mile will be granted at close of the course to students who attend five-sixths of the lessons and whose progress is satisfactory and who are resident more than four miles from the centre.*

Poor attendance was reported in 1911 when the class held in Derrykeeghan was discontinued. Fortunately, this pattern of low attendance was not a continuing feature in later years. Classes in agriculture at local centres provided a most convenient means whereby farmers, their sons and workers could learn of new findings and modern methods relating to farming. Winter Agricultural Classes were conducted normally on two afternoons or evenings during the winter months. The classes were organised by the Agricultural Instructors or in later years by their successors, the Agricultural Advisory Officers. Sometimes classes would run for two winters in the same centre. The classes were rotated to centres around the county so that over a period all young farmers would have the opportunity of attending one within reasonable travelling distance. In the early days, the purpose of the classes was stated as follows: *to create and engender in the minds of those attending them a spirit of inquisitiveness, which will encourage the students to think for themselves and thereby increase their knowledge by further enquiry.* Normally, the classes were attended by farmers' sons who were working on the home farms. The topics dealt with included crop and animal husbandry, soil fertility, drainage, grassland production and farm management. During the years when Winter Agricultural Classes were a significant element of agricultural education, poultry and pigs were important economic enterprises on most farms. The part of the course dealing with poultry was dealt with by the Poultry Instructress working in the county. In those early days, responsibility for management of the poultry flock on the farm tended to fall to the farmer's wife or another female family member. It was for this reason that in the early days most poultry instructors were female. Usually the Horticultural Instructor and a Veterinary Officer would give a number of lectures on their subjects at these classes. Winter Agricultural Classes had a particular advantage in that the Instructors or Advisers conducting the classes were in close contact with the home farms of the students and they were therefore in a good position to give advice and influence practices on those farms.

Meantime, Mr West, Secretary of the Fermanagh County Committee of Agriculture, told members that there were not enough applicants to take up the free tuition places being offered at Ballyhaise Agricultural College in County Cavan.

At a meeting in September 1913, the Chairman of the County Committee of Agriculture told Dr Hinchcliffe of the Department of Agriculture that: "*agricultural classes were a loss and that the instructor's time could be better spent. When a class was formed in a week or two it would dwindle down to an attendance of two or three."* This view was not shared by other members and it was agreed that if the instructor could get enough students a class should be held in Derrylin over the coming winter.

Educational Visits

Educational visits by those attending classes were a popular feature and were normally held at the end of the session. Visits were organised to farms, creameries, the annual Royal Ulster Agricultural Society Show at Balmoral, Belfast, and other places of agricultural interest. A trip by bus to farms in the Strabane area by the 1938/39 classes was typical of the many educational visits for winter class students over the years.

Agricultural Classes were suspended from the outbreak of the Second World War but were started again in November 1944 in Derrygonnelly and Lisnaskea.

Agricultural Colleges established

The importance of agricultural colleges or schools was realised early in the 20th century. Formal agricultural education was under the direct control of the Department of Agriculture and Technical Instruction in Dublin. It established three institutes in what is now Northern Ireland. The Ulster Dairy School, later Loughry Agricultural College and now Loughry Campus of the College of Agriculture, Food and Rural Enterprise (CAFRE), was opened near Cookstown in 1908. Greenmount Agricultural College, now CAFRE's Greenmount Campus, was opened for students in 1912 and in 1914 the North West School at Strabane was established. Prior to that Ballyhaise Agricultural College in County Cavan served west Ulster.

Scholarships to encourage young farmers to attend agricultural institutes were introduced in Northern Ireland in 1922 under the Ministry of Agriculture for Northern Ireland and administered by the County Committees of Agriculture. The Fermanagh County Committee allocated four scholarships to enable farmers' daughters to attend the North West School, Strabane. The course there included instruction in the following: poultry keeping, butter making, cooking and housewifery (including sick nursing).

In 1923 a scholarship, worth £65, was introduced to enable farmers' sons to attend Greenmount Agricultural College. In 1926, two of these scholarships were awarded by the Fermanagh County Committee of Agriculture. In 1928/29, a Greenmount scholarship was awarded to Cecil Patterson, Derrylin, who was later to become County Agricultural Executive Officer in Armagh. William T. McClintock, from Cooneen, Fivemiletown, was granted an award to Greenmount in 1930/31 and was destined to become the County Agricultural Executive Officer in Fermanagh. During 1934, three Fermanagh boys were awarded scholarships to the College. These were N. J. Earls of Belleek; C. J. W. Nixon, Lisbellaw (who eventually became Chief Horticultural Officer of the Ministry of Agriculture) and J. W. Jordan of Brookeborough (who later became a lecturer in the Faculty of Agriculture in Queen's University, Belfast).

At the end of the Greenmount College year in 1937, a Fermanagh scholarship holder, W. J. Browne, Mullygarry, Letterbreen, received great praise from the Principal, who stated that he *"was one of the most satisfactory students we have had for many years."*

A Training Scheme for farm workers was introduced in

Derrylin and Irvinestown Winter Agricultural Classes on joint outing to North County Londonderry in 1939
Back row: left to right; Douglas Brown, Harold Fawcett, Harry Keys, Stanley Potters, Benny McBrien, James Lunny and John Cox.
Second row: Thomas Pat Gunn, Hugh Cassidy, Jack McBrien, Peter Maguire, Roland Hurst, Frank Blaney, George Hoey, Thomas Johnston, Arthur Farry, Michael McManus, Alphonsus Gunn, James Willis and James P. Gilleece.
Third row (sitting): Eugene Murray, Paddy John Lunny, James Sweeney, Messrs W. T. McClintock, County Agricultural Executive Officer, D. T. Ritchie, Agricultural Instructor, A. W. Ritchie, owner and editor of the Fermanagh Times newspaper, Joe McAloon and W. J. Phair.
Front row: Bertie Keys, William Swanston, Sonny Gilleece, Johnston Elliott, Pat J. Lunny, Gordon J. Keys, James Watterson and James Lee.
(Courtesy of Mr J. McAloon).

Dr James W. Jordan
(Courtesy of Miss S. Jordan).

1946. Under this Scheme, an approved farmer could obtain a trainee for thirteen weeks at a cost of ten shillings per week. The trainees received an allowance from the Ministry of Labour and National Insurance.

Greenmount Agricultural College reopened in 1948 after being closed during the war years. Loughry College (formerly the Ulster Dairy School) reopened in 1949 and offered courses in poultry keeping, dairying and housewifery.

Queen's University

The Northern Ireland Ministry of Agriculture established research divisions in conjunction with the Faculty of Agriculture, which was established at Queen's University, Belfast, in 1924. University degrees in agriculture and associated subjects were awarded by Queen's from that time. The Agricultural Research Institute at Hillsborough, County Down, became an integral part of university teaching facilities for the Faculty of Agriculture in the University. Northern Ireland farmers, with the agreement of the Ulster Farmers' Union, contributed £10,000 of the additional £130,000 rates relief earned for agriculture in 1928 towards the establishment of the Institute.

In 1937 Mr J. V. Courtney, Aghadrumsee, won a Ministry of Agriculture scholarship worth £380 to study agriculture at Queen's University. Mr Courtney subsequently had a very successful career in the Ministry of Agriculture for Northern Ireland. He served as County Agricultural Executive Officer in Armagh and later held a similar post

Winter Agricultural Classes held in Springfield and Tempo on an outing to Riversdale, Ballinamallard, in 1950.
Back row: left to right; George Kells, Seamus McCaffrey, Norman Dundas, Andrew Dickson, David Porteus, ? and John Murphy.
Second row: James McKeaney, William Thompson, Cecil Haddick, ?, A. Price, Gerald Brown, Jim Coulter and Norman Young.
Seated: ?, Messrs William Gilpin, Agricultural Inspector; J. C. Johnston, Horticultural Instructor; George Pollock, Agricultural Advisory Officer; W. T. McClintock, County Agricultural Executive Officer; G. Parker, Veterinary officer in charge of Riversdale; Howard Thompson and Ivan Loane.
(Courtesy of Mr I. Loane and Mr S. McCaffrey).

in County Tyrone. He was honoured by Her Majesty the Queen by being appointed OBE for his services to agriculture.

Mr John Vincent Courtney OBE BAgr (Courtesy of Mr J. Courtney).

Agricultural Course at Enniskillen Technical School

The County Fermanagh Education Committee in co-operation with the Enniskillen Technical College and the Advisory Staff of the Ministry of Agriculture in County Fermanagh in 1953 initiated a *'Day school of Agriculture'*. It was a two-year course and involved instruction in agricultural and related subjects. The agricultural element of the course was taught by an Agricultural Adviser from the Ministry of Agriculture's Advisory Staff in Fermanagh. The course catered for up to 36 students each year.

The students also received practical instruction in a field dedicated for the purpose on the Tempo Road. Mr Moreland Ingram BAgr, who later became Principal of Strabane Agricultural School, was the first Agricultural Adviser to teach the class. In 1954, two students from the course received awards to attend Newton Rigg Agricultural College in Cumbria for a one-month course. The successful students were Graham Flack from Ederney and Robert Henderson from Trillick. When Mr Milby Gregg BAgr was the Agricultural Adviser involved in teaching the class a reporter from the Fermanagh Herald produced a press article on the course. The press article read as follows: *It was men like Cahir Healy, MP, and Patrick Reihill of Irvinestown Rural District Council who agitated at Local Government level and the former also at Parliamentary level, for years, for an agricultural bias in technical education in a county like Fermanagh.* The report continued: *It was the first Technical School Agricultural Class in the Six Counties at Enniskillen where dynamic Principal, Mr David Hanna, was the right man in which to put such an extremely important experiment.*

Mr David Hanna (Courtesy of Mrs Hanna).

Students who attended the agricultural class at Enniskillen Technical School in 1959 (Courtesy of Mr B. McGirr).

Students from the agricultural class at Enniskillen Technical School on a farm visit to Mr Bobbie Thornton, Derryhowlaght, Florencecourt.

Mr Sam McEwen instructing students on tractor operation at the field on the Tempo Road.

The reporter was given an informative guided tour of the plots where the students were working in the two and a half acre field on the Tempo Road. He wrote: *One acre was devoted to grazing and the remainder to tillage. All classes of vegetables and an amazing variety of potatoes, as well as oats, rye, wheat, and barley are grown. Half a dozen grazing plots are differently treated with fertilisers and lime and the results noted and the effects on the four or five cattle that graze there are also noted. An amazing improvement has taken place in young animals only a few months on these luscious grasses. An electrified fence is used to confine the animals to the area chosen for a particular week. A tractor is demonstrated and worked as part of the programme. Pupils take home young suckers, feed them; care for them as instructed and keep details for lengthy reports on progress.* In 1967, a Pig Project Scheme was in operation whereby interested students kept a School owned pedigree Large White sow at their own home farm and after fulfilling certain conditions they became the proud owners of the sows.

Mr Eric Boyce with Gerald Maguire of Bellanaleck ear marking pigs under the Pig Project Scheme.

Mr Francis Walsh, who like Mr Gregg and the other Agricultural Advisers who taught the course had a Bachelor of Agriculture degree, taught rural science in the Technical College and was involved in teaching the course which by 1967 had trained 300 students. The agricultural training classes at the Enniskillen Technical School continued until the courses at the new Enniskillen Agricultural College had been well established. During this time, the Agricultural Advisers who succeeded Mr Milby Gregg were: Mr William (Bill) C. Martin, Mr Robin C. Stevenson, Mr Robin Jamison, Mr Sam McEwen, Mr David Todd, Mr Robert Hamilton and Mr Eric Boyce, who subsequently joined the staff at Enniskillen Agricultural College.

Increased emphasis on Agricultural Education

In January 1957, Mr W. T. McClintock, Fermanagh's County Agricultural Executive Officer, addressed the Enniskillen Rotary Club. He stressed that farming was now a scientific business that benefited from research work. He said education, through demonstration work and lectures, was a major part of the County Agricultural Advisory Service's work. Preparation of young people for attendance at an agricultural college was also an important duty. The Ministry of Agriculture was now giving increasing attention to the value of agricultural education.

Mr Tom Moore, Deputy Chief Inspector of the Ministry of Agriculture, at the Fermanagh County Committee of Agriculture in September 1958, announced that the number of places at Greenmount Agricultural College was to be increased from 45 to 60. The Chairman, Captain Brooke, welcomed the news and said *"I think it is terribly important that we have enough places in those colleges"* and went on *"If our younger generations do not get first class facilities for education in agriculture, they are going to take up something else where they can get a first class education. The future of the County depends on the agricultural industry."*

In the 1960s, the Ministry of Agriculture intensified its efforts in agricultural education. Mr W. T. McClintock

addressed the County Committee of Agriculture members on a visit to Loughry College in June 1960. His address was as follows: *"Within the past quarter century a revolution in farm practice has taken place. The demands for increased food in the war years introduced mechanisation and today the tractor and an array of machinery is to be found on practically every farm. Rural electrification has been making headway even where capital charges are high and almost prohibitive in the more remote areas. Fertiliser use is a recognised annual practice on every farm. Diseases, pests and weeds are now under control; today a sprayer in an hour can wipe out an acre of rushes and weeds and leave a clean pasture. Eradication of bovine tuberculosis is at last a fait accompli, and other diseases as time and manpower become available will be dealt with in the same way. On the scientific field, rapid continuous advances are being made with research workers delving into problems, which affect everyday farm practice. The question is how to keep abreast of such progress. A farmer today simply must keep in touch with current events and developments. He gets his information from the Advisory Service, Agricultural Institutes, books, periodicals and broadcasts. The field covered is very wide indeed, but it is imperative to keep up with the times, otherwise he must fall by the wayside. With changing technique and economy, the farmer has a difficult task indeed in keeping up-to-date: to succeed he must be highly trained and keep fully informed in this scientific and multi-branched industry.*

It will be evident, therefore, that agricultural education has assumed an immensely important role and we who are responsible for it, have a considerable task. Indeed, we are not always free of blame for not being able to get the information, for with the volume of work spent on the various schemes and inadequacy of qualified technical staff, sufficient time and attention cannot always be allocated. Our work on education is two-fold in its approach:-

Firstly – The general approach to all farmers takes the form of requested farm advisory visits, lectures, farm walks and demonstrations and circulation of relevant literature. These are used to reach the maximum number in the shortest possible time. Also many of the various schemes lend themselves to helpful discussion and advice. Secondly – The direct and more important approach through our Winter Agricultural Classes, Technical Agricultural Classes, courses at the Agricultural Schools and Queen's University, Belfast.

There are two Winter Agricultural Classes held each year; also first and second year classes at the Technical School. Altogether seventy students were in attendance in the past year. Boys often proceed from these classes to Strabane Agricultural School and Greenmount Agricultural College. There are four short terms at Strabane, two for boys and two for girls. These are becoming increasingly popular; last term there were 28 boys attending the Strabane course, seven of them from this County. Greenmount can take between 40 and 50 students for the year course: developments are taking place with the object of an 80-student body. Each year three or four boys from this county attend.

The course at Loughry College provides a sound general course in poultry-keeping and dairying for girls: also there is the three-year Diploma course. The College has 35 to 40 students per year, but is also in process of development and expansion. Advanced studies can be made through the Faculty of Agriculture at Queen's University, wherein the past year there were 26 first year students, 15 second, 10 third and 13 fourth year students. Those successful in completing the course are awarded the degree of Bachelor of Agriculture.

This is but a brief outline of what is taking place. The need for further education is realised by the County Committees, the Ulster Farmers' Union, the Young Farmers' Clubs movement, and every facility and encouragement is being given today by all these bodies, which is greatly appreciated by the Ministry of Agriculture, whose primary concern ever must be agricultural education."

Fermanagh's case for an agricultural college

When giving evidence at the Babington Committee in 1943, Mr W. T. McClintock stated that there were no facilities for practical agricultural instruction and that there was a case for a county farm and institute in Fermanagh. In 1961, the Minister of Agriculture, Mr H. W. West, stated that the Government planned to build four new agricultural colleges in order to cater for the 600 new entrants to the industry who required education. The Fermanagh County Committee of Agriculture, which had been asking for a college from 1958, was concerned that Fermanagh was going to miss out on this development. *The Impartial Reporter's* account of the meeting at which the topic was discussed was headed *'Fermanagh Ignored?'* The opening paragraph of the press report was as follows: *Is every county in Northern Ireland to have an agricultural college except Fermanagh, which needs one most? It was stated that Armagh had just been given one and that the Ministry was contemplating one in County Derry and that Tyrone already had two and that Antrim and Down had one each.* The press report indicated that the issue should be pursued by the Fermanagh County Committee of Agriculture and the County Branch of the Ulster Farmers' Union. It stated: *they will get nothing by speech-making and must hammer on the door of the Ministry of Agriculture to find out the reason for the opposition to Fermanagh and see that it is overcome.* It was pointed out that a considerable number of young men take up farming in Fermanagh each year and that they do not go to any of the existing agricultural colleges for two reasons: (1) The distance from home; and (2) because they are not taught how to deal with conditions in Fermanagh where the heavy clay land is a problem that requires special treatment. It was claimed that farming in Fermanagh was completely different from the other five counties and the county should have some sort of a school of agriculture. The report continued: *Fermanagh deserves it, as it has pioneered the way in agricultural classes in technical schools, and it should insist upon getting it. It must be marked out for special treatment.*

Farmers' Union support

On the 4th May 1962, Miss Mary C. Wilson, County Secretary of the County Committee of the Ulster Farmers' Union, wrote to Mr W. T. McClintock, Secretary of the Fermanagh County Committee of Agriculture. She informed him that her Committee had passed the following resolution at their meeting on 1st May: *The members of the County Committee of the Ulster Farmers' Union consider that an agricultural college should be established in Co. Fermanagh under the new development scheme.* The letter also stated that if the resolution was accepted by the County Committee of Agriculture it was suggested that a joint deputation of the two committees should ask to be received by the Minister of Agriculture. Mr McClintock responded on 27th June 1962 indicating that the resolution was adopted by his committee and that Mr George A. Cathcart JP, and Mr William Swan JP, had been appointed to a joint deputation to meet the Minister. A sub-committee of the County Committee was also appointed to progress the case for an agricultural college in County Fermanagh. Mr William Swan when referring to meetings of the sub-committee in January 1964 stated: *"The time was ripe for an institute in County Fermanagh, on a smaller scale than the colleges in existence – it very soon would be imperative for all boys becoming farmers to have training at an agricultural centre – in Fermanagh rather than one outside the county."*

Success

Pressure continued to have a college built in Fermanagh and in 1965 success was achieved. The Minister of Agriculture, Mr H. W. West, on a visit to the Fermanagh County Committee of Agriculture at its March meeting in 1965, announced that Fermanagh was to have its own agricultural college in the near future and that efforts were being made to acquire land for the purpose.

The Chairman of the County Committee, Captain John W. Brooke, in welcoming the news paid tribute to the Minister. He said: *"It was one of the great credits to Fermanagh not only to produce lots of Ministers of Agriculture, but really first-class Ministers. We are terribly proud of the way you are representing us".* Mr William Swan in welcoming the news about the college said: *"This is a great step forward and the Minister must be commended on accepting and looking at our requests. I think the Ministry is absolutely right. For years I have felt there is absolutely no hope for farmers staying on farms without a trained background."*

The Minister that day also announced that his Ministry was to establish a veterinary research laboratory in the Omagh area. At the meeting, tributes were paid by Mr Tom Moore, Deputy Chief Agricultural Officer, to Enniskillen Technical School for its very successful agricultural course. He congratulated the Principal, Mr David Hanna, on building up the course. He said Fermanagh was better provided for in this respect than any other county.

The County Committee of Agriculture and the County Branch of the Ulster Farmers' Union were far-sighted in getting the first of the planned new colleges. Land had been purchased in Counties Armagh and Londonderry as sites for new colleges, they were never built. The facilities at Greenmount, Loughry and Enniskillen proved adequate to cope with the demand for places. As an increased number of places became available at agricultural colleges Winter Agricultural Classes were phased out.

References:

Files of *The Impartial Reporter* and *Fermanagh Herald* held in Enniskillen Library.

Minstry/Department of Agriculture's *Monthly reports* and *Agriculture in Northern Ireland.*

Records of the County Fermanagh Agricultural Executive Office.

Last Will and Testament of Anne Hall, Public Record Office of Ireland (1841).

The Rt Hon H. W. West MP PC (Courtesy of Department of Agriculture and Rural Development).

Mr William Swan JP (Courtesy of Mr B. Swan).

Chapter 17
Enniskillen Agricultural College

In April 1965, Mr Harry West, the Minister of Agriculture, announced in the Stormont Parliament that two adjacent farms near Enniskillen had been purchased by his Ministry for the purpose of establishing an agricultural college. The farms were the 150 acre holding of Mr Richey Wilson at Conerick and the adjoining 90 acre farm of Mr Daniel Brady at Levaghy. Mr West was pressed in the Commons by Mr Cahir Healy MP and Mr Eddie McAteer MP to inform the House regarding the price paid for the farms. The Minister refused to give the information at that time, as the legal formalities had not been completed. The Press report stated that it was understood that the farms had cost in the region of £44,000.

By October 1966, work was underway with the new Enniskillen Agricultural College at Levaghy, Enniskillen. It was the intention that the first 30 students would be enrolled in September 1967 for a one-year course in agriculture. As well as starting work on the hostel, developments had also commenced on the 200-acre College farm. Mr Robert Houston BAgr, the Principal of the new College, and previously Deputy County Agricultural Executive Officer in Fermanagh, told a visiting reporter that: *"The main object of Enniskillen Agricultural College will be to train young men going back into farming."* He also said that the emphasis would be on grassland farming, and the most profitable way of converting grass into milk, beef and lamb. In addition, the College would provide comprehensive training in all aspects of farming. A limited area would be cultivated for demonstration purposes. It was pointed out that while the College facilities had been planned initially for a class of 30 students it was designed in such a way that enlargement to cater for double the number could be made should the necessity arise in the future. Each student would have his/her own study bedroom.

Mr West, when addressing farmers at an 'Open Day' at the Grassland Experimental Husbandry Farm at Castle Archdale in April 1967, referred to progress with the

Enniskillen Agricultural College hostel and farm buildings under construction.

College and said that the buildings were now at an advanced stage of construction. Although work was a little behind schedule, due to the exceptionally wet winter, it was hoped that the College would be completed and ready for opening in the autumn.

On the College farm the plans were to have a herd of 40 dairy cows and their followers, 40 beef-type cows, 30 to 40 beef cattle, a flock of 30 to 40 ewes and 1,000 laying hens.

College Open

Twenty-nine students enrolled at the College in September 1967, twenty-eight sat the final examination and of these 26 were awarded certificates. Seventeen of the students came from County Fermanagh, seven from Tyrone, three from County Down and two from County Londonderry. The top student in the final examinations was Richard Kenneth George Latimer, Gortgorgan, Knockaraven, Enniskillen.

The new Minister of Agriculture, the Rt Hon Major James Chichester-Clark MP, visited Enniskillen Agricultural College in March 1968 during its first year of operation to address the Fermanagh County Committee of Agriculture. The Minister emphasised the value of education and praised the new College. He encouraged Committee members to impress the importance of getting farmers' sons to attend an agricultural college and to take advantage of the various schemes and courses. The Minister went on to say: *"I am sure you all know my Ministry considers agricultural education to be one of its most important functions and since it is clear that the future prosperity of the industry is going to depend not only on industrious hard-working farmers, but also well-trained farmers, we are convinced that every young farmer and farm worker of the future will require at least a one-year course of training. This is the target we have in view in our plans, but of course providing the necessary facilities will not by itself achieve this end. It is essential for everyone in the industry to make sure that the facilities are fully utilised".* Referring to the geographic spread of this year's students, he said: *"I am convinced that this inter-mixing of young men from various counties is itself an important part of their education and we intend to encourage this."* The Minister said that the College had been planned when Mr West was Minister and he was very pleased to see the former Minister present.

The Minister then went on to pay tribute to the architects and builders and to the College staff. He congratulated the Principal, Mr Houston, and his staff for the fine work they did in getting the farm units established and the course started.

Official Opening

The Marquis of Hamilton, MP, deputising for Viscount Brookeborough, officially opened the Enniskillen Agricultural College on Friday 5th July 1968. The Marquis, referring to the absence of Lord Brookeborough,

The official opening. From left: Mr A. E. W. Steen, Ministry of Agriculture, The Architect, The Rt Hon Major James Chichester-Clark, Minister of Agriculture, The Marquis of Hamilton MP, Mrs Evelyn Houston, Mrs Chichester-Clark, Mr Robert Houston, Principal (Courtesy of Mrs R. Houston).

Students and staff in 1973
Front row from left: Mr McCullagh, Mrs Eadie, Mr Hyland, Mr Kennedy, Mr Houston, Miss Fahy, Mr McIlmoyle, Mr Scott, Miss Irvine.
Second row: Miss Irwin, J. P. Brannigan, G. L. Campbell, J. P. Kelly, W. F. Deering, M. J. McCartan, P. J. Kelly, J. W. Surphlis, J. G. Foster, C. B. McDonald, Mr Walker.
Third row: C. Loane, K. W. J. Douglas, M. McCann, R. S. Armstrong, R. A. McKelvey, D. S. Sayers, W. R. M. Breen, R. E. K. McMinn, T. G. Wilson.
Back row: E. J. Latimer, C. V. Tubman, K. Watson, A. Ferguson, R. A. Funston, P. J. Graham, J. W. K. Miller, T. J. Aiken. (Courtesy of Mrs R. Houston).

due to illness, said that no one had done more for Northern Ireland Agriculture as both Minister of Agriculture and Prime Minister for 20 years and it would have been fitting that he could have opened the College, which was in his own constituency.

Ministry's Policy on Agricultural Education

The Rt Hon Phelim O'Neill MP PC, Minister of Agriculture, when referring to the closure of Strabane Agricultural School in a speech at Stormont, in January 1971, said it did not affect the Ministry's policy of providing places for all those seeking agricultural education. He said that over the last ten years the number of places in the agricultural colleges had more than trebled and this year would comprise 370 – a greater number than ever before. He said that this year there would be 200 places at Loughry Agricultural College, 140 at Greenmount and 30 at Enniskillen. The Ministry in the meantime had produced a film entitled *'Investment in Time'*, which promoted the benefits of agricultural education and life at an agricultural college.

At the Loughry College Prize Day in June 1971 Mr West, again Minister of Agriculture, in his address said that he considered the research, advisory and educational work of the Ministry to be the foundation on which farming progress was built. He pointed out that during the past ten years the changes in farming in Ulster had been *"quite revolutionary"*. Farms were becoming larger and much more specialised than was the case in pre-war days. Farming required a knowledge of modern business methods as well as knowledge of how to look after livestock and grow crops. Mr West said he was convinced that the farmer who intended to remain in farming and make a decent income must now prepare himself by getting a good basic education in the scientific and business aspects of modern farming. Mr West said that there was an old saying *'a person in business today using yesterday's methods should not expect to remain in business to-morrow'*. Attendance at an agricultural college would help the young farmer of the future to appreciate the need for as well as understand the methods of modern technology. It would also encourage him to alter his system of farming accordingly. Mr West said that his Ministry was prepared to increase still further the facilities for agricultural education should the demand increase.

The Minister in concluding his address stated: *"At present farmers are thinking a lot about what difference it will make to them in the likelihood of entry to the European Economic Community. I feel the main difference will be the rate at which our industry will have to adapt itself to change is likely to be accelerated and thus the need for a future farmer to be properly equipped with a college education will be all the more urgent."*

Mr West speaking at Enniskillen Agricultural College Prize Day in July 1971 stressed the need for every young man who intended to go into the farming industry to take at least a one-year course at an agricultural college. He also said: *"I have no doubt that the need for agricultural education is going to be far greater under EEC conditions than at present."* Mr West felt it was a tragedy to see the Ministry of Agriculture having to advertise for students for a college such as they had in Fermanagh. He said agriculture was the basic industry in Northern Ireland, and the economy of the country depended largely on the progress of this industry.

Mr West went on to tell the students that they were going out to face a challenge. At no time in the life of the farming industry was the challenge that they would have to face be as serious as at present. Entry to the EEC presented a great challenge. This would not be easy but he felt that those boys and girls who had been trained and specially prepared would be able to face the competition best. Those who were not equipped for the job ran the risk of being left behind.

Mr West said it was difficult to say precisely how entry to the Common Market would affect their agricultural industry but there were three factors to be considered. The first was that the Northern Ireland farmer would face greater competition on the English market; secondly, food costs were likely to be much higher and thirdly cattle were likely to be dearer than at present. He said that the surest way farmers could prepare themselves was to seek out and get all the knowledge they could obtain concerning the agricultural industry.

Mr West paid tribute to the Fermanagh County Committee of Agriculture and Mr W. T. McClintock, the County Agricultural Executive Officer, for proclaiming the need for an agricultural college in Fermanagh. Mr West said that the College provided a focal point for the agricultural industry in the county.

Progress at the College

Mr Robert Houston, Principal of the College, writing in *Agriculture in Northern Ireland* in 1972, updated progress in development of the College. He stated that the dairy herd had been increased to 50 cows with 30 followers. The beef enterprise consisted largely of 50 Aberdeen Angus cross Shorthorn cows. Hereford and Aberdeen Angus were

Students and staff in 1984

Front row (left to right): Mr McBride, Miss Mitchell, Mr Haydock, Mr Fulton (Principal), Mr O'Neill, Mr Fay, Mr Carson, Mr Knox.

Second row: F. G. Carraher, K. Winters, E. M. Quinn, P. A. McKenna, W. T. Nethery, A. G. Hemphill, M. C. West, R. F. Kee, P. A. Kelly, D. J. G. Hume, M. J. Hurst.

Third row: G. McAvoy, D. R. Ellison, E. T. O'Malley, C. Keys, J. H. Burton, A. G. McLoughlin, A. R. Burleigh, J. T. Scott, P. E. Maguire, P. B. McGovern.

Fourth row: E. A. Scott, G. R. Monteith, G. A. Russell, W. Sayers, R. J. K. Smyth, R. F. Cummings, M. F. Bellew, S. H. Flack, D. Stewart, T. A. Maguire,

Fifth row: C. R. Brown, J. Harris, K. G. Ferguson, W. R. Gilmour, C. M. Beatty, D. J. Hall, D. J. Taggart, W. A. Keatley, R, J. Barnhill, A. A. J Hemphill.

also being used for crossing with the Friesians. Hereford, Charolais and Simmental bulls were used on the suckler cows to illustrate breed differences to students. Two groups of suckled calves were retained from the suckler herd for fattening. One group was finished during the winter with the other group being finished from grass the following summer.

A sheep flock consisting of 36 crossbred ewes were mated with a Suffolk ram for early fat lamb production. The progeny of 40 sows, Landrace and Large White, was reared and fattened to bacon weight. There was also a poultry enterprise, which gave experience of egg production, pullet rearing and broiler production.

Mr Houston emphasised the importance of profitability of the farm enterprises. A Gross Margin of £120 per cow was obtained from the dairy enterprise with an average yield of 1,000 gallons per cow. The suckler cows left a Gross Margin of £60 per cow and the beef-fattening unit left a Gross Margin of £20 per head. The ewe flock had a lambing percentage of 175 and a Gross Margin per ewe of £10. The sow herd produced over 20 weaned pigs per sow and the Gross Margin per fat pig was £7.17. Gross Margins in the poultry enterprise were 46p per hen, 21p per pullet and 3.9p per broiler.

Mr Robert Houston, First Principal and later Deputy Chief Agricultural Officer of the Department of Agriculture.

Castle Archdale becomes part of College

Mr Robert Fulton, MAgr, MS(Agr), UDP, NDP, MIBiol, who had been appointed Principal of the College in 1977, in succession to Mr Robert Houston who had been promoted to the post of Deputy Chief Inspector of the Ministry of Agriculture, gave an update on progress at Enniskillen in 1981. He stated that the College now had residential accommodation for 36 students and that in 1971 the Grassland Experimental Farm at Castle Archdale had become an integral part of the College estate.

Mr Robert Fulton.

The College was run as two departments – the College Department and the Experimental Husbandry Department at Castle Archdale. The College had three main functions: education and training; research and development; and demonstration and advisory. The main function of the College Department was education and training with the main emphasis on the Certificate Course in Agriculture. Thirty-six students, who came mainly from Fermanagh and West Tyrone, attended the one-year course, which was considered to be the basic requirement for the future farmer or employee. The course covered general agriculture with the emphasis on animal production with theory and practice receiving equal attention. In addition, the College co-operated with Fermanagh College of Further Education in providing the Foundation Course in Agricultural Industries and with Loughry Agricultural College in the provision of staff and facilities for training courses in stock and farm skills.

The College farm comprised 90 hectares of farming land with a further 15 hectares at Riversdale making up the College estate. The farm was an integral and important part of the teaching department of the College and was run on commercial lines with the physical and financial data obtained being used in the course and at demonstrations. There were separate farmlets and farmyards for the dairy, beef/sheep and pig enterprises with a small arable/grass farmlet at Riversdale. The dairy unit comprised 55 Friesian cows plus replacements with plans to increase cow numbers to 65. The beef unit had 50 suckler cows plus replacements, with suckled calves and 20 home reared bull calves being fattened on the farm. The sheep flock consisted of 60 crossbred ewes, housed intensively before lambing, with all lambs grass finished. The pig unit had 60 sows, some pure bred, but mostly crossbred, with all progeny finished.

The Grassland Experimental Husbandry Farm at Castle Archdale remained an integral and important part of Enniskillen Agricultural College until a decision by the Department of Agriculture and Rural Development to disengage from Research and Development work at the Centre led to its closure in February 1995.

Course development

In addition to the full-time residential College Certificate Course, which was the main provision since the College opened, a part-time College Certificate in Agriculture course had been established by 1984. Emphasis at College was on *training people to do the job*. Fifty per cent of the marks awarded were for practical assessment. Mr Donagh G. O'Neill, previous Director of the Castle Archdale Experimental Husbandry Farm and Mr Robert Fulton's successor as Principal, revealed in his 1984/85 Prize Day speech that three-quarters of the students were returning to the home farm but only half regarded the home farm as being capable of providing full-time employment.

Twenty-eight of the students were entered for the National Certificate in Agriculture and 18 per cent of these obtained distinctions with a further 32 per cent obtaining credits in the examinations. These were the best results of all the competing colleges in the United Kingdom. The Youth Training Programme, now in its second year, was also another important College course based on partnerships. The College was the lead partner with the other partners being farmers, the Job Centres and the Further Education College in Enniskillen.

In September 1986 there were 44 students enrolled, the largest number since the College was established. In that year, half the students came from Fermanagh and the other half, apart from one, came from West Tyrone.

Agricultural Training Schemes

The importance of training for those involved in the agricultural industry had been recognised for many years. A post-war short-term Training Scheme for farm workers had been introduced in 1946. Under this Scheme, a farmer

Mr Donagh O'Neill.

Livestock skills were an important aspect of all College courses. Mr David Boyd instructs Edward McGirr on an aspect of sheep husbandry.

could obtain a trainee for thirteen weeks at a cost of ten shillings per week. The trainees received an allowance from the Ministry of Labour and National Insurance.

The Ministry of Agriculture introduced the next Training Scheme in March 1971 to help meet the needs for a properly trained labour force on Northern Ireland farms. A number of short practical training courses (8 to 10 weeks) on pig rearing and fattening, milk production, beef production, poultry rearing, egg production and certain aspects of crop production and horticulture were provided. The aim of the courses was to provide sufficient training and practice to enable each employee to work efficiently with a minimum of supervision

The Minister, Mr West, visited Loughry Agricultural College in January 1972 to see the Training Courses in operation. The Minister addressed visitors, including leaders of the industry and journalists, and stated that it was now essential to have highly educated management and skilled labour. He said this would be even more important when the United Kingdom joined the Common Market and would have to face greater competition. It was the basic policy of the EEC that the needs of the community should be produced wherever this could be done most cheaply. *"This will mean,"* said Mr West, *"that food will tend to be produced in those areas with natural advantages such as soil, climate and farm structure. However, the greatest natural resource is the human resource."*

He said that the Agricultural Training Scheme was very much a joint effort between farmers and the Ministry and if it were not for the tremendous co-operation that they had been able to obtain from the farming community, the Ministry simply could not continue with the Agricultural Training Scheme.

Practical skills, such as ploughing, were popular with students.

Proceeding to differentiate between education and training, the Minister said that in the educational courses provided by the Ministry, the emphasis was placed on instruction in basic principles of the science and practice of modern farming. The courses were designed to equip students to understand and cope with future development.

Responsibility for the training courses rested with Loughry Agricultural College initially but was transferred to Enniskillen Agricultural College for trainees within its catchment area during the 1986/87 academic year. Over the years a very wide range of training opportunities was provided at Enniskillen. The courses ranged from very practical skills such as welding and use of chain saws right through to management courses using computer skills in business management and farm diversification.

Boost to student numbers

The number of students undertaking education and training courses at Enniskillen College in 1987/88 had reached 85 with 48 of these being on the residential one-year course. In addition, 390 farmers and farm workers had been trained on 34 courses. The enrolment in 1988 recorded the highest number of Fermanagh students on the College residential course and accounted for 28 out of 48 students. Training received a boost in 1988 with 443 trainees on 43 courses. During the 1988/89 year, five of the students were girls. Mary West had been the first girl to attend the College back in 1983.

Mr Gerry Burns MBE, Chief Executive of Fermanagh District Council, guest speaker at the 1988 Prize Day, presenting the cups won by the top NCA student, Miss Jolene McGovern.

National Vocational Qualifications in Agriculture (levels 1 to 6) had been introduced in 1989 with the Enniskillen students obtaining results which were amongst the very best in the United Kingdom.

The introduction of a part-time College Diploma Course in Agriculture, also in 1989, marked the beginning of higher level agricultural courses at the College. The Diploma introduced much more farm management than

Miss Ann Mallon.

was involved in the College Certificate course. General farm management was dealt with in the mornings with advanced beef or dairy management in the afternoons. Twenty-three students enrolled on the Diploma course in October 1989, which involved attendance on one day per week at the College.

Student numbers increased significantly during the 1990s. In the 1994/95 year, the total enrolment was 163, which at that time was a record for the College. However, this was substantially exceeded the following year with 283 students on the rolls and in the 1998/99 year with 300 students. Miss Ann Mallon BSc, replaced Mr Roy McClenaghan, BAgr, Dip Agr Comm, as Principal in September 1993 following his appointment as Principal of Greenmount Agricultural College. At Prize Day in the following June, Miss Mallon reported a significant increase of 18 per cent in the numbers undertaking training at the College. In reinforcing the contribution of the College to the development of those people who attended the education and training courses, she said: *"The future development of the agri-food industry in Northern Ireland requires competitive, forward looking, market-led production and processing businesses managed by well informed and competent people."*

The year 1995/96 was the record for College Certificate course students when 66 enrolled in September. Twenty-five students were on the second year of the College Diploma course. At this time, the College Diploma course was being replaced by the National Vocational Qualification Level 3 in animal production. In its first year 75 students were enrolled.

In his 1998 Prize Day report Professor Long reported that 300 students were enrolled on a range of agriculture and equine courses which were delivered on a full and part-time basis. He said that the education and training courses provided at the College reflected a strong focus on the requirements of the agriculture and equine industries to enable students and trainees to pursue successful careers in the agri-food industry. In relation to the agricultural courses

The planting of a tree to mark the service of former Principals took place in December 1989. Mr Robert Houston, the first Principal, is filling in the soil and is watched by Mr Robert Fulton (behind Mr Houston). Mr Donagh O'Neill, the third Principal is holding the tree and the Principal at that time, Mr Roy McClenaghan (with blazer), is in the centre. Other members of staff present were from left: Messrs Mark Carson, Jim Freeburn, John Sands, Alex Gordon, Michael Graham, Martin McKendry, Seamus McAlinney, John Fay, Gerard Nicholl, Gavin Duffy, Ken Ogle, James Kerr (Countryside Management), George Bleakley, Norman Chittick. Front row beside Mr McClenaghan from left: Mrs Margaret Porter, Mrs Noreen Acheson, Mrs Mary Connolly and Martin Mohan. Mr Eddie Bleakley is standing between Messrs O'Neill and McClenaghan.

two-thirds of students were enrolled on the National Certificate in Agriculture (NCA) and National Vocational Qualifications courses at levels 2 and 3. A Higher National Certificate (HNC) in Agriculture, on a modular basis, had been introduced during the year. Its purpose was to develop production, management and marketing skills required in the agricultural industry.

Silver Jubilee

Mr Harry West, former Minister of Agriculture, was the guest speaker at Prize Day in 1993 to celebrate the College's 25 years of service to the agricultural industry in the west of the Province. It was very appropriate that Mr West should have been the special guest at this celebration as he, when he was Minister, was instrumental in having the College built in Fermanagh. A small copse of 25 trees representing 25 years of student education was planted by a student from each of the 25 years.

The Principal at the Prize Day, Mr Roy McClenaghan, informed those present that during the 25 years 944 students had completed the College Certificate courses. The anniversary also marked the beginning of a three-stage major refurbishment programme for the hostel. This was completed in October 1996 and officially opened by Mr John Murray CB, Permanent Secretary of the Department of Agriculture. The Principal in referring to the future strategy said that farming was at a crossroads, and that if the next generation of farmers was to survive they must regard *the consumer as king* producing what the consumer wants, when the consumer wants it and in the manner the consumer wants it. He then detailed how the College would meet the new demands through education and the development of the farm enterprises. The Silver Jubilee celebrations also coincided with the introduction, in partnership with Fermanagh College, of the first equine course at the College. The Principal stated: *"When you are situated in the middle of a rural environment, with a lot of potential for tourism and leisure activities, and there is a demand for education and training from the equestrian industry it seemed appropriate that the College should utilise some of its resources to help meet this need."* From this small beginning equine courses would develop to become the major educational provision at the College.

Facilities Development

Mr Sam Morrow, who succeeded Miss Mallon as Principal in January 1995, reported on progress with development of the facilities at the College at Prize Day in June 1996. The third and final phase of renovation of the hostel building, the first having been started in January 1993, was underway. The renovation programme involved the student bedrooms, dining room and kitchen, library and computer rooms together with recreational facilities. Other improvements involved the assembly hall, lecture theatres, laboratory and cloakroom facilities. During the year an additional 32 hectares of land convenient to the College had been purchased. This acquisition, together with the farm building developments and other new facilities, enabled greater opportunities to demonstrate farming and equine systems and for student practical work.

Industry advice

Advice from the industry in relation to the provision of appropriate education and training courses was always important to the College. An arrangement for the provision of this advice was formalised during the 1995/96 year, when a representative Agricultural Education Advisory Committee was formed to serve the needs of the College. A similar body to advise the College on the educational and training needs of the equine industry was formed during the 1997/98 academic year. Both committees were highly supportive of the College's educational programmes. Advice from the Equine Advisory Committee, soon after its formation, led to the introduction of the First Diploma one year course in equine studies. This proved to be a good feeder to higher level courses.

Mr Harry West, former Minister of Agriculture, presented a display board at the 1995 Prize Distribution listing the names of the Principals since the College was established. Along with Mr and Mrs West are former Principals, Mr Donagh O'Neill, Miss Ann Mallon, Mr Roy McClenaghan, Mr Robert Fulton and the Principal at the time, Mr Sam Morrow. Missing on the day was the first Principal, Mr Robert Houston.

The role of education and training in developing the competitiveness of the agriculture and equine industry and in sustaining economic growth was made clear in the Principal's address in June 1998. Professor Long indicated that this role was to develop individuals' competences, which comprised knowledge, skills and experience.

In his 1999 Prize day address, the College Principal, Professor Eric Long BAgr, PhD, referred to the College's year of success in the classroom, on the farm and on the turf. He said there were 274 students enrolled in a wide range of courses in agriculture and in equine studies as well as many part-time on life long learning. Lifelong learning was defined as *the continuous development of the competences that are essential for economic prosperity and social inclusion with the aim of ensuring that the existing workforce is adequately skilled to do the job.* A wide range of business management, computer, livestock production, nutrient management planning and countryside management courses were delivered during the year to meet specific industry needs.

A notable achievement in the 1988/89 year was the award of the Charter Mark in recognition of the excellent customer service provided at the College. Enniskillen was the only 'land based' college in the United Kingdom at that time to achieve this standard of excellence.

Management of change

Mrs Joanna McVey OBE, Chairman of the Northern Ireland Rural Development Council, and Managing Director of *The Impartial Reporter*, was the special guest at the 1999 Prize Day. In her address, she referred to the challenges facing the rural community. She said: *"The challenge is, how do we equip ourselves to manage change and to minimise the threat? How do we address progress which escalates at an ever increasing rate and magnitude? And how do we achieve this whilst retaining the integrity and well-being of our community, so that future generations can continue to live and work where generations before them have lived and worked? How do we, in fact, ensure a viable future for our local agriculture industry?*

Managing change requires a willingness to adapt. To have a breadth of vision, to be strategic and to remain relevant are all prerequisites. So are the ability to build on existing strengths and to identify and seize opportunities, to accept nothing less than the best, to be flexible and ready to co-operate; to be able to respond to the demands of an increasingly competitive market place.

These are the qualities we need if we are to manage and shape our own futures. And an educational approach that embraces of this, and helps people to achieve this end, must lie at the heart of any successful management of change."

Joanna McVey and Professor Long.

Mrs McVey continued: *"I have no doubt that Enniskillen College of Agriculture has established such an approach – and is doing it very well indeed".* She then referred to an earlier visit to the College and said: *"The abiding impression I came away with was a dedicated team of professionals who were not only totally committed to achieving this end, but who were already well on the way to doing so. Their aim is to take an increasing resilient, adaptable and quality-based agri-food industry through into the next millennium."*

Milestone

Prize Day in June 2000 was the occasion when the University of Ulster conferred BSc (Hons) Degrees on the students who had satisfactorily completed the four-year course in Equine Studies at the College. The College Principal, Professor Long, in explaining the background to the new degree course said: *"Last autumn 12 students who had successfully completed the HND Equine Studies programme at Enniskillen College and also at other colleges progressed to the final year of the BSc (Hons) Equine Studies programme following the completion of a summer bridging course. The graduation of the first cohort of Equine Studies Degree students was a milestone for the College."*

Her Majesty's Inspectors' report

Towards the end of Mr Donagh O'Neill's five year term as Principal Her Majesty's Inspectors, in conjunction with the Northern Ireland Department of Education, carried out an inspection of the College in February 1989. This was the first inspection of an agricultural college in Northern Ireland. It was a very detailed inspection which involved examination of the curriculum, courses, talking to the students and finding out the views of the local agricultural community. The outcome of the report was assessed as first-class, which made the College Principal and his team of lecturers, domestic, administrative and farm staff justifiably proud.

Opportunities for experience abroad

Through the generosity of the Vaughan Trust, students from the College have had the opportunity of broadening their experience in study tours outside Ireland. The first of these awards was made in 1975 which enabled the three top students, accompanied by a member of staff, to visit a country within the EEC. In addition, six students received financial support to enable them to visit a main agricultural show in Great Britain. Later, the Vaughan Trustees sponsored an Easter Study tour to Great Britain for all the students and members of staff.

The range of support from the Vaughan Trust for the College increased over the years. For example, students during Mr Donagh O'Neill's term as Principal had the opportunity of visiting the Royal Canadian Dairy Fair and studying milk production methods on leading farms in Canada.

In the early 1990s, the Youth Training Programme students had a study tour in the Irish Republic and all the College Certificate students visited an agricultural college and farms in Wales. Prize-winners in the College examinations gained valuable Vaughan Trust awards to enable them to undertake study visits to Germany, Holland and England.

In 1990 there were 102 full-time and part-time students attending the College. Forty-seven of these students were on the College Certificate course in Agriculture and 20 on the part-time College Diploma course. The opportunities for broadening the experience of agricultural students at the College were developed, again through the generous sponsorship of the Vaughan Trust and the initiatives taken by the Principal, Mr Roy McClenaghan, and his staff. A major initiative was the development of a partnership with Maison Familiale Rurale, a French agricultural college in Limoise, central France. This provided an opportunity for College students to learn more about the marketing and production techniques required to meet the needs of European consumers and to apply these techniques, where appropriate, in the west of the Province. In this exchange, College Diploma students visited the French college and were hosted on French farms. By 1993 over 100 students from the College had been to Limoise. A reciprocal arrangement applied for the French students. The partnership developed further in that the host farmers had the opportunity of study visits to each others' country. The Fermanagh and West Tyrone farmers on their French visit attended the Paris Agricultural Show, the Rungis Market and leading French farms.

Skills enhancement

In the 1990s, College competitions were organised which gave students an opportunity to enhance their practical skills with livestock and machinery. The 'Young Handler of the Year' competition developed skills in showing livestock.

NVQ Level 2 students on a study tour in Perthshire in 1999. They were accompanied by Mr Francis Kelly, Instructor at the College.

Mr Donagh O'Neill, Principal, (back row, centre) with the four top prize winners on the study tour to Canada in November 1987.

Competition among students, such as the 'Young Handlers' event, was encouraged.

The 'Young Driver of the Year' tested students' skills in handling a tractor, a car, a mini-digger and a Land Rover.

Equine industry

There was a very clear demand from the equine industry for education and training in the early 1990s and this was responded to positively by Enniskillen Agricultural College. Subsequent reports on the industry both in Northern Ireland and the Republic of Ireland confirmed this need.

A report commissioned by the Northern Ireland Council for Equestrianism (NICE), compiled by Mr Kenneth G. White, BAgr, Dip Comm, in 1997, indicated a demand for formal equine qualifications. He estimated that there were 29,000 equines, including 11,000 ponies, in Northern Ireland. A survey showed that 72 per cent of breeders indicated that further training would make their businesses more profitable. Farriers, trainers and stallion owners all stated a need for further training in various aspects of horse production and management. Direct employment within the industry in Northern Ireland in 1993 was 3,328. Expenditure in the same year within the sector in the Province was estimated at £32.8 to £37.8 million.

A study published in 1996 by Alison F. Corbally BEd, MEquineSt, University College, Dublin, on the Irish Sport Horse industry (non Thoroughbreds) showed that it was worth £100 million in 1993 and employed 12,000 people. There were 66,100 horses and ponies (including Thoroughbreds) in Ireland. The number of tourists participating in equestrian based activities grew by 35 per cent from 1990 to 1993.

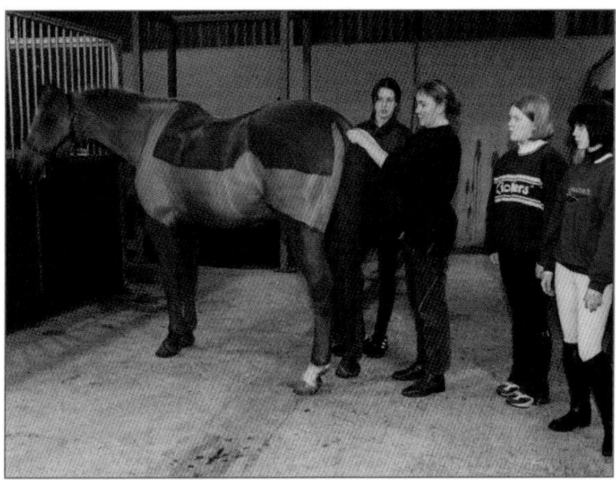

A plaiting demonstration to National Diploma students by Miss Kirstie Hardie. Students from left are: Shelley Annan, Andrea Cleary and Jenny Richardson.

Karen Hennessy and Katherine Quinn, University College, Dublin, produced a report for the Irish Horse Board in 2007 entitled: 'The Future of the Irish Sport Horse Industry'. Their key recommendations highlighted the need for education and training. They stated: *Education is a key factor in developing the future of the industry. Two critical areas are (a) the education and training of professionals, ensuring standards and accreditation within the industry and (b) the education and training of participants including owners, breeders, riders, parents and volunteers. Co-operation across the industry is essential for the provision of comprehensive education and training programmes.*

In his address at the Enniskillen Campus Prize Day in 2009, Dr Dean Harron, guest of honour, stated that the Irish equine industry supports 16,500 jobs in the Thoroughbred Sector alone. He said that there were 10,000 small breeders with 1,000 of these being in Northern Ireland. He revealed that there were 12,000 Thoroughbred foals born in Ireland every year which was more than in England, France and Italy together. There were 12,000 Thoroughbred horses in training representing an investment of £240 million by owners for training fees. Horse racing is a big tourist attraction accounting for 100,000 visitors to Ireland each year. Among the attributes quoted by Dr Harron for success in the industry were: academic and practical abilities, communication skills, computer skills, decision making ability, team work and attention to detail.

Quite clearly an industry of this magnitude needs comprehensive formal education and training provision. This need was recognised at Enniskillen College of Agriculture back in 1993 and the provision has developed steadily from that time.

Students involved in the Racing Unit activities at the College. Mr Kenneth Johnston, Senior Lecturer, is on the left with Marita O'Loughlin, Jackie Kidd, Alison Doyle and David Mathers. Professor Long is on the right. The horses are Finoel, Faylin and The Moderator.

The BTEC National Diploma in Business and finance with Equine Options

The development of a close working partnership with Fermanagh College led to the launch in 1993 of a BTEC National Diploma in Business and Finance with Equine Options. Eight students enrolled on the first year of the two-year course. There were 60 applicants for 18 places for

The hostel and main yard of Enniskillen College of Agriculture, later the Enniskillen Campus of the College of Agriculture, Food and Rural Enterprise (CAFRE).

the course starting in September 1993. The introduction of this course triggered a demand for more advanced and specialised equine courses. The College responded positively to this demand. The first specialised course in equine studies was introduced in September 1994 when 18 students were enrolled on a part-time NVQ in Horse Care.

Ulster Lakeland Equestrian Park, Necarne, Irvinestown.

Higher level equine courses

The early success of and continuing demand for the National Diploma course was followed by the launch of a BTEC HND in Equine Studies which began in September 1995 when 11 students enrolled. This was the first course of its kind in Northern Ireland. As in the case of the National Diploma a partnership was in place through which Fermanagh College taught the finance and business elements of the course. A major attraction for students participating in this course was the use of the facilities at the Ulster Lakeland Equestrian Park, Necarne, Irvinestown, which were available for practical work and also provided hostel accommodation. These facilities were made available to the College through agreement with Fermanagh District Council. This course proved popular with 18 students being enrolled in September 1996 for their first year.

Practical work at the College was facilitated through the development of the equine unit, which during the 1995/96 academic year consisted of six riding horses, two yearlings, two breeding mares and a foal. Excellent stabling and other facilities appropriate to the needs of the equine unit, to complement the 40m by 25m demonstration shed constructed in 1990/91, were provided over the years.

In the following year a part-time NVQ Level 2 in horse care was introduced which met with immediate success when 30 students were enrolled. In the next year NVQ Level 3 and a Higher National Certificate (HNC) in Equine Studies programmes complemented the College's full-time equine course provision.

Honours degree in equine studies

The success of the existing courses led to a demand from students and the industry for university degree courses in the subject. Negotiations with the University of Ulster, and with the support of the Fermanagh University Partnership Board, had a successful outcome when it was announced that a BSc Honours degree course in Equine Studies with Diploma in Industrial Studies (DIS) would commence in the autumn of 1998. Facilities for practical work with horses had been enhanced considerably in the meantime with the College equine unit now consisting of 20 horses – 15 owned by College (6 riding horses, 4 Irish Draught mares, 4 x 2yr olds and one foal) and 5 horses on loan from owners to the College. During the 1997/98 year, the number of horses on loan to the College had increased to 12 and the breeding unit had been enhanced with the gift of a Thoroughbred mare from the Irish Thoroughbred Breeders' Association, Northern Region.

The first cohort of BSc graduates in June 2000. Front row from left: Claire Guyer (University of Ulster), Professor David Eastwood (University of Ulster), Adele Ramsey, Charlotte Banks, Kelly Keogh, Professor Eric Long. Middle row: Fiona Moore, Lisa Thompson, Anita Watson, Back row from left: Jane Morrow, Senior Lecturer; Claire Graham, Karen Clinton, Marita O'Loughlin, Susan Young, Lorraine Latimer.

Wider experience for equine students

The opportunities for practical experience for students in the equine industry were considerably widened in 1997 when a Horse Racing Club was formed. Students in succeeding years would experience considerable success in Point-to-Point races wearing the College colours.

Another major development at that time was the establishment of a partnership with Michigan State University (MSU). This partnership enabled students from the College and the University to undertake courses relating to their studies at each others' campus on a reciprocal basis. This brought tremendous benefits to the students not only in terms of education but also in the cultural experience. During the 1997/98 academic year four students from MSU undertook courses at Enniskillen College.

Opportunities for widening experience also came through industrial placement during the second year of the HND course in Equine Studies when in the 1997/98 year students were placed in Great Britain, New Zealand and the United States of America.

The long-term practical experience opportunities for the College equine students were considerably enhanced when the College leased the facilities at the Ulster Lakeland Equestrian Park at Necarne, Irvinestown, for a period of 25 years commencing 1st April 1998.

During 1997/78, the College expressed its appreciation to the Northern Region of the Irish Thoroughbred Breeders' Association for providing support required to initiate the Flo Milling Scholarship, which aims to provide equine students with the opportunity to experience Thoroughbred breeding in other regions and thereby assist with the development of the locally-based industry. The inaugural scholarship enabled a National Diploma second year student to study Thoroughbred breeding in Kentucky.

Courses for farmers and the wider community

Technical updates for practising farmers were introduced in 1990. These covered production and management aspects of the main farming enterprises to be found in the west of the Province. Over 1,200 training days by way of updates had been carried out during the 1992/93 year. The following year the number of training days

provided had increased to 1,700 involving 1,500 farmers. Courses entitled *'Women in farming'* were an innovation in 1991. Women on the farms have traditionally played an important role in the book keeping associated with the farm business. The introduction of these courses was very timely and coincided with increasing bureaucracy associated with running a farm business.

Throughout the 1990s 'Open Weeks' were a feature of the College's annual activities. During the designated week each year the College was open to the public. Special displays featuring every aspect of farming and other topics of interest to families were provided. These evening events were exceptionally well attended by a wide section of the public.

Enniskillen Agricultural College, later the Enniskillen Campus of CAFRE, hosts the Enniskillen Group of the Riding for the Disabled Association (RDA) each week. Mrs Marie Morrow and Mrs Maeve Hannon, who have been Organisers of the Group, are with the RDA pony 'Punch'.

The Countryside and Farming

Making the wider public aware of how food is produced and engendering an appreciation of the countryside were important aspects of the College's work during the late 1980s and 1990s. A farm and lakeland trail was established in a partnership involving the Castle Archdale Grassland Experimental Centre and the Department of the Environment's Castle Archdale Country Park. This enabled holiday makers visiting the Country Park to see how modern farming was conducted in harmony with the natural environment.

Energy crops

Willow growing for energy production was also a feature of the trail. A combined heat and power unit had been installed at the College to utilise the willows grown at Castle Archdale. The willows were harvested every three years, air-dried and chipped. The gas produced through a gasification process powered an engine coupled to a generator that had the potential to make the College self-sufficient in electricity. The unit at the College was an experimental prototype, which in practice, was unable in the long term to sustain the level of output necessary to supply the College's electricity needs. Nevertheless, it proved a valuable experimental unit and the lessons learned from its operation enabled more sophisticated and functional units to be established elsewhere.

Farm and Lakeland Trail

This trail was established at the College in 1989 to encourage students and school children to be more aware of the countryside. A walk, incorporating a bird hide and tree planted areas, was developed along the edge of Drumgay Lough. Wildlife and the flora of the Lough could be observed on one side and farming activity on the other.

A *First Nature* environmental education programme for 5 to 8 year olds was introduced at the College in 1994. Visitors to the College were always welcome, not only to see agricultural items of interest but also to visit the farm and Lakeland trail. During the 1994/95 year over 7,500 people visited the College during the year.

Farming at the College

The value of practical work for students and the maintenance of high standards of animal and crop husbandry always received high priority at the College. The emphasis by the Principal in the early 1990s on 'learning by doing' and adoption of the mantra 'Do as we do - Not as we say' gave an indication of the high standards at the College and on the importance placed on practical work. Farming under the soil and weather conditions prevailing in County Fermanagh is seldom easy and the College over the years had to face the challenges being experienced by other agricultural producers. For example, Mr O'Neill, the Principal, and his staff, like other farmers in the west of the Province, had to deal with extremely difficult weather conditions during the summers of 1985 and 1986. The summer of 1985 was one of worst summers in living memory and the following summer was little better. The impact of the adverse weather on increased costs of production of a grass-based enterprise is illustrated by the results from the College dairy herd. The Gross Margin was reduced from £27,400 in 1984/85 to £18,900 in 1985/86. Concentrate usage increased from 0.8 tonnes to 1.4 tonnes per cow. The better farming conditions during 1987 enabled the profitability of the College dairy herd, as expressed by Gross Margins, to increase from just under

£20,000 in 1986/87 to almost £35,000 in 1987/88. This resulted from good yields, lower costs and good calf and cull cow prices. The average yield per cow was 5,160 litres with meal feeding at 0.21 kg per litre. The Gross Margin per cow was £588. The profitability of the beef and sheep unit was equally impressive yielding a Gross Margin of £28,000, which was four times the level of 1986/87. The stocking rate for the beef and sheep unit was 2.3 cow equivalents per hectare. The 24-month beef from dairy bred steers produced a Gross Margin of £625 per hectare. The pig herd was also profitable giving a Gross Margin of £14,000.

The College beef unit buildings.

Examples of the efficiency of the College's 60-sow pig herd can be gleaned from physical and financial indicators. In the 1989/90 year, 2.3 litters per sow were being achieved. The beef cattle enterprise was equally impressive at that time with beef animals being sold at 540kg at 15 months of age. However, the College experienced the same problems as other farmers from 1996 in marketing these young bulls because of the Bovine Spongiform Encephalopathy (BSE) crisis. The productivity and efficiency of the dairy herd had been further enhanced at this time with an average yield per cow of 5,400 litres of milk being produced with a meal usage of 900kg. The College suckler cow enterprise now consisted of two herds of 25 cows each – one spring calving and the other calving in summer. The spring calving herd consisted of Aberdeen Angus cross Limousin cows mated with a Charolais bull while the summer calving herd was based on the Limousin herd. Higher outputs from grassland had been achieved through extended grazing techniques.

Development of the sheep enterprise gathered pace in the early 1990s. The College, in partnership with other farmers, took a leading role in developing the Erne Lamb Group in an effort to improve marketing and get better returns from the market. Texel rams were introduced for comparison with Suffolk crosses. Suffolk/Cheviot ewes were compared with the traditional Greyface and later a Charollais ram was crossed with Texel Greyface cross ewes. Dutch Texels were imported in 1992 in an effort to produce leaner and heavier

Leslie Armstrong on left and Gary Hetherington who won a Northern Bank sponsored Farm assessment competition. They are accompanied by Leslie's parents Mr and Mrs James Armstrong from Lisbellaw. Mr McClenaghan, Principal, and Mr Johnston, Senior Lecturer, were present. The awards were presented at Balmoral Show in May 1991.

lamb carcases which were in demand by the trade. It was found possible to keep lambs from this breed to 25kg, which still met the stringent supermarket specification for leanness. Rams from the Dutch Texel flock were used subsequently on commercial farms with considerable success. The College 60-strong pedigree Dutch Texel flock was providing rams for the Greenmount Agricultural College quality lamb production systems in 1997.

Russell Scott with Mr Kevin O'Donnell, Lecturer at the College, in May 2000. Russell won the sheep section of the 'Young Handlers' competition

One of the College's great strengths was its accessibility to the local community. The farm enterprises, over the years, proved to be an excellent training resource which was used to great advantage by the Agricultural Advisory Service.

Future business competitiveness

In his 1999 Prize Day address, the Principal referred to the extremely challenging year faced by the farming community as a result of adverse weather conditions and

other factors. He went on to say that farmers had to look more seriously on the production of quality products in line with market requirements, using farming systems which minimise costs and incorporate positive countryside management, if they were aiming for future profitability and business competitiveness. He then detailed how the College had adapted its management policies with the aim of improving its resources for education and training. The College was developing a low-cost milk production system to make best use of grazed grass. Targets were to achieve 4,125 litres of milk from grass with a production cost of 9 pence per litre. Rotational grazing for beef cattle enabled a batch of steers to achieve a daily liveweight gain of 1.1kg per day. Turning to the equine unit, he said that students had foaled five mares including the first Thoroughbred foal to be born at the College.

'Suckler 2000'

In the autumn of 2000 the College beef unit was the centre for a major initiative by the agricultural industry designed to give Northern Ireland's important suckler beef sector a timely tactical boost by lifting the quality of breeding animals in readiness for a stronger, export led market for finished cattle. The initiative was led by Mr Stanley Lytle of the Department of Agriculture's Agricultural Development Service, Mr Alex Cromie, Senior Lecturer at the College and staff from Greenmount Agricultural College. Other agencies involved were the National Beef Association (NBA), the Livestock and Meat Commission, AI Services and the breed societies. The purpose of this campaign was to address the negative influence of the Holstein breed through better cow breeding and the use of better bulls. The chairman of the NI Branch of the NBA stated at the event: *"Everyone in the beef sector has a firm eye on quickly re-establishing its important export markets and this will be more easily done if more of the cattle that come forward for slaughter are bred from better sires and dams and more of the carcase can be used for high price cuts."* The College's beef enterprise formed the focus for the *'Suckler 2000'* event. The excellent conformation and growth rates of the double-muscled Charolais calves produced by the College's Aberdeen Angus cross Friesian suckler herd showed the potential for producing top class beef animals from dairy bred cows. The progeny of Aberdeen Angus sires crossed with the College's Limousin suckler cows showed how premium market prices and higher profitability could be obtained.

Prince Charles is welcomed to the College by Mr Roy McClenaghan, Chief Agricultural Officer, and Professor Eric Long, Principal of the College.

Visit of HRH the Prince of Wales

The highlight of the year 2000 was in June when HRH Prince Charles visited the College. He combined a visit to the College facilities with an inspection of locally produced food, which was on exhibition in a large marquee at the College. The Prince met local farmers and leaders of the industry as well as locally based food processors. In his address, the Prince said: "*I have been very pleased to see this afternoon some encouraging examples of co-operation between government, industry and the local community working together to enhance the fabric of rural society. I do congratulate you on what you are doing to find new opportunities for niche markets, to promote local products and services, and to develop new skills for people through education and training.*"

The Prince then launched the third year of the Ulster Farmers' Union Food Initiative urging all shoppers to ask for local produce. Mr Douglas Rowe, from Boa Island, President of the Ulster Farmers' Union, commenting on the Food Initiative said: "*It is encouraging the sale of Northern Ireland products not only at home but more of it sold at a better price abroad. As farmers, we deserve a bigger share of the end price. It's unfair that that for the last four years we as primary producers have been at a loss-making situation where the processing industry goes from strength to strength and retailers have been reporting record profits. Some figures would say that farmers get £1 in every £30 of the housewives' budget on food. We need to improve on that.*"

Prince Charles toured the College facilities. He took a particular interest in the equine breeding project initiated in 1998 to provide the HND students with the opportunity to develop equine breeding competence through a 'learning by doing' approach. He was impressed by the students' Racing Club, which had a membership of 40. The College in the year 2000 won the *'Leading Owner'* award after eight wins during the Point-to-Point season.

HRH Prince Charles and Professor Long.

Prince Charles was then shown some of the farm enterprises. He saw the Suffolk Sheep early lamb production system and the muscling traits of lambs, which were the progeny of Dutch Texel sires. He witnessed the quality calves, which would make top class beef produced from Aberdeen Angus cross Friesian cows mated to double-muscle Charolais bulls and from Limousin cows mated with Aberdeen Angus bulls.

Mr Seamus McAlinney, Head of CAFRE's Enniskillen Campus and guest speaker, Mr Joe Hernon, Chairman of European Federation of Thoroughbred Breeders' Associations, congratulate Orla McGlynn, a student on the Honours Degree in Equine Management at the Campus Awards Ceremony on 23rd June 2010.

References:

Ministry/Department of Agriculture *Monthly Reports* and *Agriculture in Northern Ireland.*

Enniskillen Agricultural College Prize Day reports.

Files of *The Impartial Reporter* and *Fermanagh Herald* held in Enniskillen Library.

Records of the Fermanagh County Agricultural Executive Office.

Corbally, Alison F., Report on *The Irish Sport Horse Industry (Non Thoroughbreds). University College, Dublin. (1986).*

Hennessy, Karen and Quinn, Katherine, Report for the Irish Horse Board entitled: *The future of the Irish Sport Horse Industry.* University College, Dublin. (2007).

Chapter 18
Fairs and markets

Farmers, as primary producers of food, have always been vulnerable to exploitation when marketing their produce. The fact that farm units were generally small meant that an individual's ability to influence the market was practically non-existent. Periods of glut at certain times of the year were almost inevitable for seasonal farm produce. In many cases this produce passed through many middlemen before it reached the final consumer. When the cost of processing and the profit margins of the intermediaries were taken into account the farmer generally received a small proportion of the final sale value of the product.

Products like farm produced butter and eggs were normally taken to the local market and there received whatever amount the buyers were prepared to pay. Fat pigs in the early years of the century were normally killed on the farm and the carcases were taken, like butter and eggs, to the local market, where they were subjected to the same sort of price negotiation as applied to the other products. Livestock was sold in fairs, which had centuries of history behind them, before they were replaced by livestock marts.

Tempo Fair Day in 1900 (Courtesy of the Langham family).

Fairs

From the beginning of the century until the 1950s, fair days were held in practically every town and village in Fermanagh. They were held on a stipulated day during the month. Many towns had a fairgreen but in most cases the stock would be herded along the streets. Cattle and sheep were normally walked to the fair while weaned and store pigs were transported using horses and carts. A hessian sheet was used to cover the body of the cart to prevent the pigs from jumping out.

Enniskillen Fair, held on the Fairgreen, with an overflow into Belmore Street and the Gaol Square, was the main market for horses in the county as well as for cattle and other classes of stock.

Fairs were much more than places where livestock alone was bought and sold. Travelling salesmen, who sold everything from second-hand clothing to all sorts of provisions that could possibly be of interest to country people, were regularly present.

Clothing salesman in Tempo Fair in 1900 (Courtesy of the Langham family).

Farmers brought their stock for sale to the fair in anticipation of getting a willing buyer to purchase their animals at a reasonable price. Those intending to sell stock normally attended other fairs to get an impression of prices in advance of bringing their animals to market. Prices were agreed by negotiation and seldom were the animals sold to

the first enquirer. Negotiation usually involved arriving at some sort of middle ground between the asking price and what the prospective buyer was offering. Usually, a third person would be a dealmaker between the seller and buyer. Final agreement would be concluded amid much hand slapping and spitting. When the price had been agreed there was the important matter of a luck penny, which was again subject to negotiation! After a successful transaction, arrangements were made for the safekeeping of the stock for the duration of the fair and then for their onward journey to their new abode.

The September fair in Enniskillen in 1934 witnessed the largest sale of store cattle for many years. The Great Northern Railway transported 1,000 head of cattle from Enniskillen on that day. The number of cattle certified under the Fatstock Scheme at the fair was 500. Because of the large numbers of cattle for certification the Ministry of Agriculture, at the request of the County Committee of Agriculture, granted a second day in the month for this purpose.

The development of the Land Rover, first produced in 1948, provided a big step forward in livestock transport for farmers. In the early 1950s, a farmer who had a Land Rover and a two-cow Rice trailer was regarded as being very well established and progressive.

Dealers

Dealers at fairs were plentiful and up to all the tricks of the trade. They owned cars before most farmers which enabled them to drive out the roads leading to the towns where farmers would be walking their stock to the fair. The dealers would try to buy the stock on the road before they got to the market. They would usually have a story about the poor trade and how obliging they were in relieving the farmer of his livestock. Movement of livestock from the farm to the fair was on foot until tractors and trailers with cattle crates and other forms of transport became more common towards the late 1950s.

Hiring fairs

The principal towns and villages held hiring fairs twice a year in May and November. Farmers who were looking for workers for summer and harvesting work would engage employees at the May fair and those requiring help for winter and spring work would attend the November fair. The farm workers usually lived with the employer's family. They were generally treated as family members during the period of their employment. Workers were hired at an agreed sum for the period of employment.

Mr John Fawcett of Rosculton, Springfield, hired James Griffin at the Derrygonnelly Hiring Fair on 24th May

Irvinestown Fair Day in 1950 (Courtesy of Mrs Breege McCusker).

1931 for six months for £10 10s 0d. As well as payment for the work, the hired man was fed and maintained in the household. Payment was made in instalments. For example, James Griffin received 8d on 10th June, then 3s 0d on 15th June and £2 12s 6d on 29th June. As part of the remuneration James's mother was given 10s 0d on 7th July. Amounts varying from 2s 6d to £1 2s 0d were paid at regular intervals until 21st November, when John received the outstanding balance of 17s 1d and this completed his contract. Payment was not always in cash. Sometimes goods rather than cash would be given. In the case of John Flynn, a previous employee of John Fawcett, he received boots to the value of £1 2s 6d on 19th June 1929 and a packet of Players cigarettes on 12th October worth 6d.

Mr William K. Parke in his book *A Fermanagh Childhood* gave an account of the hiring fair in his native Derrygonnelly. It read as follows: *The hiring fairs were held on the 24th May and the 24th of November. The May fair was the more important for it was then that the men were hired for the summer's work. The men and girls who were offering themselves for hire stood around on the footpath at a particular part of the street. The men fell into different categories. There was the top class man who could work a pair of horses and a mowing machine, and was a good milker, knowledgeable with cattle, an early riser and clean. This type of man demanded the top hiring wage and could afford a certain amount of latitude in choosing his employer. Others fell into lower categories right down to the young boy who had just left school or the man who required constant supervision. These men received a low wage and at times found it difficult to secure hiring, often being forced to emigrate.*

During the 1930s, a top man received around £20 for the summer six months with food and lodging and around £15 for winter. The lower bracket might be £10 or £15. The girls were hired either by so much a month or for the whole six months and their wages fluctuated from £1 10s 0d to £2 per month, together with food and lodgings.

Some farmers, who had the name of serving inferior food or providing bad accommodation, or maybe demanding that a man worked longer hours than usual, found it difficult to hire a good man. There were also farmers who had inferior equipment or lived in a remote area and they also found difficulty in hiring people.

The hired men took a few days holiday at hiring time. They also got 'Holy' days, the Twelfth of July and Sundays off but the milking, foddering and cleaning out was done before they left. They worked a twelve-hour day until about seven thirty in the evening except during the hay saving time when, if the weather was good, they might work until midnight. They worked six days a week, together with the essential work on Sundays and overtime pay was unheard of.

The wages might seem small but profits in farming at that time were small, in fact just at subsistence level. Hundreds of young men and women left our area during this period on the emigrant ships, many never to return – these included boys and girls with whom I played around the village.

Livestock markets

Fairs, which had been such important market places for farmers, were replaced by livestock markets, known locally as marts, from the middle of the twentieth century. The Ulster Farmers' Mart in Enniskillen was developed by the Johnston family from County Armagh. Mr James Johnston purchased the lease, including the market rights, of the Fairgreen and the Gaol Square from Mr F. R. Browne in 1947 and set about establishing the livestock mart.

Mr James Johnston (Courtesy of Mr Stuart Johnston).

A dinner, hosted by the Mart Company and attended by 100 farmers, was held in Enniskillen on 22nd March 1951 to celebrate the first year's trading of the Mart. During the year, 22,766 animals were sold through the new facility.

The sale every Thursday attracted 1,400 to 1,700 stock from the western counties of Eire and County Fermanagh. An advertisement by the Mart stated that: *Enniskillen was situated at the terminus of the Sligo and Leitrim Railway and is the gateway from the west and affords an opportunity to the Northern farmer to obtain first quality stock at the minimum*

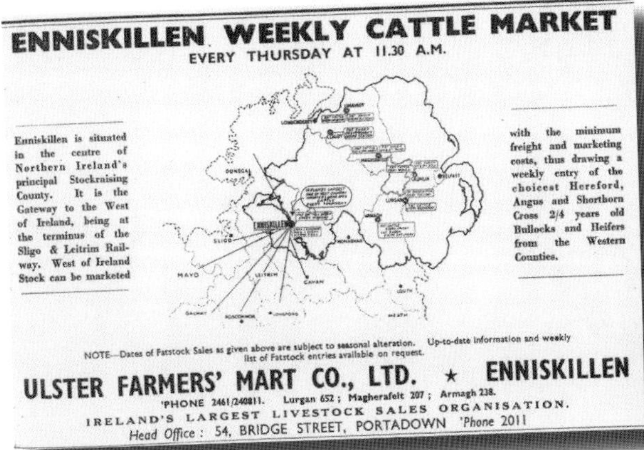

Advertisement for the Ulster Farmers' Mart as it appeared in The Farmers' Journal in 1955.

freight cost. These cattle are healthy and thrive well when changed to new pasture, and get into beef quickly. The Ulster Farmers' Mart is the largest in Ireland and provides facilities second to none for the Fermanagh farmer, as it offers an outlet for his stock by bringing buyers from all over the Six Counties as well as from England and Scotland.

Railways were regarded as a superior means of transporting cattle over a distance. Animals were not subjected to the same stresses arising from sudden braking and sharp cornering which were likely to be the case when cattle lorries were used.

In addition to the cattle and sheep sales on Thursday, Enniskillen Mart also had a pig sale every Wednesday when upwards of 400 to 500 store and weanling pigs were on offer. In the early days of the Mart, after the cattle were sold through the sale-ring they were driven to collecting yards in the vicinity, where they were kept until they were taken to be loaded on the train for their onward journey. The yards where stock was kept belonged to McLaughlins, Mackens, and Shannons. The charge for keeping the stock was three pence per animal.

Stock from the West of Ireland

An advertisement in the *Belfast News-Letter* in April 1951 extolled the services provided by Enniskillen Mart. The Mart undertook the despatch of purchased stock free of charge by the excellent road and rail transport. The store cattle on offer were stated *to be very high quality of both bullocks and heifers from Western Ireland's best thriving districts, and consists of Hereford, Angus and Shorthorn-cross aged bullocks and heifers of outstanding quality; also the choice of Fermanagh home-bred store cattle, cow heifers, grazing cows and store bulls.* Also on offer were *upwards of 100 young dairy cows and heifers from Fermanagh and western counties.*

The Mart in the 1960s (Courtesy of Mr Stuart Johnston).

The proximity of the Mart to the railway station (foreground) was a great asset when trains were running.

During the 1950s through to the 1970s, seventy per cent of the cattle sold in the Mart were from the Irish Republic. On the other hand, a number of butchers in the north west of the Irish Republic bought their beef cattle in Enniskillen. After entry to the EEC, farmers in the Irish Republic tended to fatten their cattle rather than export them as stores. At the end of the twentieth century, 90 per cent of the cattle sold in Enniskillen Mart were produced on Fermanagh and Tyrone farms.

At a Fatstock Show in the Mart in the late 1970s, Captain R. O. Hermon of Irvinestown is being presented with the cup for the best animal in the Show by Mrs Maureen West, wife of Mr Harry West, Minister of Agriculture. Also in the picture from left front row: Ms Kitty Jeffers, who worked in the mart office; Messrs Tommy Allen, Portadown; Tommy Allingham, Garrison; Kyber Hanley, who worked in the Mart; Simon Carson, beef cattle exporter from Belfast; Jimmy Johnston, Managing Director of the Mart. Behind Captain Hermon and Mrs West are Stuart Johnston, now Managing Director of the Mart; George McNally, cattle exporter from Armagh. Back row from right: Norman Graham, auctioneer; Bob Benson, manager of the Mart; Billy Jones, Managing Director of County Cars, Enniskillen (Courtesy of Mr Stuart Johnston).

Fair days continued after the Mart was established and were still operational in the late 1950s. Farmers found the marts to be more satisfactory because each animal on entering the sale-ring was displayed to all the potential buyers at the same time. This offered the seller the prospect of realising the full market price rather than, perhaps, being talked into accepting a price that was below true market value.

Fairs brought considerable business to towns and villages. When these communities saw that the ending of fairs was in sight many of them established small marts with the aim of keeping the business in the area and for the convenience of local farmers. Marts were established in Lisnaskea, Irvinestown, Fivemiletown, Belleek, Garrison and Derrylin.

Messrs William Stirling, buyer from Scotland; Henderson Richie, buyer from east of the Province; Robert Stirling, another buyer from Scotland and brother of Robert Stirling; Bob Benson, Manager of the Mart; Tommy Waite (arm over rail), cattle haulier; Jack Leahy, Newtownbutler (left elbow on rail). (Courtesy of Mr Stuart Johnston).

The official opening of Garrison Mart in the summer of 1960 was performed by Mr W. T. McClintock, County Agricultural Executive Officer, front centre. Others in the picture are left to right: Messrs Joseph Gray, Knockmore, Derrygonnelly; Patrick Gallagher, Tullyrosmearn, Garrison; John Hagan, local Ministry of Agriculture Inspector; Tom Brown, Cleans, Springfield; Wesley Acheson, Glen West, Garrison; Patrick Casey, Hotel, Garrison.

Derrylin Mart, registered as Derrylin Livestock Sales Limited, was typical of the marts established in the villages and small towns. It was a company limited by shares and was incorporated on 31st October 1962. Its main objectives were to take over as a going concern the business of Derrylin Attested Sales and carry on the business of auctioneers and salesmen dealing in the sale of livestock, including cattle, pigs, sheep, horses, and wool. Membership of the company was limited to 50. The first shareholders with a one pound share each were Messrs Patrick Francis Blake, Derrylin, and William Swan, Drumany, Thompson's Bridge, Enniskillen.

Enniskillen Mart's move to Lackaboy

In the early 1990s, Enniskillen town was developing rapidly and the Mart was experiencing severe problems with traffic congestion. In addition, the premises, built around 1950, were in need of modernisation. Dunnes Stores Ltd wished to establish a supermarket in the town and they regarded the Mart site as a suitable location. Negotiations between Dunnes and the Ulster Farmers' Mart had a successful outcome. The Mart Company owned land at Lackaboy on the Tempo Road in Enniskillen and this was an ideal out-of-town site for a new auction centre. The new state-of-the-art mart buildings at Lackaboy were complete in 1994 and from that time a successful business has been carried on there.

Partnership with Fermanagh Farming Society

From the establishment of the Mart in 1950, there has been a very happy working relationship between it and the County Fermanagh Farming Society, the organisation that runs the annual Fermanagh County Show, in Enniskillen. While the Mart was located at the Fairgreen site, it hosted the Annual Agricultural Show. When the Mart moved to Lackaboy, the Show also moved to that site. Through the generosity of the Johnstons, who own the Mart, the Fermanagh Farming Society possesses a five-acre showground adjacent to the Mart property. When the Annual Show is being held in August each year, the showground is used for showing the livestock and the Mart yard and buildings are used for trade exhibits and for the home industries displays.

References:

Blair, May, *Hiring Fairs and Market Places.* Appletree Press, Belfast (2007).

Files of *The Impartial Reporter, Fermanagh Herald, The Farmers' Journal* and *Belfast News-Letter.*

Notebook from 1929 -1931 of Mr John Fawcett, Rosculton.

Parke, W. K., *A Fermanagh childhood.* Friar's Bush Press, Belfast (1988).

Documentation from Messrs Patrick Blake and Bertie Swan relating to Derrylin Mart.

The new Mart and Auction Centre at Lackaboy (Courtesy of Mr Stuart Johnston).

Chapter 19
The Milk Marketing Board and Fermanagh Creameries

The Ministry of Agriculture retained control of the milk industry until 1st April 1955 when its role as the marketing authority was transferred to the producer controlled Milk Marketing Board for Northern Ireland (MMBNI). The Board's main function was to purchase all milk from producers and sell it to best advantage for liquid consumption or manufacturing. In 1956, only 35 million gallons of the 100 plus million gallons of milk produced in Northern Ireland were used for human consumption. The remainder was processed. The Board administered the guaranteed price, which was linked to a Standard Quantity.

The MMBNI board consisted of ten members elected by producers and three members appointed by the Ministry of Agriculture. The setting up of the MMBNI and the new economic conditions prevailing at the time gave milk producers tremendous confidence, which was reflected in increased milk output.

From 1957 until the 1970s an Ulster Dairy Queen, selected from the six County Dairy Princesses, was a milk promotional initiative by the Northern Ireland Milk Marketing Board. Miss Philomena O'Reilly, a member of the staff of the Ministry of Agriculture in Enniskillen, was the Fermanagh Princess and the Ulster Dairy Queen in 1965 (Courtesy of Mrs Bronagh Reilly).

Messrs James Johnston, Geoffrey Rogers and George Cathcart at Derrygonnelly Creamery Annual General Meeting in 1955 (Courtesy of Mr Basil Fawcett).

Mr Claudie Stinson, Manager of the Derrygonnelly Creamery garage, filling the Creamery milk tanker with petrol in 1953 (Courtesy of Mrs M. Stinson).

Milk processing

After the ending of war-time restrictions diversified forms of milk processing expanded into products such as cheese, evaporated, condensed and dried milk. National and international companies, including factories owned by the MMBNI, undertook this processing. In Fermanagh, the Scottish Co-operative Wholesale Society

(SCWS), Irvinestown, Springfield, and Fivemiletown and Brookeborough Co-Operative Creameries pasteurised and bottled milk for the local trade. Derrygonnelly and Springfield together manufactured dried skim milk powder at the plant in Derrygonnelly. Butter was manufactured at all locations.

Creamery amalgamation

The Erne (Kesh) and Irvinestown Societies amalgamated to form Fermanagh-Tyrone Farmers Limited and built a new creamery in Irvinestown in 1965. The assets and goodwill of the SCWS were acquired by the above organisation jointly with Derrygonnelly, Augher, and Fivemiletown and Brookeborough Co-Operatives in 1969. The new business at the SCWS site was known as United Creameries Enniskillen Ltd, which continued to produce butter and bottled milk. The existing societies had a vision to create a new dairy factory in Enniskillen and entered discussions with the MMBNI. At the same time the MMBNI was negotiating with Unigate (Fermanagh Creameries Ltd) and decided to support their Lisnaskea venture. The local societies realised that there was not a large enough milk pool in the catchment area to support two new factories and decided to place United Creameries Ltd into voluntary liquidation in 1972. The assets and goodwill of United Creameries Ltd were distributed among the four societies that had invested in the project.

Bulk milk tanks

In June 1969 Mr John K. Lynn CBE, Chairman of the MMBNI, defended the Board's handling of the recently introduced bulk milk tank collection system. A bonus, contributed by the purchasers of the milk, was paid to farmers who installed bulk tanks amounting to ¾d per gallon for the first year, ½d for the second and third years and ¼d for the fourth year. Farmers who were using tanks had to meet the capital costs although a Farm Improvement Scheme grant was available to eligible farmers. Some milk producers, however, who were continuing to use creamery cans, apparently thought that they were subsidising the bulk tank users.

Milk can at Barrs of Boho.

Unigate factory at Lisnaskea.

The MMBNI introduced a Bulk Milk Tank Rental Scheme during 1974. The annual rent was £1 for each 10 gallons capacity. The rent was deducted from the producers' milk cheques. The rent covered the cost of the tank installation, maintenance, automatic washing unit and insurance against losses due to breakdown. In addition, small mobile milk tanks of 50 gallon capacity were available for use with smaller herds or where the bulk milk tanker was unable to gain access to the dairy.

West Ulster Farmers Ltd

Further creamery amalgamations took place in 1978 with the formation of West Ulster Farmers Ltd when the societies at Derrygonnelly and Springfield joined with Fermanagh-Tyrone Farmers Ltd. In the new structure, they were joined later by the Killen Society in west Tyrone. The new organisation's plan was to concentrate all milk processing in Irvinestown and maintain some local services at the other sites. Springfield supplied farm requisites, Killen was the liquid milk centre and Derrygonnelly remained open to receive milk in cans until the entire farm milk supply moved to collection by tanker in 1982. At this time Lough Erne Creamery Ltd, a private enterprise venture, established a cottage cheese manufacturing unit in Derrygonnelly in premises rented from the Derrygonnelly branch of West Ulster Farmers Ltd. The cottage cheese production in Derrygonnelly had a relatively short life. It was eventually taken over by West Ulster Farmers Ltd, with production being transferred to the Irvinestown site.

Springfield Creamery lorry (TK Bedford) on its milk collection round on the last day of can collection in 1982. The driver was Mr John McClean and his helper on that occasion was Mr Jack Little. Mrs Betty Little is standing beside her husband outside their house at Mullaghmore, Boho (Courtesy of Mrs Betty Little).

Mobile milk tank.

Mr William Dickson CBE, Chairman of the Board of Directors of West Ulster Farmers Limited, and Mr George Fawcett, Manager.

Bulk milk tanker.

The Irvinestown plant

On the formation of West Ulster Farmers Ltd and the concentration of milk processing in Irvinestown, production was based on the separation of milk into cream and skim milk. The cream was made into butter and casein was extracted from the skim milk. Casein, a milk protein, was in demand as an ingredient in the food industry. The production of casein was economically attractive at that time due to the level of subsidisation from the European Community (EC). When the level of financial support from Europe was reduced, casein production became uneconomic and the Irvinestown company then switched to the production of mozzarella cheese from whole milk. This product was a major ingredient in pizzas and was much in demand by the fast-food industry. The Irvinestown company opened a new factory for its production in 1992. The financial success of the new venture was short lived due to a rise in the price of milk, which made the process uneconomic. The increased milk price resulted from the EC policy of 'deregulation' which brought to an end the Milk Marketing Board's ability to manage the pricing of milk for different processed milk products.

Demise of the Milk Marketing Board

The Northern Ireland Milk Marketing Board, established in 1955, had brought considerable prosperity to the Northern Ireland milk industry. The Board purchased all milk from producers and then allocated that milk to the processing industries at prices, which each process could stand economically. In this way, maximum returns were obtained for the producer. The liquid milk market always commanded a much higher price than, say, butter or cheese manufacture. In 1934, Sir Basil Brooke stated that only 30 per cent of production went to the liquid milk market. Dr George Chambers, in 1980, said that only 18 per cent of the total milk produced was sold to the liquid market with the remainder going at much lower prices for manufacturing into butter, cheese, milk powder, cream, yoghurt and other dairy produce. With the ending of the role of the Milk Boards on 28th February 1995, management of the sale price of milk to the end users was no longer possible.

Over the lifetime of the Northern Ireland Milk Marketing Board, members from County Fermanagh served with distinction. Mr George A. Cathcart OBE, JP, from Bellanaleck, served from 1955 until 1980 and for a time was Vice Chairman of the Board. Mr William C. Wilson MBE from Lisbellaw, was a member from 1956 until his death in 1962 and he was succeeded by his sister Miss Mary C. Wilson MBE whose membership terminated in 1968. Messrs Ronnie Farrell, Lisnaskea, and Harold Hamilton MBE were members from 1980 and 1990 respectively until the winding up of the Board in 1995. Mr Hamilton, who had been Vice Chairman of United Dairy Farmers Ltd, the

Irvinestown plant of West Ulster Farmers Ltd in 1990 (Courtesy of Mr George Fawcett).

new dairy co-operative set up after the dissolution of the Milk Marketing Board from its formation, succeeded Mr Robin Morrow CBE as Chairman in March 1998.

Economic pressures

After the MMBNI ceased operations, processors had then to either arrange direct contracts with producers and/ or purchase milk at auctions conducted by United Dairy Farmers Ltd. The impact of this new development on West Ulster Farmers Ltd was that they had to pay a much higher price for milk than heretofore and the production of mozzarella cheese became very uneconomic. As indicated earlier, the outcome was the closure of the mozzarella plant in mid 1995 with the loss of 40 jobs. The Irvinestown plant from that time relied on cottage cheese production, which earlier had been transferred from Derrygonnelly. In the meantime, the subsidiary operations at Killen, Springfield and Derrygonnelly had been wound up with a farm supply business being maintained only at Irvinestown.

Closure of Fermanagh Creameries Ltd

The Fermanagh Creameries Ltd cheese factory at Lisnaskea, which started production in November 1972, utilised a large volume of milk produced in Fermanagh and from further afield. It also provided valuable employment, which peaked at over 200. The company was originally part of the giant UK Unigate organisation but was sold to another English company, Dairy Crest plc, in February 2000. Sadly, the new owners soon concluded that they no longer required the Lisnaskea plant and it was closed down at the end of the year of acquisition.

Fivemiletown and Brookeborough Co-Operative Agricultural and Dairy Society Ltd

The creamery at Fivemiletown, which is located just across the Fermanagh border with Tyrone, derives a significant proportion of its milk supply from County Fermanagh farms. It continues to thrive and has diversified and contracted over the years to meet changing circumstances and economic opportunities. For many years, butter production was its mainstay. It first produced bottled milk in the 1940s. As well as its milk-based industry, the Society diversified later into a subsidiary garage business establishing the Auto Service Station in Fivemiletown. The garage provided a repair service for vehicles and agricultural machinery and also an agency for the sale of cars. The garage business was subsequently extended into Enniskillen with a car sales operation based in premises on the Sligo Road. Subsequently, the garage business was disposed of with the company concentrating solely on milk processing, specialising in cheese manufacture. Cheddar with speciality soft cheeses, including goats' cheese, together with butter manufacture, became the company's sole lines of production at the end of the century.

Milk processing into 21st century

The first decade of the twenty-first century witnessed the ending of all milk processing within County Fermanagh. Soft cheese production at West Ulster Farmers' Irvinestown plant ceased when the manufacturing rights of the product range were sold to Augher Co-operative Agricultural and Dairy Society Ltd. In the early part of the twentieth century there were 29 creameries and auxiliaries located within Fermanagh processing milk. In the early years of the next century there was none. The only local plant processing milk produced in County Fermanagh is at Fivemiletown just across the border in County Tyrone. Furthermore, much of the milk that is purchased by consumers in Fermanagh is most unlikely to have been produced in the county. The nearest pasteurising plant, privately owned, which retails milk in Fermanagh is based in Omagh, County Tyrone. Another major retailer in Fermanagh is Ballyrashane Creamery, which is based near Coleraine in County Londonderry. Despite the fact that there is no longer milk processing in the county, milk produced on Fermanagh farms is very much in demand and is transported by purchasers for processing at a number of factories in both Northern Ireland and in the Republic of Ireland.

References:

Chambers, Dr George, *The Rise and Fall of an Indigenous Industry: Milk Processing in County Fermanagh from the Seventeenth Century to the Present Day* published in *Fermanagh History and Society*, edited by Eileen M. Murphy and William J. Roulston. Geography Publications, Dublin (2004).

MacLurg, Alastair, *Ulster Farmers' Union – The History of its First Seventy Years 1917-1987.*

Ministry/Department of Agriculture's *Monthly Reports* and *Agriculture in Northern Ireland.*

Files of the *The Impartial Reporter* and *Fermanagh Herald.*

Records of West Ulster Farmers Ltd.

Chapter 20
Marketing of Pigs

The efforts by Fermanagh farmers to co-operate in the marketing of their pigs had met with considerable success. The Fermanagh Pig Breeders' and Feeders' Association had been established in 1927 at the instigation of Mr W. H. West, Secretary of the Fermanagh County Committee of Agriculture. Mr West had been encouraged by the achievements of the co-operative movement particularly for the benefit of dairy farmers. The benefits of co-operation for the farming community had been championed by Sir Horace Plunkett. Sir Horace addressed a large and representative meeting in Enniskillen Townhall back in October 1912, under the chairmanship of Mr J. Porter Porter of Belleisle. Sir Horace stated at that time that the greatest challenge for farmers was how to market their pigs. He emphasised that they could not dispose of them or any other produce to the best advantage unless they not only perfected their own organisation but also formed it in conjunction with other organisations throughout the country. He said he came as a representative of the farmers of the whole of Ireland seeking to pursue a policy which would lead to the salvation of the threatened agricultural industry of this country. The co-operative policy he and others were fighting for could be classed under three heads – better farming, better business, better living. He said that they wanted to see science introduced into the farming industry as it had been introduced into every other progressive business and to see life in agricultural districts less dour. They wanted to see the profits which ought to be and could easily be added to the farming industry applied to give farmers a more advanced social life, so that the young and enterprising amongst them would not be tempted to leave the country for the town and in Ireland to leave their country for America.

Sir Horace stated that a close study of progressive agricultural countries showed that farmers' prosperity was in proportion to their degree of organisation. Denmark was given as an example where co-operation among farmers had improved the standard of living and outlook of the small farmers.

The Agriculture Marketing Act (NI) 1933 opened up the potential for farmers to obtain a greater share of the final value of the foodstuffs which they produced. Many of the advantages of co-operation were achieved through the operation of the Marketing Boards, which came into being following the 1933 Marketing Act.

The Northern Ireland Pigs Marketing Board (PMB)

The 1933 Act empowered the Ministry of Agriculture to regulate the marketing of agricultural products and conferred powers on Boards administering such schemes. The Pigs Marketing Scheme (NI) Approval Order, 1933, came into operation on the 1st October of that year. The scheme gave the newly formed Board power to fix the price of pigs and to regulate sales by a producer. The setting up of the Pigs Marketing Board under producer control, backed by statutory powers and the support of the Ulster Farmers' Union (UFU), gave farmers for the first time an assured outlet for their pigs. This was a successful arrangement and during the first five years of the Board's existence pig numbers in the Province doubled. Prices for the pigs were negotiated between the PMB and representatives of the curers, the Pig Industry Council.

Large White Ulster sow.

Wiltshire Cure

Export demand at this time was for 'Wiltshire' style bacon rather than the traditional 'roll and ham' produced from the Ulster breed of pig. Large White York pigs were better suited to the 'Wiltshire' cure and in time, this accounted for the demise of the Ulster pig as a commercial breed.

Large White York boar.

Factories, with the PMB as major share holders in partnership with cross channel firms experienced in bacon production and marketing, were set up at Colin Glen, Dunmurry and Cookstown to produce 'Wiltshire' cured bacon. With UFU agreement, the PMB took over the purchase of all live pigs and the control of export of pigs to Great Britain. The PMB established twenty-nine centres throughout the Province for pig collection. At these centres the Board selected the type of pigs required by the factories and in doing so minimised the pig numbers that were exported live.

Pig grading

The issue of pig grading was one of the first challenges faced by Sir Basil Brooke when he became Minister of Agriculture. Some vested interests were opposed to grading but the Minister took a very firm stand. In February 1934, when indicating his whole-hearted support for grading, he said: "*The scheme is going through, and no individual, no matter how powerful he may be, is going to be allowed to rob our farmers of the opportunities which have been given them.*" Sir Basil stated that Ulster had built up a valuable ham and roll bacon trade, but that trade might not be capable of great expansion. He was anxious to encourage that trade but if they were to double and quadruple their output the greater part of the increase must be lean 'Wiltshire' cured bacon. There was only one way to do that – to pay the producer the extra price in accordance with the leanness of his pork. A quality grading system was therefore vital. He went on to say that he would not allow any grading system to be in the hands of the curers or any other interested party. Under the Pigs Marketing (Grading) (Northern Ireland) Order 1934 all dead pigs for curing into bacon and hams in Northern Ireland were graded at the curers' premises by Veterinary Inspectors of the Ministry of Agriculture. The weight class at that time attracting the top price was around 1cwt 1qr 14lb and a Grade A pig, determined by how little the shoulder fat measured, was worth 59s 2d paid by the curer. From this amount, the producer paid a levy of 4s per pig.

Prize for the best bacon carcase being presented by the Ulster Dairy Queen and Dairy Princesses at Enniskillen show in 1959.

Problems with the PMB

Problems arose with the functioning of the PMB in 1938 and 1939. The Government in Great Britain in 1938 had offered financial assistance to the pig industry. The aid was in connection with direct annual contracts between individual producers and curers. In Northern Ireland, the Ministry of Agriculture maintained that similar direct contracts between producers and curers in the Province would be the best way to ensure the same price for producers as that pertaining in Great Britain. The PMB was not convinced that annual contracts would suit the small producers in Northern Ireland but claimed that the financial assistance given in Great Britain, where there was no marketing board, should be given to the PMB for its bulk contracts with the curers. This disagreement on policy, together with allegations of irregularities in the PMB's administration, led to an enquiry into the PMB's operation. The outcome was the dissolution of the PMB in February 1939. Despite these difficulties pig production levels in Northern Ireland had increased steadily from 1934 until the outbreak of the Second World War in 1939 largely encouraged by the activities of the PMB.

Parity with Great Britain

In September 1939, the price of pigs was set at a lower price than that pertaining in Great Britain. The UFU supported the Pig Producers' Association in taking a case to the High Court arguing that Northern Ireland producers were entitled to the same prices as those on the mainland. The action was successful and established the principle that under wartime regulations the same prices for produce applied throughout the United Kingdom.

Impact of the Second World War

With the outbreak of war in September 1939 all fatstock marketed in the UK came under the control of the Ministry of Food. The Ministry of Agriculture for Northern Ireland, as agents for the Ministry of Food, took over responsibility from the PMB for the purchase of live pigs at collection centres with effect from 15th January 1940. The sale of dead pigs to curers continued in force. Pig prices were set by the Ministry. Due to the shortage of imported feeding stuffs, the number of pigs marketed in Northern Ireland declined steadily from a peak in 1939 to its lowest level in 1947 representing a drop of almost 80 per cent. Following decontrol on 1st July 1954 the PMB's trading powers were restored which gave it a monopoly in the purchase of all bacon pigs.

Babington Committee

The UFU had made strong representations to the Babington Committee set up in 1943 for the restoration of their entitlements under the Marketing Act of 1933 particularly in relation to their rights to have their own marketing schemes. The Babington Committee reported in 1946 and made a number of recommendations in relation to the pig industry. These included: restoration of the PMB, development of an efficient pig processing industry, pig breeding based on Large White pigs, and the establishment of a Pig Recording and Litter Testing Station.

Expansion

The availability of imported feeding stuffs after the war once again, together with the profitability of the enterprise, enabled producers to increase very significantly the number of pigs marketed in Northern Ireland. A substantial expansion in pig production took place from 1947. In 1950, numbers were approaching those pertaining at the beginning of the war and by 1955 there were over one million pigs in the Province, which was almost double the pre-war numbers.

In May 1965 it was announced that the PMB and Swift and Company of Chicago had formed a jointly owned company, Ulster-Swift Ltd, to construct and operate a £900,000 pig processing plant in County Fermanagh. Present at the launch were: Mr R. Williamson, general manager PMB; Mr F. R. Kirkwood, secretary, PMB; Mr I. G. D. Parry, director of Ulster Swift; Mr Porter M. Jarvis, chairman of Swift and Company; Mr A. E. Swain, chairman of the PMB and of Ulster-Swift; Mr E. R. Summer, director of Ulster-Swift; Mr C. B. Lawerenson, director of Ulster–Swift; Mr W. Swan, member of PMB and director of Ulster-Swift (Courtesy of Mr Bertie Swan).

PMB re-established

A newly constituted PMB was appointed in June 1954 and it became the statutory marketing agency for all pigs. The PMB was comprised of eleven members elected by producers and three appointed by the Ministry of Agriculture. The PMB negotiated prices with the curers and those together with payments under the Fatstock Guarantee Scheme determined the prices paid to producers. The year 1954 proved difficult for the PMB and for producers. Difficulties in agreeing prices with curers, insufficient curing capacity, and smuggling of pigs into Northern Ireland from the Irish Republic, meant that live shipments to Great Britain were necessary and this did not prove a very profitable operation.

This experience indicated an urgent need for greater curing capacity in Northern Ireland. The pigs marketed in Northern Ireland increased from the low level in 1947 to 1957 by 733 per cent. The pig industry then expanded steadily and by 1963, marketings had reached two million pigs, worth around £12 million, which accounted for almost 40 per cent of UK production. The slaughtering of pigs on farms ended in 1963.

The shortage of processing capacity was addressed by extensions at the factories in Cookstown and Colin Glen, the acquisition and expansion of Belfast Food Products and by the opening of a new Ulster-Swift factory in Enniskillen in 1966 which had a weekly throughput of 3,250 pigs.

The PMB at that time owned a 43 per cent share in the total curing capacity in the Province.

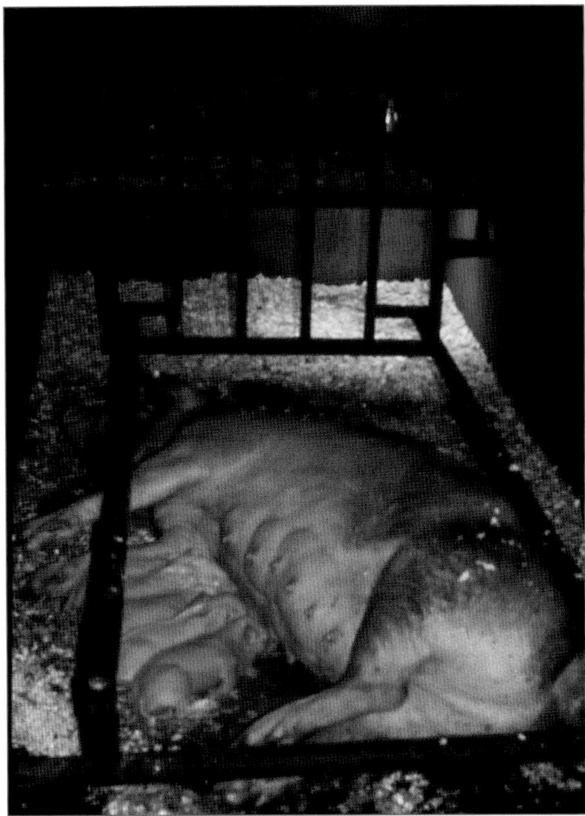

Sow and litter.

Pig fattening house.

Difficult times

The boom of the early 1960s was short-lived. Prices paid for pigs in Northern Ireland continued to be similar to those on the GB mainland but the cost of feeding stuffs was considerably higher. Minimum import prices for grain into the UK and GB's self-sufficiency in cereals gave rise to the significant differential in feed prices. Because of poorer profitability, levels of pig production in Northern Ireland dropped from 41,500 per week in the last quarter of 1965 to 29,000 per week in the comparable quarter of 1966. This decline in output led to serious consequences for the processing industry. The first casualty was Belfast Food Products, which went into liquidation in 1971.

The Ashton Committee

The Ashton Committee, set up by the Ministry of Agriculture to make recommendations on the PMB's operations, reported in June 1970. It made two recommendations: firstly, the PMB monopoly on purchase of pigs should cease and secondly, the quota system to supply curers should stop and be replaced by a direct contract system between producer and processor. The second recommendation from the Ashton Committee was that the PMB should liquidate its partnership interests in factories and limit its participation in the processing industry to one wholly owned factory.

These recommendations were not accepted by the industry and the PMB's monopoly in the purchase of pigs was maintained. The PMB's interests in factories was put into the complete control of PMB Investments Ltd – a body that had previously been set up to manage the Board's shares in the processing factories.

Smuggling

Pig smuggling did not always result in one-way traffic. In 1968, there was a considerable movement of pigs to the Irish Republic, where prices were more favourable.

Major James Chichester-Clark.

The Uniport factory (previously Ulster Swift) at Enniskillen.

Mr William Swan JP (Courtesy of Mr Bertie Swan).

Entry to the EEC led to even more cross-border traffic in pigs. In 1972, the Department of Agriculture introduced Legislation (Movement of Pigs Order) in an effort to control smuggling. Despite these measures, it was difficult for the PMB to maintain a steady pig supply. In 1975, the Board established supply contracts with level delivery bonuses in an effort to maintain a regular supply of pigs. A successful challenge in the European Court in 1978 proved that the PMB's powers to purchase all bacon pigs produced in Northern Ireland were not compatible with EEC competition rules.

Minister's views

The Minister of Agriculture, the Rt Hon Major James Chichester-Clark speaking at the new Enniskillen Agricultural College in March 1968 said that Northern Ireland must sell two thirds of all its produce to consumers in the UK.

Some of the marketing of this produce was entrusted to Marketing Boards, which the Minister said were constantly under review in order to make them more efficient and to bring more profit to the producers. He said it was his intention to reduce the number of members on the PMB from 14 to 9 in order to increase the efficiency of that Board. He indicated that an inquiry into pig production and marketing in Northern Ireland would help to advise whether the present set-up was right or whether it could be improved. He questioned the future of the 'Wiltshire Cure' and wondered if bacon would be in the same demand in ten years time. Mr William Swan, local member of the PMB, emphasised that it was most important to keep the pig industry alive as they had one of the most up-to-date bacon factories in the UK located in Enniskillen. He pointed out that the two major problems were feed costs and remoteness and believed that some aid from the Remoteness Grant should be directed to the pig industry.

The Minister referred to the problems in meat marketing and said that the Ministry had been under pressure to set up a meat marketing board but felt that if they had had one in the dreadful conditions in 1967 it would have broken down.

Decline of the PMB

Because of the EEC ruling the Northern Ireland Marketing Act of 1964 was replaced by a Marketing Service Order, which was compatible with EEC law. Consequently, a Voluntary Marketing Board was established. The new Board was now responsible to its registered producers instead of the Government. The producers who entered into voluntary contracts with the Board became the registered producers who elected the Board members. The PMB Investments

Ltd was wound up and the operation of the Board's factories came under the supervision of a committee of the new Board. Under the new arrangements, there was no longer any control over the considerable movement of pigs to the Irish Republic. Some producers who sold their pigs directly to curers, thus bypassing the Board, exacerbated the problems. In addition, two curers only bought pigs directly from producers. The outcome of these developments was that the PMB ended the allocation system to curers and offered the pigs to the highest bidder. The number of pigs purchased by the PMB in 1984 and 1985 was only about a quarter of that in 1965. In 1985, the price being received by producers was well below that of producers in Great Britain – a big turn around from the situation prevailing in earlier times. The number of producers registered with the PMB declined steadily. There were over 13,000 in 1969 and only 854 in 1985. The reduced numbers were due to the decline in the pig population and fewer producers as units were becoming larger. Lack of loyalty to the PMB was also a major factor in that producers dealt directly with curers. This all led to the demise of the PMB and the end of a scheme, which aimed to influence the marketing of pigs by the producers for the benefit of producers. The PMB's assets were subsequently sold.

Pig Production Development Committee

A body, called the Pig Production Development Committee, was established in 1996 under the Pig Production Development Act (Northern Ireland) 1964 for carrying on some of the functions previously undertaken by the PMB. Its primary purpose was to provide services and facilities for the benefit of those engaged in the production of pigs. This body had two representatives from the UFU, one from the British Pig Association, one from the NI Pig Breeders' Association and four appointed by the Department of Agriculture (two of whom represented the interests of the defunct PMB, and two represented the curers).

Mr William Rea MBE JP, Tullynagowan, Brookeborough, (left) in light-hearted discussion with Mr Michael McCullagh MRCVS, Divisional Veterinary Officer, at a conference on pig diseases. Mr Rea served for many years as a member of the Northern Ireland Pigs Marketing Board.

Pig Numbers in Fermanagh

Table 20.1 Pig Numbers in Fermanagh

Year	1920	1930	1938	1940	1942	1943	1945	1950	1955
Total pig numbers	14,188	18,464	34,987	27,853	21,556	18,675	13,841	16,312	36,000

Year	1960	1965	1971	1975	1980	1985	1990	1995	2000
Total pig numbers	59,000	70,148	54,839	25,653	21,900	17,432	14,993	11,473	*
Herds			1,502	696	408	259	148		

Source: Economics and Statistics Division census data, DARD.

**Figures for Fermanagh and Tyrone were amalgamated due to data confidentiality constraints (Pig numbers were very low in County Fermanagh).*

The above census data show how the pig population in Fermanagh rose and fell in line with the profitability of the enterprise and other factors such as availability of suitable bought-in feed. At the end of the century pig keeping, like the poultry enterprise, had become a very specialised industry with small profit margins. Only large scale highly efficient production units became economically viable.

References:

Files of *The Impartial Reporter* and *Fermanagh Herald* held in Enniskillen Library.

West Archive – Clogher Historical Society. Monaghan.

Ministry/Department of Agriculture's *Monthly Reports* and *Agriculture in Northern Ireland.*

MacLurg, Alastair, *Ulster Farmers' Union – The History of its first Seventy Years 1917-1918.*

Department of Agriculture's County Fermanagh Agriculture Development Committee records.

Chapter 21
Animal Health

During the twentieth century there was a continuous campaign through education and control measures to limit the damage caused by livestock diseases to the agricultural industry. Many diseases could be controlled by the farmer having taken veterinary or other advice. However, there have been a number of diseases which would have been impossible to control or eradicate without a concerted effort at local, county, province-wide and indeed an all-Ireland basis. Diseases that fall into this category include: Sheep Scab, Ox Warble Fly, Bovine Tuberculosis (TB) and Brucellosis (contagious abortion), Swine Fever, Foot and Mouth Disease, Anthrax and Bovine Spongiform Encephalopathy (BSE). The Ministry of Agriculture's Divisional Veterinary Officer in Enniskillen, among his other responsibilities, had the duty of controlling the spread and elimination of these diseases in County Fermanagh.

Sheep Scab

Sheep Scab is one of the most contagious diseases of sheep. The disease, caused by a parasitic mite, seriously affects the welfare of sheep. It has a significant impact through its effect on the condition of ewes, the growth rate of lambs, damage to wool and reduced quality of sheepskins. Scab can be introduced to a flock by animals returning from market or from a neighbour's sheep. It is not surprising therefore, that the eradication of Sheep Scab has been a high priority throughout the century. Despite a compulsory dipping programme, outbreaks of Sheep Scab were a source of concern for the County Committee of Agriculture and the County Fermanagh Diseases of Animals Committee in 1935. Under the Sheep Dipping (Ireland) Order 1915, all sheep had to be dipped on two occasions, separated by an interval of not less than seven or more than fourteen days. Sheep dipping baths were provided by the Committee at centres throughout the county and sheep had to be dipped in the presence of a Veterinary Inspector. The cost was 2d per sheep. Although Sheep Scab was virtually eradicated at this early stage, occasional, often isolated, outbreaks have been confirmed over the years. These were usually caused by bought-in sheep or brought-in animals and were dealt with urgently so that the disease was kept under control. Occasional cases of Sheep Scab continue to appear and are dealt with as they arise.

Sheep dipping in progress at Marlbank.

Ox Warble Fly

These large flies, commonly referred to as *'Gad Flies'*, are parasitic on cattle and deer. Adult Ox Warble Flies are active in the hottest part of the summer. They lay their eggs on the hairs of the legs. It is the darting behaviour of the flies, while they are depositing their eggs, that frightens cattle and makes them 'gad' or gallop. The eggs hatch in about four days and the larvae penetrate the skin and migrate through the tissues eventually reaching the animal's back. In the following spring the larvae appear under the skin and form a breathing hole and remain there for about a month. They then enlarge the breathing hole, wriggle out, fall to the ground where they hatch and give rise to the next generation of flies. The welfare of infected animals obviously suffers and there is serious damage to the hide. The Warble Fly Order, operating from 1936, required that all animals should be dressed with an appropriate insecticide. In the early years the insecticide used was *Derris* which was applied to the animal's back when the warbles appeared. In 1964, a new very effective method of warble fly control was introduced. It was a systemic insecticide that killed the larvae in the animal's body before they reached the animal's back. The treatment involved pouring the systemic insecticide onto the animal's back where it was absorbed and in the process killed the Warble Fly larvae. A Warble Fly Scheme commenced on

1st September 1966, whereby officers of the Divisional Veterinary Office visited farms and dressed all eligible animals. The Divisional Veterinary Officer informed the County Committee of Agriculture that all cattle in the county, apart from those that were sick, had been dressed for warbles using this new material during 1966 and 1967. This resulted in the incidence of warbled hides dropping from 50 per cent to one per cent. In 1969, Warble Fly was made a notifiable disease. In 1981, the Divisional Veterinary Officer in County Fermanagh reported that Warble Fly was no longer a problem. As a precautionary measure from then on all cattle were inspected on a regular basis for Warble Fly infestation when tests for Brucellosis and TB were being undertaken. The last confirmed case of warbles in Northern Ireland was in 1996.

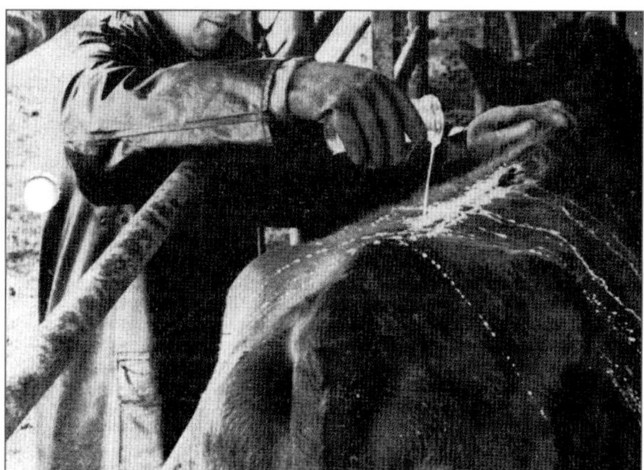

Pour-on treatment for Warble Fly.

Tuberculosis (TB) Eradication

In October 1945, the Cashel Branch of the Ulster Farmers' Union put forward a resolution to the Fermanagh County Committee of Agriculture urging the Ministry of Agriculture to take blood samples from all cows in Northern Ireland for the purposes of detecting and eliminating TB. This resolution was supported by the County Committee of Agriculture and forwarded to the Ministry. In the following May, the Ministry responded stating that it was not in a position at present to place a Tuberculin Test at the disposal of farmers generally, either free of charge or for a small fee. In March 1947, the Minister, the Rev Robert Moore, referred to ongoing research work and expressed hope that a much more efficient means of dealing with TB in cattle was on its way.

The Tuberculosis (Attested Herds) Scheme became operative in 1949 and was revised with effect from 1st September 1954. This was a voluntary scheme. Herd owners were advised to have their animals tested and those animals that reacted to the Tuberculin Test were to be removed from the farm. If the number of reactors did not exceed ten per cent of the total stock of cattle on the farm application could be made to join the scheme. A number of repeat tests were then carried out on the remaining animals on the farm at not less than 60 day intervals. When two successive tests were clear the herd would qualify for registration in the Register of Attested Herds. There was financial encouragement to become Attested. Bonus payments of 1½d per gallon of milk or 30s per year for each animal in the herd were payable for a period of six years. Record keeping, including births and deaths, was a condition of the scheme and animal movements were by permit only issued by the Ministry. In April 1957, Mr W. A. Taylor, Divisional Veterinary Officer, told the Fermanagh County Committee of Agriculture that the county was lagging behind every other area in the matter of Attestation.

In January 1958, a meeting on animal health, including discussion on Tuberculosis, was held in the Townhall, Enniskillen, at which the speakers were Professor H. G. Lamont and Mr J. S. Ogg of the Ministry of Agriculture. A press article in advance of this meeting billed it as *'likely to be the farmers' meeting of the year'*. By February 1958 there were 367 Attested Herds in County Fermanagh involving over 10,000 cattle. This represented the smallest response of any county. In Northern Ireland at that time a total of over 7,700 herds more than 215,000 animals had achieved Attested Herd status.

Slaughter of TB reactors

The Minister of Agriculture, the Rev Robert Moore, in early 1958 expressed his intention of prescribing areas for the complete eradication of Bovine Tuberculosis by the slaughter of reactors, if necessary, and the payment of compensation. In March 1959, Mr H. W. West, Parliamentary Secretary to the Ministry, stated that 46 per cent of cattle in Northern Ireland were Attested and that full attestation was the aim by 1960.

By 31st May 1960 there were 3,824 herds Attested in County Fermanagh. A further 1,866 herds were in the Supervised category. At this time almost 88 per cent of the cattle in the county were either fully Attested or were on their way towards that status.

Compulsory Testing and Compensation

From 1st January 1960, Orders were in force enabling the Ministry to carry out compulsory testing of cattle not already in the Attested Herds Scheme and to remove for slaughter, subject to compensation at 75 per cent of market value, all animals which react to the test. No cattle were permitted to be tested after that date with Tuberculin except by the Ministry or with the Ministry's authority. Entry of untested cattle into Northern Ireland was prohibited after that date.

Steady progress was made over the years with the TB eradication programme. However, total elimination of the disease has proved to be a challenge and constant endeavour by farmers and the Divisional Veterinary Office staff has been necessary to keep the disease completely under control. By April 1978 ten herds in the county were under restriction. In June 1979 the number of herds with problems had increased to 50 and these were mainly in the south of the county bordering the Irish Republic. The problem continued during the next two years with 37 closed herds, again mainly in the south of the county. From 1981 to 1992 the number of infected herds fluctuated between 20 and 50, but rose rapidly after that and peaked at 98 in 1993.

Following intensive control measures TB was reduced to around 50 infected herds by the end of 1994 and the situation remained about this level until 1997. After this, infections began to rise again and by the year 2000 had reached a level of about 150 infected herds.

Towards the end of the century there were two noticeable changes in TB infection in Fermanagh. Firstly, TB infection in cattle was no longer localised in the south of the county, but was much more widespread with 'pockets' of heavy infection in areas to the north and west of Enniskillen. Secondly, infection within herds was often more severe than in earlier years and larger numbers of cattle within herds would become infected and would have to be removed. In earlier years, outbreaks often had no more than a few infected animals removed followed by clear tests and restriction.

Brucellosis or Contagious Abortion

Brucellosis is the name given to the infectious disease of man and animals caused by the bacterium, *Brucella*. It causes the condition in humans called Undulant Fever and in cattle Contagious Abortion disease. The scourge of this disease in cattle was being publicised in 1955. It was pointed out that the disease was responsible for heavy losses in cattle including dead calves, cull cows and reduced milk output. Upwards of 80 per cent of cows which become infected with the disease abort only on one occasion and, thereafter, develop an immunity or tolerance but then became carriers of the disease. The use of vaccination in protecting susceptible animals against infection seemed to be the best solution at that time with Strain 19 vaccine being promoted for that purpose. However, after the introduction of the Brucellosis Eradication Scheme in 1964 it was made clear that the use of the vaccine was not enough to ensure freedom from the disease. The Brucellosis Control Order prohibited the use of the vaccine on animals above the age of eight months.

In Northern Ireland, herds producing Grade A milk had been tested and were free of Brucellosis. From early 1958 herd owners voluntarily submitted their herds for testing and those that were free of the disease were added to a register. In order to prevent the sale of infected animals from herds, that were subject to testing, to other herds the Brucellosis Control Order (NI) 1962 was introduced and subsequently replaced by the 1964 Order. Under this Order the bulk milk from each producer in Northern Ireland was tested at the creamery or processing factory to which it was sent. Six per cent of samples gave a positive result. This process identified the herds which had a Brucellosis problem and compulsory testing was introduced in January 1963. Cows were individually tested by the Ministry and those found to be infected were valued by the Ministry and slaughtered with the farmer receiving 75 per cent of the market value of the infected animals. With regard to cattle breeding herds it was considered, at that time, that they had less infection than dairy herds. In 1966 Mr H. W. West, Minister of Agriculture, stated that an Order had been made declaring Northern Ireland an eradication area in respect of Brucellosis in cattle. He said: "*This is a formal statutory step which declares Northern Ireland to be a country which has reached an advanced stage in the eradication of this disease. Additionally, however, it gives my Ministry powers to control the movement of cattle into Northern Ireland.*" He went on to say that the Department of Agriculture and Fisheries in the Republic of Ireland was working in very close co-operation with the Ministry of Agriculture for Northern Ireland in the operation of the controls.

Mr J. M. McMenemy MRCVS, Divisional Veterinary Officer (1955 – 1969).

By 1967 three-quarters of the total herds in Northern Ireland were Brucellosis free. Eight out of ten milk herds and six out of ten beef herds were free of the disease. It became the declared policy of the Ministry to clear Brucellosis from cattle in Northern Ireland by 1970. New measures to control the movement of animals were introduced in 1967. Under the Order, no owner of an infected herd was permitted to sell any animal, aged nine months or over, without authorisation from the Ministry. From1st April 1967, sales and markets were required to set aside certain days for the sale of certified stock only. At the end of November 1968 over 96 per cent of herds in Northern Ireland were certified clear of Brucellosis.

New measures were introduced by the Ministry of Agriculture on 1st January 1969 to speed up the final eradication of the disease. Imports of cows and in-calf heifers from the Irish Republic were only permitted if they were fully certified and from a 'Clearance Area'. In 1969, for the first time, every herd had been brought into the Ministry's Brucellosis Testing Scheme and had been tested at least once. An appeal was made to farmers to do everything in their power to prevent the introduction of disease into previously clear herds.

Brucellosis free

On 15th December 1971, the Minister of Agriculture, Mr H. W. West, declared the Province to be free of Brucellosis. He stated: "*It is therefore with particular pleasure that I am able to announce to this House today that the incidence of Brucellosis in our national herd has now been reduced to a level which satisfied me that that the country can be declared a Brucellosis Free area.*" At the same time an appeal was made to farmers to continue co-operating with the Ministry not only to maintain this satisfactory state but to assist in eliminating the last vestiges of the disease from livestock. At that time over £2.8 million had been paid out in compensation for reactor cattle and in-contacts during the eradication period

Mr B. H. Hart MRCVS, Divisional Veterinary Officer (1969 - 1979).

In June 1973, a special appeal was made by the Veterinary Division to herd owners to assist in the final elimination of Brucellosis which was classed as one of the last remaining causes of severe losses in the Province's cattle herds. It was stated that the level of infection in Northern Ireland in 1971 was minimal but that progress in 1972 and 1973 had not been maintained. The basic cause was the introduction of infection into herds that were previously clear. It was pointed out that 50 per cent of breakdowns occurred in herds which were adjacent to or in the vicinity of existing infection. The appeal was for herd owners to reduce this prolific spread by careful management and livestock control. Precautions were to be taken to ensure that the disease did not spread. Care was to be exercised in relation to manure and slurry disposal. The risks of sharing machinery were also highlighted. The proper maintenance of fences in order to prevent straying of cattle was emphasised. Infection could survive in land for up to three months and therefore grazing of this land by stock other than bullocks or sheep was to be avoided. Farmers were reminded of their responsibility to their neighbours in taking all necessary precautions against the spread of the disease.

Biennial testing for Brucellosis

In 1977 steady progress was reported in the eradication of the disease in Fermanagh with the number of infected herds down from 50 to 39. In the following year the number of infected herds was down to 22. In 1982 there were no herds in County Fermanagh under restriction due to Brucellosis infection. On 26th July 1982 Northern Ireland's herds were declared 'Officially Brucellosis Free' (OBF). Throughout the 1980s the prevalence of the disease continued to be reduced and on 13th April 1988 a European Community Commission recognised that since the Northern Ireland herds had been OBF for more than four years and that at least 99.8 per cent of herds were free from the disease, the annual tests could be replaced by biennial tests.

County Fermanagh remained free of Brucellosis until 1989, when one case of infection was confirmed. There were no further cases of infection until 1999 when two cases were confirmed and by the end of 1999 there were five confirmed cases. In 2000 there were 24 confirmed cases of Brucellosis in County Fermanagh and infection was generally in the south of the county, extending as far north as the Maguiresbridge area.

Swine Fever

Swine Fever is a highly contagious disease of pigs which causes fever, skin lesions, convulsions and usually death within 15 days. It was a relatively common disease in Northern Ireland prior to 1935 but the rapid expansion in pig numbers and the cessation of bacon imports resulted in the disease being brought under control and eventually eradicated. Since then there have been few cases of Swine Fever, except for a few sporadic outbreaks during the Second World War years. These were traced directly to the feeding of insufficiently boiled swill containing scraps of bacon from foreign ships. The pig industry then enjoyed freedom from Swine Fever until the mid 1950s.

From October 1956 until August 1957, over 50 outbreaks of the disease were confirmed in Northern Ireland, necessitating the slaughter of 7,000 pigs. The first of these outbreaks was linked to a specific group of store pigs purchased from a source which was difficult to trace. From this source the other outbreaks spread over a wide area by interchange of store pigs from salesyard to farm and from dealer to client. When these outbreaks were under control the Ministry took steps to prohibit public sales of pigs and the importation of live pigs and pork products.

Restriction of the movement of pigs was introduced under the Swine Fever Order (Northern Ireland) 1957. Under the Order which applied from 20th May 1957 the movement of pigs, over 10 weeks of age or over 56 lb weight, was prohibited. The exceptions were when pigs were being slaughtered or when sows were being being moved temporarily for mating. Other exceptions were pigs over five months of age when they were being moved from one farm to another for retention for breeding purposes. Pigs under the limits mentioned were required to be moved directly from the breeders' premises to the fatteners' premises and pig dealers required movement licences for this purpose. Records of movements were a necessity and all vehicles had to be cleansed and disinfected after pigs had been transported. More severe restrictions were introduced on 8th July 1957 when movement licences became a requirement. Licences were issued at 19 centres throughout County Fermanagh. A new Swine Fever Order was introduced in February 1958 which imposed further restrictions. These included restrictions on or the prohibition of the re-sale of purchased pigs except for slaughter or for breeding only with the written consent of the Ministry. Pigs could only be transported in vehicles owned by the seller, the purchaser or the Ulster Transport Authority. All pig farmers were required to keep written records of the number of pigs on their premises and of all movements of pigs. The ban on the movement of pigs was lifted in February 1959, although record keeping was a continuing requirement. In the same month Mr H. W. West, Parliamentary Secretary to the Ministry of Agriculture, stated that the stern measures taken had brought the disease under control. Pigs slaughtered under this measure from 1st April 1958 had numbered 1,335 involving compensation payments of £12,500. The last case of Swine Fever in Northern Ireland was in 1958.

Foot and Mouth Disease

This is a highly contagious and sometimes fatal disease of cloven-hoofed animals including cattle, sheep, goats and pigs. In early September 1912 an outbreak of Foot and Mouth disease in County Fermanagh was the subject of discussion. The Enniskillen Urban Council discussed the restrictions placed upon fairs and markets arising from the disease outbreak. It was claimed that because a few isolated cases of the disease had been discovered the Department had restricted practically the whole county. Mr James Dawson MRCVS, the Department's veterinary surgeon, attended the September meeting of the County Committee of Agriculture and assured members that the disease was in fact Foot and Mouth. The Chairman, Canon Hall, said that all they could do now was to use every endeavour to shorten the time of restriction by assisting the Department in their efforts to stamp out the disease. There were no cattle, pigs or sheep at the Enniskillen September Fair Day that year. The outbreaks of the disease were recorded in the Kinawley district in the townlands of Drumhervin and Corravehy. Mr Thompson, Departmental Inspector, reported further outbreaks of the disease on farms in Cornaskeogh and Stragowna. Another outbreak was reported at Swanlinbar, four miles from Kinawley. In November the Department of Agriculture made an Order which reduced the restricted area to that within a radius of seven or eight miles from the infected farms. By January 1913, the Department of Agriculture had issued an Order removing the restrictions on the movement of animals in Fermanagh and elsewhere in Ireland apart from a district still scheduled in the neighbourhood of Mullingar.

An outbreak of Foot and Mouth Disease occurred in County Down in June 1931, which meant that the ports of Great Britain were closed to the importation of cattle from Northern Ireland for a period of nine weeks. Northern Ireland had been free of the disease during the previous 19 years. There was a very serious outbreak of the disease in England and Scotland in the 1960s. In the years prior to that there had been sporadic outbreaks but not on the same scale as in the 1960s. The disease outbreak peaked in England in 1967 with 2,210 outbreaks involving over 196,000 cattle, 97,000 sheep and 113,000 pigs.

Throughout the 1960s the Ministry continued to issue warnings about the need for the utmost care in order to avoid Foot and Mouth disease spreading to Northern Ireland from England and Scotland. There were no confirmed cases of Foot and Mouth Disease right up to the end of the century. However, in 2001 an outbreak occurred in the Cooley Peninsula in County Louth and also a confirmed case in

Coagh, County Tyrone, and another in County Antrim. There were no cases in County Fermanagh.

Animal Welfare

It became illegal to offer horned animals for sale after 1st February 1969 and this requirement has been rigorously enforced at markets and elsewhere by the Divisional Veterinary Officer's staff. Pedigree cattle were exempt from this requirement and could be sold in marts or elsewhere if they were segregated.

Mr Michael McCullagh MRCVS, Divisional Veterinary Officer (1979 – 1998), in serious discussion with Mr Robert Sheridan, Gorteen, Florencecourt, on a farm walk.

Anthrax

Occasional outbreaks of Anthrax infection were diagnosed over the years. There were serious outbreaks of Anthrax infection in two herds in County Fermanagh in 1985 and 1986. The last confirmed case of Anthrax in Northern Ireland was in 1990.

Bovine Spongiform Encephalopathy (BSE)

BSE, as it was commonly known, was a new disease in County Fermanagh towards the end of the century. The first case of BSE to be identified in Fermanagh was in the Kesh area in 1988, in a cow which came originally from County Antrim.

The number of affected herds began to increase year by year and peaked in 1993 when there were 50 confirmed cases in County Fermanagh. After this the number of affected herds decreased and by the end of the century was reduced to six. Generally few herds had more than one infected animal, occasionally two, and very rarely three confirmed cases. See Chapters 36 and 37 for further information on the disease and its impact on the agricultural economy.

References:

Files of *The Impartial Reporter* and *Fermanagh Herald* held in Enniskillen Library.

Ministry/Department of Agriculture's *Monthly Reports* and *Agriculture in Northern Ireland.*

Reports of the County Fermanagh Agricultural Development Committees.

From left: Mr David Brown MRCVS, Divisional Veterinary Officer (from 1998), with Mr Seamus McAlinney MAgr, Head of Enniskillen Campus (CAFRE), formerly Enniskillen College of Agriculture; Mr Kenneth Sheridan, Granshagh; and Mr Richard Trimble, Group Secretary, Ulster Farmers' Union.

Chapter 22
Poultry

Poultry, for many years, was an important enterprise on practically every farm in County Fermanagh. Right from the establishment of the County Committee of Agriculture, at the beginning of the twentieth century, efforts were made to enhance the productivity of poultry through breeding and improvement in husbandry under the Poultry Scheme. Lectures were given by the Poultry Instructor on everything relating to the breeding and management of hens, turkeys, ducks and geese. The Instructor's role was to advise poultry keepers on all aspects of husbandry by way of farm visits and lectures. In addition, the Instructors had a responsibility to improve the breeding of poultry. Mr J. E. Ferris, the County Committee's first Poultry Instructor, made the following comment in his report for 1906: *The egg stations have done good work, and have been an incalculable benefit to the poultry keeping community.* He continued: *1393 settings of eggs having been distributed during the past season, which clearly indicates that the efforts being made to place the poultry industry on a more satisfactory footing are meeting with success.*

Egg stations

In 1906 there were 14 egg distributing stations, each earning a Premium of £5. These were selected farms where pure breeds of hens and ducks were kept for the production of eggs for breeding purposes. For example, Miss Stewart had Brown Leghorns and her farm produced 150 settings of eggs; Mrs Robinson had Black Minorcas and Indian Runner Ducks and 133 settings of eggs were produced from that unit.

Indian runner ducks.

Other breeds of hens at the time were White Leghorn, White Wyandotte and Buff Orpington. In those days chicks were hatched and reared by a broody hen, often referred to as 'clocking hens'. In 1906 there were 11 turkey Premiums, each worth £2, granted by the County Committee. The Poultry Scheme in 1935 offered Premiums in respect of: (a) one pure-breed of hens and ducks to supply settings of eggs; (b) American Bronze turkey cocks and (c) stations to distribute goose eggs.

Mrs Armstrong, Keeranbeg and family, with White Wyandottes in the 1940s (Courtesy of Miss J. Armstrong).

Light Sussex cock and hen (Courtesy Mr V. Graham).

Turkeys

In December 1945 an account was given in the Ministry of Agriculture's *Monthly Report* of turkey production on the unit of Mrs Robert Allen, Kilturk Cottage South, Newtownbutler. It was stated that turkey rearing was that branch of poultry farming that was left almost entirely to women folk. Credit was given to the Turkey Stations Scheme under which facilities were provided whereby owners of turkey hens could obtain the services of an approved American Bronze turkey cock of good type, at a reduced fee. Turkey cocks on these stations were expected to mate at least 25 hens, other than those belonging to the owner of the cock, at a fee not exceeding two shillings. Mrs Allen had been breeding and rearing turkeys for about 30 years producing 30 to 40 birds each year. The young turkeys were hatched out under a broody hen sitting on eight or nine eggs. Each turkey hen laid two clutches of eggs in a season. When the turkey hen became broody again turkey chicks were introduced to the nest. Mrs Allen produced selected cocks for supply to Station holders. From the 1950s the American Bronze breed was gradually replaced by Broad Breasted White turkeys which had greater growth rates, larger breasts and better food conversion. The Beltville White turkey breed was first introduced by North Antrim Turkeys in 1952. Free range production was also replaced in large measure by intensive methods from that time.

A bronze turkey cock on a west Fermanagh farm.

Turkey and Geese Stations were still a feature of poultry improvement in 1952 when the Premiums were worth £3 10s 0d and £2 10s 0d respectively. It was still a common sight in country districts in Fermanagh in the 1940s to see women taking turkey hens to a turkey cock in the district for mating or as it was commonly referred to as 'tramping'. The normal method of transport was by bicycle. The turkey hen was placed inside a hessian bag, with its head out, secured on the rear carrier rack of the bicycle.

Egg Marketing

From an early date, after the setting up of the Northern Ireland Ministry of Agriculture, the importance of marketing eggs to best advantage was appreciated. The first Egg Bill was introduced in 1924 and this brought a remarkable change in the reputation and quality of Northern Ireland eggs which, by 1931, were commanding a higher price than other eggs entering Great Britain. The Minister of Agriculture, Sir Edward Archdale, stated in the Northern Ireland Parliament that the Ulster code of legislation had been adopted by other countries. England had adopted Northern Ireland grades, their standard for freshness and their system of code marking. Even Denmark had adopted Northern Ireland's grades and practice of buying by weight.

As with other agricultural products during the Second World War, the Ministry of Agriculture, acting as agents of the Ministry of Food, took control of the marketing of eggs from January 1940. Egg prices were fixed for the years 1939 and 1940 under the Marketing of Eggs Acts (NI) 1924 – 1938. The difficulty in importing feed during the war restricted the growth of the industry and egg rationing was the outcome. After the war the poultry industry expanded rapidly.

Importance of poultry

Poultry and eggs were regarded by the Minister, Sir Edward Archdale, as the most important branch of Northern Ireland agriculture. The export of eggs from Northern Ireland ports in 1926 was almost equal in value to the total amount realised for eggs exported from the whole of Ireland in 1904. He attributed the success of this enterprise largely to the work of County Agricultural Committees and their Poultry Instructors.

Sir Edward Archdale when addressing delegates of the World's Poultry Congress at a dinner in the Ulster Hall in Belfast, in August 1930, informed them of the importance of poultry in the Northern Ireland agricultural economy. The Congress had been held in the Crystal Palace in London and a visit to Northern Ireland was part of the programme for delegates. Sir Edward told those attending that ten Poultry Instructors had been appointed across the Province and that 970 poultry stations had been established. He said: *"In the wave of agricultural depression following the war one of the few branches of Ulster's agricultural industry which has continued to prove profitable had been poultry keeping. This was reflected in the increasing importance which eggs and poultry occupied in agricultural output figures."* He then referred to the success of the Marketing of Eggs Act, with Ulster eggs commanding top prices in the London market. He stated: *"It has been our object to make education and legislation to go hand in hand, and I think we are succeeding. Our poultry population is now twice as dense as that of any other part of the British Isles, and is still increasing."* He went on to say that the value of agricultural output in Northern Ireland in 1930 was between £14 and £15 million and of that sum no less than £3.5 million was represented by the value of the country's eggs and poultry. Sir Edward stated: *"eggs and poultry are the largest single item in our agricultural industry, exceeding in value the whole cattle trade, the whole pig trade, the whole of the dairying industry, and, finally, the value of the whole crops output of Northern Ireland. Few people realise that our output of eggs and poultry exceeds the gross value of the ship building industry."*

Incubators

Incubators were being used in 1929 and were a big advance on the practice of hatching chicks under a broody hen. Mr J. G. Rhynehart, of the Ministry of Agriculture, informed the Fermanagh County Committee of Agriculture that the Ministry would subsidise four incubators in the county that year and in subsequent years. Incubators cost about £10 and the Ministry would contribute half the cost. It was pointed out by Miss Callery, Poultry Instructress, that nine or ten Station-holders already had incubators.

In advancing a case at that time for Mrs F. R. Browne's poultry farm at Lakeview, Enniskillen, to be considered as a demonstration farm, Miss Callery wrote as follows: *This farm is run on very up-to-date lines. The stock kept include the principal utility breeds viz. White Wyandottes, White Leghorns, Rhode Island Reds, Light Sussex, and some good first crosses of these breeds have been bred to a very high standard of egg production and general utility requirements.*

Lisnaskea Poultry Club outing to E. F. Fairbairns' hatchery in late 1960s. Seated from left: Mrs E. M. Armstrong, Keeranbeg House; Mrs Moore of Coaghroe. Standing from left: Mrs Andrew Wigham, Castlebalfour; James Hall of Tullynevin; Unknown (Courtesy of Miss J. Armstrong).

Poultry Clubs and Foxes

Poultry Clubs, which had a great social as well as an educational value, were promoted strongly by the Ulster Farmers' Union (UFU) in 1933 when that organisation appointed a Poultry Organiser. At that time poultry was regarded as the only profitable enterprise in the depressed state of the farming industry. As all poultry were free range at that time foxes were a real threat.

The UFU in September 1936 and the Ballinamallard Poultry Club in January 1937 sent resolutions to the County Fermanagh Committee of Agriculture asking for a scheme to control foxes. The County Committee responded positively and introduced a scheme offering five shillings per fox brought to a police station with a total budget for the county for the year of £30. Other Poultry Clubs were formed later at Lisbellaw and Lisnaskea.

Mr William Dunn with a large dog fox (Courtesy of Mr W. Dunn).

Local successes

Performance testing by way of Egg Laying Tests was initiated at the Stormont farm in 1923 and continued until 1958 when it was replaced by Gosford Poultry Testing Station in 1960. In 1944 local flock owners were having success in the Stormont Egg Laying Tests. Successful exhibitors included: Mrs Armstrong, Ballindullagh; Mr Harry Bamford, Cavanaleck, Fivemiletown; and Mrs Charleton, Eaglemount, Lisnaskea. Mrs E. M. Rea of Tullynagowan, Brookeborough, was a prize winner in the Laying Tests in 1946. Other winners were Mrs A. J. Veitch, Drumlone, for White Wyandottes; Mrs W. Johnston, Mountdarby, Coranny; and Mrs P. J. McElroy, Lismalore, Brookeborough.

Success was not limited to the Egg Laying Tests. In May 1945 there was a feature in the local papers entitled: *'Fermanagh*

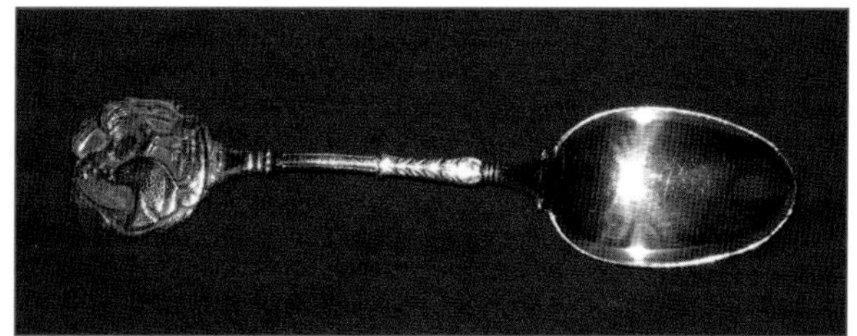

Silver spoon presented by the Ministry of Agriculture to Mrs E. M. Armstrong, Keeranbeg House, Magheraveely, for success in the Stormont Laying Tests in the 1940s (Courtesy of Miss J. Armstrong).

man's success with poultry'. The article described how Mr Thomas Kernaghan, who farmed 10 acres at Greenhill, Brookeborough, had made a success of the enterprise.

Accredited Hatcheries

The Accredited Farm Scheme came into operation in 1935 for the purpose of supplying hatching eggs from pure breds and first crosses to commercial hatcheries which were a recent development. Accredited Farms, unlike the egg distributing stations, could keep two pure breeds and could use these for cross breeding. In 1945/46 a Register of Accredited Hatcheries appeared for the first time. The purpose of the scheme was to ensure that all chicks supplied were vigorous and healthy. These gradually replaced the small private hatcheries and also the small breeding farms which sold eggs for hatching and also chickens as hatched to neighbouring farms. The first of these Accredited Hatcheries serving the Fermanagh area belonged to Mr John McCarney of Fivemiletown. By January 1950 there were three additional hatcheries serving Fermanagh. These were Erne Hatchery, Queen Street, Enniskillen; Enniskillen Hatcheries, Ballycassidy, Ballinamallard; and E. F. Fairbairn Ltd, Tempo Road, Enniskillen. It was normal practice in those days for day-old chicks to be transported by public transport and left off at some pre-arranged collection spot for the poultry keeper.

Deep litter

As well as breeding developments, changes in housing methods brought about a revolution in poultry keeping. Up until the early 1950s most poultry were on free range. The introduction of deep litter whereby hens were housed all the time was a considerable advance and was strongly promoted by the Poultry Advisory Service. This was a major advance on free range in relation to increasing output, labour efficiency and ease of management.

Good ventilation and insulation were two prerequisites for a successful deep litter house. Natural lighting with well distributed windows (equivalent in area to 5 to 7 per cent of floor area) and whitewashed internal walls were also essentials. A source of artificial light to extend the day

Mr Dick Cullen, who had a shop in Clabby, setting out on his country run. An empty egg case can be seen on the top of meal bags.

Mrs Ellen Bannon, Kilnamadoo, Boho, feeding her mixed flock of laying hens in 1950 (Courtesy of Sister Edel Bannon).

length to not more than 14 hours was allowed. Peat moss or wood shavings were the source of floor litter and it was recommended that the building up process of this material should begin in August. This enabled the bacteria, which made the system work, to develop during favourable warm weather. It was important that the litter was kept dry and loose in order to provide a suitable scratching medium for the birds and to keep diseases, parasites and vices under control. The application of small quantities of hydrated lime was helpful in achieving this. The maximum stocking density in a deep litter house was 3 square feet per hen.

The objective of the deep litter system was to keep the hens in a controlled environment which would favour egg production. Another benefit was that droppings did not have to be removed on a regular basis. It was important to have proper atmospheric conditions in the house, so that evaporation of the moisture content of the droppings could proceed actively through bacterial activity. Keeping the temperature up to a reasonable level during the colder months was particularly helpful. Lofts, barns and other types of housing were adapted for this new system of keeping hens. In addition, new deep litter houses were erected in Fermanagh under the Marginal Land Scheme. This led to improved productivity from hens and also eased management. Wire floors were the next major development in poultry housing.

A deep litter house on the Elliott farm at Drumconnis, Ballinamallard.

Hybrid hens

In the mid 1950s, hybrid poultry made their appearance. These were crosses, developed commercially, which produced birds of uniform type. They were bred to eat the minimum amount of food and produce a large number of good sized eggs. These hybrids had names like White Link, Brownegger and Hyline 840. At the same time similar developments in turkey breeding led to the production of broad breasted strains.

The Ministry of Agriculture's Gosford Poultry Testing Station, Armagh, served to test commercial hybrid stock and in this way informed commercial egg producers as to the best performing stock. Samples of hatching eggs were drawn, hatched and reared at Gosford with the pullets being transferred to battery laying cages at about point-of- lay around 21 weeks. Egg output was then recorded over a 50-week laying period. In 1966 day-old pullets were brought into the station rather than hatching eggs.

Battery cages

Battery cages increased rapidly in use from 1963. This coincided with the introduction of a clean egg scheme by the British Egg Marketing Board (BEMB). Northern Ireland was used by the BEMB as the area in which to launch a pilot scheme to encourage the supply of clean, unwashed eggs. Producers were paid an incentive for eggs that were naturally clean or dry cleaned. Eggs that were washed, but otherwise of first quality, incurred a penalty. The production of clean eggs was much easier using battery cages than using the deep litter system. Furthermore, automation in relation to feeding and egg collection was easily integrated into the system.

Battery cages on the Erne Eggs production unit.

Eggs coming from the cages on a conveyor belt.

Battery cages came under political pressure within the European Union (EU) towards the end of the century on welfare grounds. EU legislation was introduced in 1999 initially specifying an increased space allowance, from 450 to 550 square centimetres per bird, with the eventual phasing out of conventional cages.

Poultry feeds

Considerable changes in feeding accompanied the changes in breeding and housing. In the 1920s yellow meal or maize meal and flaked maize, oats and home grown potatoes formed a major part of the diet. The potatoes were boiled and fed in a mixture with the other feeds. It was not until after the Second World War and the development of the deep litter system that progress was made in the use of balanced rations.

Egg marketing

In the early days the general merchant who had a travelling lorry which brought groceries and meal to the farm also bought the eggs. These merchants were licensed. From 1927, under the Egg Marketing Act, the sale of dirty, stained or soiled eggs was prohibited. Eggs were tested for quality and the use of standard egg boxes was a requirement. Under the 1947 Agriculture Act, eggs like other agricultural produce were assured of a guaranteed price, which brought stability to the market. Rationing and price control of eggs was abolished in 1954. In 1957 the British Egg Marketing Board took over marketing responsibilities.

Egg quality was the topic for discussion and demonstration for a sizeable number of producers in Enniskillen Agricultural College in February 1970. Speakers, including Dr R. H. Montgomery from the Egg Marketing Division of the Ministry, addressed the meeting which was chaired by Miss Elsie Dickson, Poultry Adviser for the Ministry in County Fermanagh. Press articles written by Miss Dickson on poultry topics appeared in the local press at regular intervals during the 1970s. Later that year, the future of the poultry industry was the subject of a meeting held in Enniskillen Agricultural College. Speakers included Mr Tom McCluggage, the Ministry's Chief Poultry Adviser, Mr Newell Bingham, Manager of Gosford Poultry Testing Station and Dr Brian McFerran, Veterinary Research Laboratories. This meeting, under the chairmanship of Mr T. A. Larmour, Deputy Chief Inspector of the Ministry of Agriculture, was held to prepare producers for the demise of the British Egg Marketing Board.

Egg quality

An Egg Quality Scheme was introduced by the Ministry of Agriculture in Northern Ireland in 1970. It was a voluntary scheme and the Ministry appealed to producers who were supplying more than 75 dozen eggs each week to participate. The purpose of the scheme was to further secure a market for Northern Ireland eggs on the English market by offering for export only those eggs of a very high quality. Egg quality was determined by shell thickness and thickness of the egg white.

Poultry Instructors and Advisers

Mr Ferris was the first Poultry Instructor employed by the Fermanagh County Committee of Agriculture. Miss Murphy succeeded Mr Ferris who in turn was followed by Miss Johnston, who had previously worked for the Roscommon County Committee of Agriculture. Miss O'Hanlon then served until she was succeeded by Miss A. M. Callery in 1926. Others who served as Poultry Instructors or Advisers in Fermanagh included Miss Hamilton, Miss Ruby Walker, Miss Magowan, Miss Terry Fahy and Miss Elsie Dickson.

Broiler growing was a new industry in the 1950s.

Decline and specialisation

The introduction of high performing breeds of poultry, together with battery cages in controlled environment houses, and ease of mechanisation all combined to turn the laying poultry enterprise into a highly commercial business. Land, other than for spreading droppings, was not required. Poultry units in specialised houses sprang up around the country and the enterprise which had been so important economically on the small farms of Northern Ireland gradually moved into the hands of a few large producers. Broiler and turkey production, which again had

The Erne Eggs production unit and the Ready Egg Products processing plant at Manorwaterhouse, Lisnaskea.

been valuable on the small farms, followed a similar pattern. Broilers, which became the basis of table poultry production, were treated similarly to laying hens in terms of breeding, feeding and management. The birds were specially bred to produce the maximum yield of meat in the shortest possible time. They were fed rations and kept under a management regime that achieved their full potential.

County Fermanagh has not been left behind in the changes that have taken place in this sector of the agricultural industry. Mr Charles Crawford of Manorwaterhouse, Lisnaskea, owner of Erne Eggs Ltd, has become the largest egg producer in Ireland and one of the largest in the United Kingdom.

Adding value

Mr Charles Crawford established Ferne Foods Ltd in 1991 at Manorwaterhouse, in a modern factory on a site located a short distance from his egg producing unit. The primary reason for this development was to create additional employment and to add value to the eggs produced on the Erne Eggs farm. The eggs were processed into egg burgers and other products for the catering trade. Later, an opportunity arose in partnership with Moy Park Ltd to diversify the factory production to include the processing of chicken. Mr Crawford sold his interest in Ferne Foods to Moy Park Ltd in the year 2000 and then set about establishing an egg processing plant adjacent to his egg producing unit. In addition to eggs supplied from the farm a substantial number are bought in from other sources. Egg products supplied to the catering trade, mainly in England, include boiled eggs, egg whites and egg yolks – the latter two in different formulations to meet the savoury and dessert demands in the market.

Rise and fall

An indication of the prosperity of the poultry enterprise can be gauged from the trend in numbers of birds kept on farms. In the early part of the century the bird population on farms in County Fermanagh was just over half a million. Numbers grew steadily to a peak of over three quarters of a million in 1912. The First World War, with the shortage of imported grain, led to a marginal decline. Numbers then climbed steadily and by 1930 were approaching 900,000. The Second World War did not have the same impact on

Lord Lyell, Northern Ireland Minister of Agriculture, centre, on a visit to Ferne Foods Ltd in the early 1990s. From left are Mr Geoff Saulters, SHS Distributors, Mr Charles Crawford, Chairman, Ferne Foods Ltd, Mr Harry Steele, Director Ferne Foods Ltd and Mr Hugh Kirkpatrick, Chief Agricultural Officer, Department of Agriculture (Courtesy of Mr Charles Crawford).

Ready Egg Products.

poultry numbers as occurred during the First World War. Farmers were better equipped to grow cereals (over double the acreage) during the latter conflict, especially oats, which was a suitable feed for poultry. Due to the relative availability of home grown oats, and an attractive pricing structure for eggs and poultry, numbers expanded very significantly. At the outbreak of the Second World War in 1939 the poultry population in Fermanagh was just under one million. In 1941 it had reached 1.35 million birds and in 1943 poultry numbers were 1.5 million. Numbers peaked during the last year of the war at just over 1.6 million. These numbers were maintained until 1950, but thereafter the population declined very steadily over the years and reached a figure of less than half a million in the year 2000, which was a lower number than existed at the beginning of the century. The pattern of poultry keeping changed dramatically during the century. At the beginning of the century practically every farmer and country dweller kept poultry. At the end of the century, Mr Charles Crawford, on an intensive poultry farm at Lisnaskea, had almost as many hens as all the County Fermanagh farmers put together at the beginning of the century.

References:

The Ministry/Department of Agriculture's *Monthly Reports* and Agriculture in Northern Ireland.

Files of the *The Impartial Reporter, Fermanagh Herald* and *Belfast Newsletter.*

MacLurg, Alastair, *The Ulster Farmers'Union – History of its first Seventy Years 1917 -1987.*

Free range geese, which are in demand at Christmas, are still a feature on some Fermanagh farms (Courtesy of James Elliott).

Chapter 23
Forestry in County Fermanagh

Mr John Phillips, District Forest Officer in Fermanagh, when writing about forestry development in the county in May 1959 pointed out that in ancient times Fermanagh was heavily wooded. He stated that there were over 100 townlands in the county with the prefix *'derry'* which means 'oak wood'. He also indicated that the mountainous areas had Scots pine and birch woodlands. Climate change and reclamation for farming purposes over the centuries reduced the area of woodland very considerably. In addition, the felling of trees during the First and Second World Wars meant that little woodland remained by the mid 1900s. One of the Ministry of Agriculture's aims in afforestation policy in the early years was to arrest rural depopulation by establishing forests in areas where land was of little agricultural value.

Native birch woodland at Knockmanoul/Drumcullion bog in early Spring.

Early years

In the early years of the century land offered by farmers to the Ministry in Fermanagh was often refused on the grounds that it was unsuitable for planting. In some cases the areas offered were considered to be too small to be of value for afforestation. Acquisitions in the early days were largely limited to old estate woodlands. Castlecaldwell Estate, extending to 300 acres, was purchased by the Ministry in 1913. In 1930 the Enniskillen Chamber of Commerce sent the following letter to the County Committee of Agriculture for consideration: *The Enniskillen Chamber of Commerce desires to point out to the Minister of Agriculture that the County of Fermanagh is rapidly becoming denuded of trees and plantations, and we respectfully request the Ministry of Agriculture to push forward extensive schemes of re-afforestation in the county both for utilitarian and ornamental purposes especially as the Government has not advanced any schemes for the benefit of County Fermanagh.* The Ministry in reply stated that efforts had been made to acquire land in the county but in situations where suitable land appeared to be available the owners either declined to sell or refused to accept the price offered.

Expansion and employment

In 1938 afforestation was being encouraged by the County Committee of Agriculture. At a meeting it was reported that 200 acres had been planted in trees at Tubrid. A member of the County Committee of Agriculture obviously approved of this action as he stated that the land being planted *'would not feed a goat'*. By the beginning of the Second World War the area owned by the Forest Service of the Ministry of Agriculture in Fermanagh was almost 2,000 acres with substantial areas at Kesh and Ely Lodge. The area had increased to a total of 2,500 acres by 1947. Twelve years later the area owned had reached 25,000 acres with 10,000 acres of that planted.

Young plantation near Derrygonnelly.

Young forest on poor hill land in west Fermanagh.

This rapid expansion in land acquisition and planting was accompanied by a corresponding increase in employment. By 1947, forty-three forestry workers were employed and by 1959 there were 250 permanent employees and a temporary work force of over 200 men. In addition to these, there were two District Forest Officers and 19 Foresters employed in the county. The Forest Service provided groups of new houses with modern facilities to accommodate forest workers. In 1959 fifty such houses had been built.

Trees planted

The choice of trees planted was limited because of the poor quality and exposure of the available land. Sitka Spruce was the main choice with much smaller areas of other conifers like pines, larches and silver firs. Fermanagh suits tree growth and can boast some of the fastest growing forests in Europe. At Castlecaldwell some trees had reached 100 feet in height after only 38 years. Forest nurseries were developed on good agricultural land at Pubble and Rosslea. In 1959 the Pubble nursery was producing two million plants per year.

Growth

By 1961, 28,000 acres had been purchased for afforestation in Fermanagh. In 1981 this area had extended to over 53,000 acres and in 1993 to over 55,000 acres, which equated to about 13 per cent of the land area of County Fermanagh. In 1993 around 41,000 acres had been planted in trees which represented 10 per cent of the total area of the land in the county. At that time it was considered that of the remaining 14,000 acres only one tenth was plantable.

Native woodland on the scarp slope of Knockmore, Derrygonnelly.

These two houses are beautifully located in mature woodland.

The remainder was largely comprised of very high exposed areas, rocky outcrops, areas of turbary, nature reserves and small areas remaining in agriculture. The remainder was largely comprised of very high exposed areas, rocky outcrops, areas of turbary, nature reserves and small areas remaining in agriculture.

At the end of the century the Forest Service owned 23,006 hectares in Fermanagh. Of this area 5,515 hectares remained unplanted. Conifers accounted for 15,205 hectares with broadleaves accounting for 1,911 hectares and mixed plantations comprising 375 hectares.

Other woodlands

Grant aided planting which was in private ownership amounted to 1,830 hectares at the end of the century. The largest proportion of this, 1,121 hectares, was mixed woodland with broadleaves accounting for 497 hectares and conifers 212 hectares.

Other woodlands in the county, estimated from aerial photography, amount to around 3,000 hectares. These native woodlands are mainly found on the shores of Upper and Lower Lough Erne, scarps, steep ground, river banks and lowland bogs.

Tree choice

Commercially, afforestation in County Fermanagh is dependent mainly on two species of Western North American origin, Sitka Spruce and Lodgepole Pine. In 1981 the forests in Fermanagh were comprised of 73 per cent Sitka Spruce, 10 per cent Norway Spruce and 10 per cent Lodgepole Pine. Norway Spruce has a higher quality site requirement and lower timber yields than Sitka

Forestry in the landscape at Florencecourt (Courtesy of the Forest Service).

Harvesting operations at Navar forest (Courtesy of Forest Service).

Spruce and is therefore being used less. Lodgepole Pine is a comparatively low yielder but will survive on poor sites with much lower fertiliser inputs than Sitka Spruce.

Environmental considerations

The Department's current planting practice dictates that in upland areas not more than 75 per cent of the planted area can consist of the primary species. At least 10 per cent must comprise open space and more than five per cent must remain for natural regeneration of broadleaf woodland. Biodiversity is a major consideration and over 10 per cent of the area must be managed with this objective as a priority.

Environmental issues are a major consideration when replanting after harvesting a crop of timber. The design for replanting takes into consideration such issues as minimising risks from wind damage, fire, pests and diseases. At least 15 per cent of the replanted area is managed in a manner giving primary consideration to conservation and enhancement of biodiversity. Areas are also being restored to semi-natural woodland or non-woodland habitat.

Avoidance of water pollution is a major concern. In the case of watercourses more than two metres wide, or lakes, planting does not come any closer to the water than 20 metres. In the case of watercourses one to two metres wide a 10 metre distance must be maintained and where one metre wide watercourses are involved a five metre space is kept.

Landscape is also an important factor. Planting widths are varied and reflect local topography and where possible they link up with other native woodland on adjacent land.

Forest values

Timber production, calculated at 73,000 cubic metres per year in 1993, was estimated to reach 100,000 cubic metres at the end of the twentieth century.

Forests have other values apart from timber production. In Fermanagh they make a tremendous contribution to recreation and tourism development. There are major forest parks at Florencecourt, the scenic drive at Lough

Mr John Hetherington, Managing Director of Premier Woodlands Limited (Courtesy of Premier Woodlands Ltd).

Sunset at Navar forest
(Courtesy of Forest Service).

Navar and other facilities at Castlecaldwell, Clonelly, Castle Archdale, Ely Lodge, Magho and Naan Island. In addition, forest land provides 25 miles of the Ulster Way. Plantations also make a valuable contribution to nature conservation as well as to landscape enhancement. They contribute to the diversity of habitat available for wildlife. Sites of high natural history interest within the forests have been carefully preserved with the establishment of six National Nature Reserves, 14 Forest Nature Reserves and many other conservation areas within the forest estate. In some forest areas excellent sporting opportunities exist for rough and managed shoots.

Private forestry

Whilst most of the forests in County Fermanagh are owned by the Department of Agriculture and Rural Development's Forest Service privately owned forests, especially on the estates and larger farms, are also important. Increasingly, private forests are managed by professionals specialising in woodland management. Premier Woodlands Limited is the largest company in Northern Ireland providing these services. Its managing director, Mr John Hetherington, is a Fermanagh man who lives at Clabby. His company specialises in every aspect of acquisition, establishment, management, maintenance and harvesting of woodlands. The company's clients vary from small farmers to large land owners and investors located throughout Ireland, Scotland and a few in England. Premier also looks after a small number of overseas investors who are attracted to owning large areas of woodland in Scotland. Private woodland establishment has changed from the 1960s to the 1980s when attractive taxation concessions led to a few large moorland areas being planted with conifers. At present attractive grant aid is leading to many smaller areas on farmland being planted mainly with native broadleaves.

Timber processing

County Fermanagh is home to one of Britain and Ireland's largest wood products suppliers, Balcas Ltd. The plant at Enniskillen uses timber grown in Fermanagh and from throughout Ireland. The company also has plants in Kildare and Scotland. Its extensive product range includes construction timber, fencing products, internal mouldings, pallet and packaging products. A new development has been the production of *brites* which is a product made from sawdust and is well suited as a fuel for domestic and larger scale central heating systems. Waste material from the sawmill is used to generate electricity for the grid. Employment is stated to be 700 with an additional 300 engaged in forest harvesting and haulage

References:

Files of *The Impartial Reporter* and *Fermanagh Herald* held in Enniskillen Library.

Ministry/ Department of Agriculture's *Monthly Reports* and *Agriculture in Northern Ireland.*

Institute of Biology conference papers on *The Biological Potential of County Fermanagh, October 1981.*

The Balcas plant at Ballycassidy, Enniskillen.

Chapter 24
Farming and the Environment

County Fermanagh is internationally renowned for its distinctive landscape and the abundance and variety of its wildlife. Its habitats include some of the best wetland sites in the United Kingdom. Colourful hay meadows, extensive areas of woodland and scrub, blanket bogs, mountains and moorland are all very important not only for their landscape value but also in supporting a wide range of flora and fauna.

An indication of Fermanagh's environmental importance is derived from the number of areas specially designated for protection by the Northern Ireland Environment Agency. This Agency is the body responsible for advising on and implementing the Government's environmental policy and strategy. Sixty-seven Areas of Special Scientific Interest have been designated in the county. These are defined as being among Northern Ireland's very best wildlife and geological sites. In addition, there are 11 Special Areas of Conservation, two Special Protection Areas and three Ramsar sites which are wetlands of international importance.

Farming threats

Throughout most of the twentieth century the farmers' main role has been to produce food. The experience of the two World Wars determined that adequate food should be produced at home. Changes in farming systems in Fermanagh over the century have also had an impact. Arable cropping, which was especially important during both wars, declined in importance from the 1960s and was replaced by almost exclusively grassland based farming systems. One impact of this was a noticeable change in bird populations. For example, Yellow Hammers and Grey Partridge were quite common when cropping was widespread but are now extinct in the county. Red Grouse which were common on heather moorlands in the 1960s are now quite rare.

Yellow Hammer
(Photograph by Andy Hay. RSPB-images.com).

Fermanagh has a distinctive landscape and a wide range of habitats.

Grey Partridge
(Photograph by Chris Gomersall. RSPB-images.com).

Corncrake
(Photograph by Chris Gomersall. RSPB-images.com).

Corncrakes, which came from southern Africa to breed during the summer months, were very common in the meadows of County Fermanagh until the 1970s. They became extinct during the 1980s. Intensification of grassland farming with earlier cutting of silage compared to the traditional crops of hay was claimed to be a major contributing factor leading to the decline and eventual extinction of the corncrake. However, there may be other factors involved as the corncrake also disappeared from those areas of the county where traditional methods of fodder with late cutting dates were maintained.

New birds have appeared or reappeared including the introduced Canada geese. Buzzards at the end of the century were quite a common site in many parts of the county.

Drainage schemes, both arterial and field, have altered habitats with consequent changes in both flora and fauna. Afforestation in the hills, where heather has been replaced by conifer trees, has also impacted on bird populations. Increased levels of fertility in farm land and intensification of livestock farming have brought undesirable changes in water quality.

Flax

Fibre crops, notably flax, required for aircraft manufacture and other purposes especially during the war years were also important. It was in connection with flax production that one of the first environmental threats was observed. The farm processing of flax involved dam retting. Flax was pulled by hand or machine, tied into beets (like sheaves) using bands made from rushes, and placed in a dam. The flax beets were packed in the dam and weighted down using stones so that all the material was under the surface level of the water. A biological process known as retting within the dam was usually completed in 7 to 10 days. The purpose of the retting was to aid scutching, the process of separating the fibre from the woody core of the plant. After retting, the flax was removed from the dam, spread on the land for drying, then tied into beets again. When perfectly dry it was stacked or put in a shed before going to the scutching mill.

Removing flax from the dam
[Courtesy of Ulster Folk and Transport Museum (NMNI)].

Canada geese are now of pest proportions on some grassland farms close to loughs.

Serious pollutant

The water remaining in the dam after the flax was removed at the end of the retting process was a serious pollutant when allowed to enter watercourses. It had a very high biochemical oxygen demand (BOD), depriving fish and invertebrates of an oxygen supply in the water and as a consequence a watercourse could be left devoid of aquatic life. The adverse effect of the process on waterways in Ireland has been documented as far back as 1913. At that time Augustus Grimble, in his book *The Salmon Rivers of Ireland,* when commenting on the deterioration of the River Deele in Donegal wrote as follows: *Then flax cultivation began, and has increased to such an extent that at length the pollution has destroyed all vestige of fish life.*

The Northern Ireland Flax Water Committee in 1923 carried out experiments on the effect of flax water on fish life. They put yearling and two year old trout into various strengths of flax water and found that even small quantities in river water caused casualties among the fish and in other life within the river water.

The Committee recommended growers to construct catch dams well away from the river bank and that the contents should not be released before January unless a heavy flood came earlier. If a catch dam could not be used it was recommended that the flax water be allowed to flow over land. Alternatively, the flax water could be allowed to flow from the retting dam through a small bore pipe slowly enough to ensure that it was very thoroughly diluted with pure water as it reached the stream. This method was regarded as highly dangerous especially if other farmers were using a similar approach on the same stream. It was recommended that this method should not be adopted without competent advice.

Undrinkable

Not only did the flax water destroy river life, it also left the water undrinkable by animals or humans. If a pollution incident of this nature occurred, a considerable length of time was required to enable the watercourse to regain its former condition. Fortunately dam retting of flax only took place for a relatively short period during the summer months, consequently the pollution risk was for a comparatively short time span. Regular warnings were issued to farmers at the critical time of the year regarding this environmental threat. Under the Fisheries (Flax Water Act) 1947 it was an offence to steep flax in any river or lake or to allow flax water to flow into any river or lake at any time. The Act also required the provision of catch dams for disposing of the flax water.

Another early potential threat to watercourses was the discharge of sheep dip from dipping baths. Many of these were constructed perilously near rivers where there was a ready supply of water to fill the dipping bath. Unfortunately locating baths on such sites left the river very vulnerable to discharges of spent dip and indeed contamination from freshly dipped sheep. This often had serious consequences for aquatic life over a considerable distance down stream.

Early awareness

With regard to farm waste pollution, the value of retaining liquid manure as a fertiliser has been recognised for a very long time. When commenting on a competition for cottages and small farms in 1906 run by the Fermanagh County Committee of Agriculture, the judge, Mr James Bradshaw, made comment on the arrangements of the manure heap when he reported on the Small Farm Section of the competition. He stated: "*In connection with the handling of the manure, it should be noted that in far too many cases the rain water from nearly all the buildings is allowed to run down either into the heap or alongside it. This should be remedied at once by the use of spouting along the eaves of the buildings.* In relation to the Cottage Section he said: *The arrangement of the manure heap is not always up to the mark. Provision may be made – and often is – for utilising the liquid, but the heap itself is too often not compactly built, it covers too much ground and therefore catches too much rain. This should be remedied at once, and the manure built on as small an area of ground as possible, and where turf mould can be obtained it should be liberally used to absorb the liquid that drains from the heap.*" It is certain that Mr Bradshaw had in mind the conservation of the maximum amount of nutrients for fertilising the land but of course at the same time pollution from this source would also have been minimised.

Silage effluent and slurry

When silage was first promoted in the early 1940s there was little reference to the risks arising from silage effluent pollution. However, quantities on individual farms at that time were small and the material being ensiled would have been relatively mature and as a consequence effluent run-off would have been minimal. The Agricultural Development Scheme of 1949 offered grants for silos and farm sewage disposal. It also covered dams for the collection and storage of flax water. Subsequent schemes had provision for farm waste disposal. It was not until the late 1950s with the advent of the Farm Improvement Scheme and the growth in popularity of silage that serious provision was made for silage effluent. The 1960s and 1970s witnessed the introduction of loose housing of stock and the move away from bedding with straw. This together with the development of loose housing systems using cubicles and slats meant that on those farms most of the animal waste, including silage effluent, was handled as slurry in

The silage effluent in this case is draining into a tank – otherwise it could cause serious damage if it gained access to a watercourse. Mr Mervyn Simpson, Farm Buildings Officer DANI, is carrying out an inspection.

A serious fish kill in a Fermanagh river caused by farm effluent.

An algal bloom in mid-summer in a sheltered bay in Lower Lough Erne. Fortunately, algal blooms of this intensity are rare and are always localised. (Courtesy of Dr Patrick McGurn).

specially designed tanks. The slurry in due course was then spread on the land. Despite the progress made in dealing with these farm wastes problems arose on farms from time to time. Silage effluent is a particularly pollutant material and in most years prosecutions were taken by the Fisheries Conservancy Board against individual farmers for causing pollution of water courses from this source. Effluent starts to flow within a few hours of grass being ensiled, peaks within a few days and can continue to run for several months. The quantity of effluent produced from silage is mainly determined by the moisture content of the grass being ensiled. If grass is wilted to around 25 per cent dry matter the effluent may only amount to a trickle but if the material ensiled is very wet, at say 15 per cent moisture content, effluent production could amount to 300 litres per tonne or 60 gallons per ton. As little as one litre of silage effluent entering a river can reduce the oxygen content of 1,000 litres of water to a critical level for the survival of fish.

Apart from point-source pollution from farmyards there are other sources of pollution entering watercourses. These include effluent from septic tanks attached to dwellings and village and town sewage works. These sources may have a similar damaging impact as silage or other farm source effluent on watercourses resulting in immediate fish kills. However, they can also have a longer term detrimental impact on water quality in rivers and lakes through causing nutrient enrichment.

In addition to point-source pollution, diffuse pollution exists. Pollution is referred to as diffuse where there is no distinct point of discharge. Farming activities can cause significant diffuse pollution problems through loss of nutrients such as phosphorus and nitrogen. This nutrient enrichment can have a long term detrimental impact on water quality in rivers and lakes.

Nutrient enrichment of Lough Erne

Fifty-four percent of the catchment of Lough Erne is within the Irish Republic. It has been shown from a study of sediments in the bottom of the lough that nutrient enrichment began at the beginning of the 20th century and increased slowly until the 1950s and then increased rapidly until 1975. The steep rise from the 1950s coincided with urban migration and the development of water supplies and septic tanks in rural areas. In addition, farming intensified during this period with increased fertiliser usage. Afforestation, requiring the use of fertilisers, was also growing rapidly at this time. Since 1974 phosphorus inflows from the different rivers have been measured. From 1974 until 1989 there had been no change in the total amount. The contribution from the Republic of Ireland per unit area of catchment was no greater than from County Fermanagh. It was estimated in 1992 that the Irish Republic contributed 45 per cent of the nutrients to the Erne system. Within Fermanagh, the Colebrooke and Ballinamallard rivers contribute significantly more than any other river per unit of land area. These river catchments include

the more intensive farming areas in Fermanagh and contain a number of towns and villages with sewage works. Higher levels of nutrient enrichment occur in wet years. However, this makes little difference to the concentration of nutrients in the loughs because of the corresponding greater outflow. Within Fermanagh, the Colebrooke and Ballinamallard rivers contribute significantly more than any other river per unit of land area. These river catchments include the more intensive farming areas in the Fermanagh and contain a number of towns and villages with sewage works. Higher levels of nutrient enrichment occur in wet years. However, this makes little difference to the concentration of nutrients in the loughs because of the corresponding greater outflow.

Eutrophication is the term used to describe the process of nutrient enrichment, where a body of water gradually changes from a nutrient poor state (oligotrophic) to a nutrient rich state (eutrophic). Lower Lough Erne is classified as eutrophic whereas Upper Lough Erne falls into the hypertrophic (very nutrient rich) class.

Phosphorus the cause

Research work at Lough Neagh by the Department of Agriculture's Freshwater Biological Investigation Unit (FBIU) and by research workers from the University of Ulster in the 1970s showed that deterioration of the water quality in the lough was due to increased algal growth which was fuelled by phosphorus enrichment of the water. The phosphorus was found to be coming from sewage works, farmyards and septic tanks and also from run-off and through drainage of farmland. At low levels of application phosphorus applied as fertiliser to farmland is held by the soil. Increasing soil phosphorus levels increases the rate at which the nutrient is lost from the soil through surface run-off and also through drainage. In peaty soils the phosphorus is not locked in the soil to the same extent as in mineral soils and losses through drainage from applied phosphorus are much greater. This is of particular significance where poor peat soils have been afforested and where substantial quantities of phosphorus are necessary to ensure reasonable tree growth rates.

The value of phosphorus as a plant food has been fully appreciated over the years. It was the element that was found to be most deficient in the soils of County Fermanagh particularly after the damage done to soil fertility following Compulsory Tillage during and after the two World Wars. Fertilisers containing phosphorus have been applied to crops and grassland over the years to increase yields and improve the quality of the produce. Indeed fertilisers with a reasonable level of phosphorus, as a fertility building measure, were a requirement for Grassland Improvement Schemes which were eligible for grant aid over the years. Increased usage of fertiliser containing phosphorus and the feeding of imported meal (which also contained phosphorus) to livestock meant that levels of the element would build up in the soil, particularly on intensive farms. It has been estimated that the amount of phosphorus in animal excreta produced had almost doubled during the period 1850 to 1990 in County Fermanagh.

Sources of phosphorus

In 1997 Lough Neagh was regarded as the most phosphorus rich lough in Ireland. It was followed by Upper Lough Erne (just over half the phosphorus concentration of Lough Neagh) and then by Lower Lough Erne (less than half of Lough Neagh's phosphorus concentration). Fifty-eight percent of Lough Neagh's phosphorus was calculated to come from agricultural sources whereas it was 73 per cent in the case of Lough Erne. In addition to the fertilisers containing phosphorus applied to farmland, substantial quantities of ground rock phosphate have been applied to encourage tree growth in the upland areas of Fermanagh which have been afforested.

Mr Connor Maguire, Agricultural Adviser, with Conor O'Harte, Newtownbutler, taking a soil sample.

Need for balance

In 1977 the concept of farm nutrient balance was being promoted by Dr McAllister and Dr Adams of the Department of Agriculture's Agricultural and Food Chemistry Division. They indicated that in Northern Ireland the nutrients contained in imported animal feedingstuffs and in applied fertiliser exceeded those contained in exported crop and animal products. They showed that soil analyses indicated that levels of phosphorus and potassium were building up in Northern Ireland soils. They stated that if phosphorus and potassium levels were already high there was no production benefit to be gained by increasing them and that there could be a pollution risk. They showed how the nutrient balance on individual farms could be calculated. The nutrients available in the excreta of the livestock during the grazing season and applied as slurry could be compared to nutrients required by the crops grown. The information gained as to whether the farm was in negative or positive balance in relation to phosphorus and potassium, together with a regular soil analysis of individual fields, was described as a useful guide in relation to farm fertiliser policy.

Castle Archdale trials

Trials at Castle Archdale carried out by Dr H. I. Gracey from Greenmount Agricultural College and the Farm Director, Mr D. G. O'Neill, from 1979 until 1982 showed that on soils with a phosphate index of 1 or 2 the application of slurry and fertiliser containing nitrogen only, gave similar yields of silage over first and second cuts, when compared to the use of a compound fertiliser which contained phosphorus. They also showed that taking silage cuts removes three times as much potassium as phosphorus. At Greenmount Agricultural College on a silage field, where the soil index for phosphorus was 4, the omission of phosphorus from the fertiliser treatment over an eight year period did not reduce silage yields.

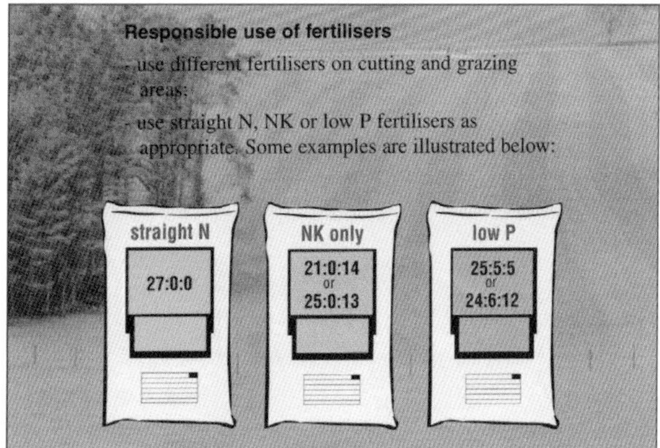

Extract from DARD's advisory leaflet on the responsible use of phosphorus fertiliser.

Colebrooke River initiative

A water quality study on the Colebrooke River was carried out in 1990 by Dr R. H. Foy of the Department of Agriculture's Aquatic Sciences Research Division, based at Greenmount Agricultural College. In that study it was shown that five of the sub-catchments were outside the good quality class. One of these was in the poor quality category. The main Colebrooke River remained in the top quality (Class 1) throughout its length.

As a follow-up to the above study, the County Agriculture Development Service in Fermanagh targeted the Colebrooke River catchment for an advisory programme during the period 1992 to 1995. The programme was specifically aimed at reducing point-source pollution from farms. All farms in the catchment were visited and assessed for pollution risk. Four hundred and thirty-four farms were visited and it was discovered that slightly over half of the farms had potential problems. In the Tempo River part of the catchment 224 farms were visited and 118 of these had potential problems. The major problems, each occurring 76 times, arose from leaking silos and polluted run-off from farmyards. Failure to collect storm water and allowing rainwater to wash across areas covered with manure or slurry caused the polluted run-off from the farmyards. Next in importance was stockyard contamination which occurred 59 times. Problems associated with leaking manure pits or middens and slurry lagoons accounted for 48 incidences. Farmers readily accepted advice and adopted a very positive approach to solving the problems identified.

Erne Catchment Nutrient Management Scheme

A comprehensive Erne Catchment Nutrient Management Scheme, funded under the EU Special Support Programme for Peace and Reconciliation in Northern Ireland and the Border Counties of Ireland, was carried out by the Department of Agriculture during the years 1996 to 2000. The object of this scheme was to establish farming practices which addressed the increasing concern about the quality of waters in the Erne Catchment area, with particular reference to phosphorus. The more intensive farms were targeted, soil analyses were carried out for each field and farm waste application plans were prepared so as to minimise pollution risks.

The Colebrooke River in winter.

In addition, farm phosphorus balances were calculated, and fertiliser recommendations given for both grazing and cutting areas. It was found that on many intensive farms phosphorus levels were adequate or high and that phosphorus requirements could be met in many cases from the application of slurry only. This had the potential to save money through the purchase of cheaper fertiliser. In a number of cases in silage cutting areas where phosphorus levels were high, potassium and sulphur levels were found to be low. Fertilisers with nitrogen and potassium, and sulphur in some cases, were all that was required for good silage yields. A reduction in the use of chemical fertiliser had the potential to deliver environmental benefits in addition to reducing production costs on farms.

Policy changes

Emphasis on food production remained an important aspect of UK Government policy throughout the 1970s. In 1975 there was a boost to home food production through the UK Ministry of Agriculture's 'Food from our own resources' initiative. Until the 1980s the farmers' public role was largely seen as a food producer. However, as food supplies were secured and surpluses were appearing there was a new recognition of the farmers' role as managers of the countryside. By that time it was realised that intensive agriculture in some cases was impacting adversely on the environment. A good example of this was the damage done to wildlife through the use of the pesticides Aldrin and Dieldrin. Headage payments on livestock, especially sheep, led to overgrazing of mountain pastures in some cases which in turn led to a change in vegetation and severe erosion.

From 1985 the European Union introduced measures to allow governments to introduce schemes which would reward farmers for farming in a way that was sympathetic to the particular environmental needs of the area. From then specific schemes for farmers, which aimed to conserve and enhance landscapes and habitats of particular environmental value, were introduced. In Northern Ireland, under the Agriculture (Environmental Areas) Northern Ireland Order 1987, two areas were selected for designation as Environmentally Sensitive Areas (ESAs). These were the Mournes and Slieve Croob in County Down, and parts of the Glens of Antrim. By 1991 these Department of Agriculture schemes were regarded to be very successful in encouraging farmers to protect and enhance wildlife habitats and improving the appearance of the countryside.

West Fermanagh and Erne Lakeland Environmentally Sensitive Area

Following the successes in County Down and County Antrim, the West Fermanagh and Erne Lakeland Environmentally Sensitive Area was designated in 1991. The boundaries of the Fermanagh ESA, with slight modification, were essentially those of the proposed Area of Outstanding Natural Beauty which had been established by the Department of the Environment for Northern Ireland. The area extended to 57,000 hectares and comprised approximately 45 per cent of the land area of Fermanagh and involved 2,600 land owners. Characteristics of this renowned landscape include small fields bounded by rich hedgerows, woodlands, hay meadows, wet pasture and traditional farmsteads. The aim of the ESA Scheme was to assist and encourage farmers to farm in a way which was sympathetic to the particular environment needs of their area and at the same time permit successful farming activity. Environmental threats from farming were also to be addressed under the scheme. Threats considered of significance were intensification including a switch from hay making to silage, increased use of fertilisers on species-rich grassland and overgrazing of heather moorland. Dereliction was also considered to present a significant environmental threat.

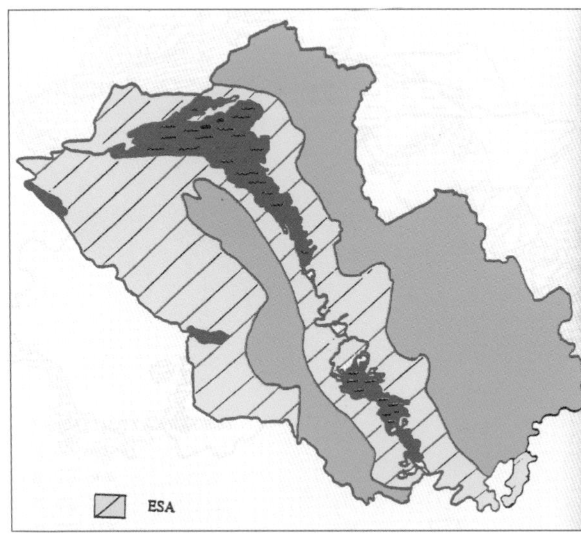

Map of West Fermanagh and Erne Lakeland ESA (indicative only).

Range of habitats

The Erne basin is one of the best wetland sites within the UK. The range of habitats makes it particularly important for breeding waders, especially snipe, curlew, lapwing and redshank. It is also valuable for over-wintering birds such as whooper swans. There is an impressive range of hay meadows particularly in the west of the county. During summer these are colourful sights with hay rattle, ragged robin, ox-eye daisy, orchids and many other wild flowers. Hedgerows, woodland, scrub, blanket bog, raised bogs, mountains and moorlands are all important habitats for wildlife and contribute significantly to the landscape. Limestone escarpments containing a rich variety of plants, many of which are unique, are to be found within the area. Numerous historic and archaeological sites exist within the ESA boundaries.

Controls

Farms which entered the scheme had a stocking rate restriction and limitations placed on fertiliser, herbicide, pesticide and lime usage. New drainage or reclamation was not permitted. Farm operations which would disturb nesting birds were not allowed.

Existing habitats and features of historic interest had to be preserved. Any new farm buildings or roads required advice to be given from the Department of Agriculture before construction commenced.

Lapwing's nest at Drumany, Thompson's Bridge.

Mr Bernard McGirr, Countryside Management Officer, DARD, in a species rich west Fermanagh hay meadow.

Mr Malcolm Finney, Countryside Management Officer, DARD, with Mr Benny Flanagan in his hay meadow discussing the stage of growth of the plants.

In addition to the above requirements, those entering the scheme who had particular habitats or features on their farms had to adopt certain management prescriptions. For hay meadows, there was a limit on fertiliser and manure applications. Cutting date was restricted until after 1st July so that the plants would have had time to produce seeds. Grazing after 1st October was not permitted.

Orchids, red clover, buttercups, hay rattle, ragged robin and a number of different grass species are evident in this hay meadow.

Fertiliser, pesticide and herbicide applications were not permitted on limestone grasslands. Stocking rates on these areas were set so as to avoid under or over grazing. Supplementary feeding of out-wintered stock was not permitted.

Superb limestone grassland at Monawilkin, Derrygonnelly.

An orchid in limestone grassland.

A well managed moorland.

Wet pastures were subject to controls on grazing. Too heavy grazing would cause poaching and too light grazing would encourage scrub growth.

Similar grazing restrictions applied to heather moorland found on areas like Cuilcagh Mountain and the Pettigo Plateau. In these areas grazing by cattle was not permitted from 1st November until 28th February. During the remainder of the year stocking levels were restricted to a maximum of 10 ewes or one cow per five hectares. Supplementary feeding of stock on these areas was prohibited.

Woodlands and scrub management under the Scheme

A study visit by senior staff of DANI to Monawilkin. Mr Donagh O'Neill, Deputy Chief Agricultural Officer, is fourth from the left. The County Agricultural Executive Officers for the six counties are Messrs Raymond Bingham, Armagh, (first left); David Wright, Down, (third left); Willis McWhirter, Londonderry, (fifth left); Sam Morrow, Fermanagh, (sixth left); Stephen McKenna, Tyrone, (seventh left); and Ezekiel Currie, Antrim, (fourth from right); Terry Chambers, Head of Farm Mechanisation and Farm Safety Branch is second from left. Dr Harry Gracey, Head of Countryside Management Division, is second from right. Bob Haycock, Head of Farm Buildings Branch, is third from right; Leslie Martin, DANI Headquarters, is on the extreme right.

Wet pasture is important for breeding waders.

A well laid hedge.

Grazing can damage woodland. Fencing stock out is therefore important.

Rath at Lisblake, Florencecourt. Crown Copyright. Reproduced with the permission of the Controller of Her Majesty's Stationery Office.

dictated that grazing by farm animals or feral goats was not permitted. Other measures required include the thinning, inter-planting and control of invasive species as necessary.

Avoidance of damage to historical or archaeological sites was a requirement. Tree planting and cultivations close to a site were not permitted and management of grazing stock in these areas and their vicinities required careful control.

Enhancement work

Environmental enhancements were encouraged as an optional part of the Scheme. These included items of a capital nature, such as tree planting, hedgerow regeneration and the renovation of traditional farm buildings. Generous rates of grant were available for these items. Eighty per cent grants were available for hedgerow regeneration, restoration of dry stone walls, tree planting, regeneration of heather, protective fencing for hedges, and renovation of traditional farm buildings.

Turf cutting – traditional and machine methods side by side. The use of the 'sausage' machine destroys the bog and is an unacceptable method of harvesting turf where the integrity of the bog is to be maintained.

A traditional isolated farm building.

Planting of native tree species is an important aspect of the scheme.

Mr Tom Phair, Feddans, Garvary, receiving the first payment in County Fermanagh under the West Fermanagh and Erne Lakeland ESA Scheme from Mr Hugh Kirkpatrick, Chief Agricultural Officer, Department of Agriculture. Also included is Mr Sam Morrow, County Agricultural Executive Officer and Mr Albert Knox, Countryside Management Officer. In the background is a wooden gate erected as an enhancement item under the Scheme. Tom Phair's grandfather, Mr Crozier Phair, was one of the participants in the County Committee of Agriculture's experiments on fertiliser use reported in the 1906 Report of that Committee.

A beautifully restored stone wall being admired by Mr Bernard McGirr, DARD Countryside Management Officer.

Provision or restoration of traditional gates and posts qualified for a 60 per cent grant.

The ESA Scheme was well received by the farming community. It has proved highly successful, raising awareness, changing attitudes and perceptions and delivering environmental benefits.

Uptake of the Scheme

At 30th September 1999 there were 1,029 signed agreements for the West Fermanagh and Erne Lakeland ESA Scheme. The table shown overleaf provides information on the agreed expenditure for each habitat under agreement.

Hedge planted on John Rutledge's farm at Derrylin. Miss Jayne Armstrong, DARD Countryside Management Adviser, is discussing establishment success.

Table 24.1 Uptake of ESA Scheme in Fermanagh

Habitat	Expenditure (£000)	Area (ha)
Improved land	183.0	6,100
Rough moorland grazing	17.3	1,735
Unimproved land	695.7	15,460
Historic sites	23.4	73
Hay meadows	142.7	1,196
Limestone grassland	88.6	984
Heather moorland	217.0	4,339
Woodland or scrubland	100.2	1,431
Wet pasture	115.5	1,014
Over-wintering area for swans and geese	2.3	33
Wildlife corridors	2.3	18
Total	1,584	32,383

Source: Countryside Management Division, DARD.

Lord Arran viewing enhancement work carried out on the farm of Mr Clive Weir, Dromard, Tamlaght. Mr Weir (centre) and Mr Sam Morrow (right), County Agricultural Development Officer, are included.

Mr Tom Crudden, DARD Countryside Management Officer, discussing a species rich pasture with Mr Vincent Mulligan, Coranny.

Details of Enhancement work

In May 1998 it was estimated that 750 participants had carried out enhancement works under the ESA as follows:

- *Over 27,000 metres of hedge had been replanted and rejuvenated*
- *Over 110 metres of dry stone walls had been restored*
- *200 traditional stone farm buildings had been renovated*
- *Over 100 hectares of heather moorland had been regenerated*

Countryside Management Scheme

The ESA Schemes were complemented by the introduction of the Countryside Management Scheme in 1999. This Department of Agriculture and Rural Development Scheme had similar aims to that of the ESA Scheme but it applied only to farms outside the ESA area.

Like the ESA Scheme its aim was to enhance biodiversity by maintaining species diversity through the positive management of wildlife habitats. It also aimed to enhance landscapes and heritage features by integrating their management into the everyday working of the farm. Participants in the Scheme were required to comply with the Codes of Good Agricultural Practice for the Prevention of Pollution. An adequate outcome of a farm pollution audit was a pre-requisite for entry into the scheme. A nutrient management plan was also a requirement of the Scheme.

References:

Gibson, Dr Chris, DANI Aquatic Sciences Research Division, *Is Lough Erne getting worse?* Paper presented at Lough Erne Advisory Committee, March 1992.

Eutrophication in Northern Ireland's Waters – Proposal for a Strategy to control Nutrient Enrichment (NI Environment and Heritage Service 1997).

Erne Catchment Nutrient Management Scheme – Specifications for Consultants (DANI 1996).

The Erne System: Sustainable Use of a Biological Resource - Institute of Biology's Conference papers 1992.

Proposals for a Water Quality Management Strategy for the River Erne Catchment (Executive Summary) (Hyder Consulting January 1988).

Foy, Dr R. H., *Water quality in relation to farming practices and Capital Grant availability.* DANI (1991).

Ministry of Agriculture for Northern Ireland's *Monthly Reports* and *Agriculture in Northern Ireland.*

Files of *The Impartial Reporter* and *Fermanagh Herald* held in Enniskillen Library.

Chapter 25
The soils of County Fermanagh

The area of County Fermanagh extends to 185,178 hectares which represents about 13.5 per cent of the total area of Northern Ireland. The basin of the River Erne system is a major physical feature of the County. The River Erne rises in Lough Gowna, County Longford, and flows through Upper and Lower Lough Erne on its way to the Atlantic. Water occupies about 10 per cent of the total area of the county. The topography of Fermanagh was significantly influenced by the Ice Age which accounts for the drumlin countryside and the 150 islands in Upper and Lower Lough Erne. Heather clad mountains are also a feature of the county with Cuilcagh Mountain at 670 metres above sea level being the highest.

Cuilcagh Mountain.

The soils in the county are variable. The geology of Fermanagh is predominantly limestone and sandstone and most of the soils are derived from these rocks. However, as a result of glaciation soils vary considerably in composition, texture and depth. There are some limestone outcrops with free draining shallow soils but extensive areas of land have deep heavy mineral soils with poor drainage characteristics.

The Fermanagh countryside viewed from Levaghy towards Trory (Courtesy of Mr John McVitty).

Limestone outcrops in west Fermanagh.

Aerial view from Levaghy across the Erne towards Belmore Mountain (Courtesy of Mr John McVitty).

Blanket bog on the lower slopes of Cuilcagh Mountain. The lowland is typical drumlin countryside with the hills having mineral soils and the inter-drumlin hollows a covering of peat.

Mineral soils in the uplands.

A raised bog from which some turf has been harvested.

A good quality lowland very productive mineral soil.

On the high ground there are considerable areas of blanket bog but the depth of this material tends to be shallow, with the exception of a few limited areas.

Raised bogs have developed on top of the original basin peat in some of the inter-drumlin hollows.

The challenge of soil classification

Over the years of the twentieth century those with responsibility for administration of agricultural affairs struggled with the difficulties of classifying the soils in Fermanagh. There was the issue during the First and Second World Wars of deciding what was arable under the Compulsory Tillage schemes. Under the Compulsory Tillage orders the amount to be cultivated was related to the area of arable land on individual farms. Decisions relating to the determination of the extent of the arable area on each farm fell to the local Department/Ministry of Agriculture officials. Officials had to make an assessment by walking individual farms and determining the properties of the soil and other conditions regarding each field's suitability for cropping. In terms of the Hill Land Schemes which operated for many years, the definition of eligible land was related largely to elevation. However, some of the land that was classified as eligible in County Fermanagh in terms of elevation would not have been eligible elsewhere in other areas owing to their greater production potential.

With the advent of the European Economic Community and the Common Market new support measures for agriculture were introduced. The Less Favoured Areas Directive, with two categories of support based on Disadvantaged or Severely Disadvantaged land classifications, brought new challenges for those involved with administration of the support measures.

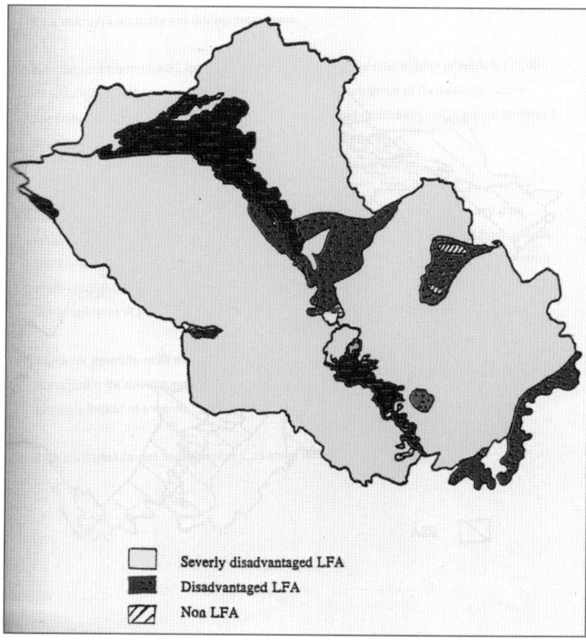

Map of Fermanagh showing LFA boundaries (indicative only).

Land classification

Morrow and Lytle, in 1981, for a presentation at an Institute of Biology Conference, had classified the soils of Fermanagh into four different categories depending on their agricultural value and productive potential as follows:-

Category A (8%) – best quality land. These soils are generally lighter in texture and better structured with relatively free draining characteristics.

Category B (50%) – second quality land. These soils are heavier in texture and have poorer structure with impeded drainage. Castle Archdale was quoted as being typical of this category of land.

Category C (24%) – gleyed soils with distinctively shallower topsoils. The subsoils vary from the heaviest clays with poor drainage to boulder strewn areas and rock outcrops.

Category D (18%) – elevated land varying from peaty gleys to deep peats.

Rainfall, in addition to the other factors such as elevation, slope and aspect, when superimposed on the various soil types, has a significant impact on agricultural productivity. In Fermanagh the areas with the highest rainfall coincide with poorer land quality and also with elevation.

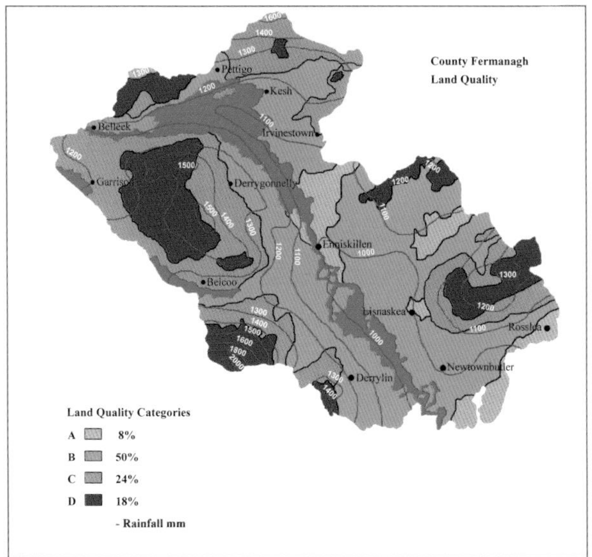

Map showing the different soil classes taking into account their productive potential, as determined by Morrow and Lytle.

Categories B, C and D were classified as a Less Favoured Area under EEC Directive 75/268. The livestock stocking rates on the different categories of land were assessed by Morrow and Lytle in 1981 as follows:-

Category A – 1.44 livestock units per hectare

Category B – 0.95 livestock units per hectare

Category C – 0.78 livestock units per hectare

Category D – 0.12 livestock units per hectare

Department of Agriculture for Northern Ireland Soil Survey (1987 – 1997)

Professor M. McG. Cooper, of Newcastle University, in 1959 when commenting on the potential of the land at the Castle Archdale Experimental Husbandry Farm, identified the need for a soil survey in County Fermanagh. It was not until the 1980s, when resources became available, that the Department of Agriculture for Northern Ireland carried out the first systematic study of soils in Northern Ireland, under the leadership of Mr J. G. Cruickshank. The Survey was completed in 1997 with one of the significant outcomes being the production of 18 soil maps of the Province at a scale of 1:50,000.

The soils in Fermanagh range from very poor draining surface and groundwater gleyed soils to highly productive brown earths. The availability of these maps facilitated the production of a generalised Agricultural Land Classification of the county broadly based on the English and Welsh system. In practice the grades are defined by reference to several physical characteristics, including slope, climatic data, elevation and stoniness. However, due to incomplete data, the interpretive map is of a generalised nature.

Under the above classification the Grades of soil are determined as follows:-

Grade 2 – very good quality land.

It is land with minor limitations which affect crop yield, cultivations or harvesting. A wide range of agricultural and horticultural crops can usually be grown but on some land in the grade there may be reduced flexibility due to difficulties with the production of the more demanding crops such as winter harvested vegetables and arable root crops. The level of yield is generally high but may be lower or more variable than *Grade 1.*

Grade 3a – good quality agricultural land

Land capable of consistently producing moderate to high yields of a narrow range of arable crops, especially cereals, or moderate yields of a wide range of crops, including cereals, grass, oilseed rape, potatoes, sugar beet and the less demanding horticultural crops.

Grade 3b – moderate quality agricultural land

Land capable of producing moderate yields of a narrow range of crops, principally cereals and grass or lower yields of a wider range of crops or high yields of grass which can be grazed or harvested over most of the year.

Grade 4 – poor quality agricultural land

Land with severe limitations which significantly restrict the range of crops and/or level of yields. It is mainly suited to grass with occasional arable crops (e.g. cereals and forage crops) the yields of which are variable. In moist climates, yields of grass may be moderate to high but there may be difficulties in utilisation. The grade also includes very droughty arable land.

Grade 4a – denotes mineral soils

Grade 4b – denotes organic soils

Grade 5 – very poor quality agricultural land

Land with very severe limitations which restrict use to permanent pasture or rough grazing, except for occasional pioneer arable crops.

Agricultural Land Classification of Fermanagh

An examination of the map covering County Fermanagh (copy below by courtesy of Agri-Food and Biosciences Institute) shows a wide distribution of the different qualities of soil. To generalise, most of the best quality land is to be found in the east of the county around Ballinamallard, Tempo and in the Brookeborough/Fivemiletown end of the Clogher Valley. Other pockets of better land are to be found along the border with the Irish Republic stretching from Rosslea to Newtownbutler. On the west side of the loughs the area south-west of Derrylin and small pockets from Enniskillen to Ely Lodge fall into the best category. The survey confirms that the land in Fermanagh is generally not of a high quality. There is no Grade 1 land. The other categories, excluding the islands, are as follows:-

Grade 2	4%
Grade 3A	8%
Grade 3B	30%
Grade 4A	6%
Grade 4B	43%
Grade 5	7.5%
Urban (5U)	*1.0%*
Disturbed (5D)	*0.5%*

References:

Cruikshank, J. G. (Editor and Main Author), *Soil and Environment: Northern Ireland.* Agricultural and Environmental Science Division, DANI and The Agricultural Science Department, Queen's University, Belfast (1997).

The Erne System: Sustainable Use of a Biological Resource – Institute of Biology Conference papers, 1992.

Information supplied by Messrs J. V. Courtney, DARD, and A. Higgins, AFBI.

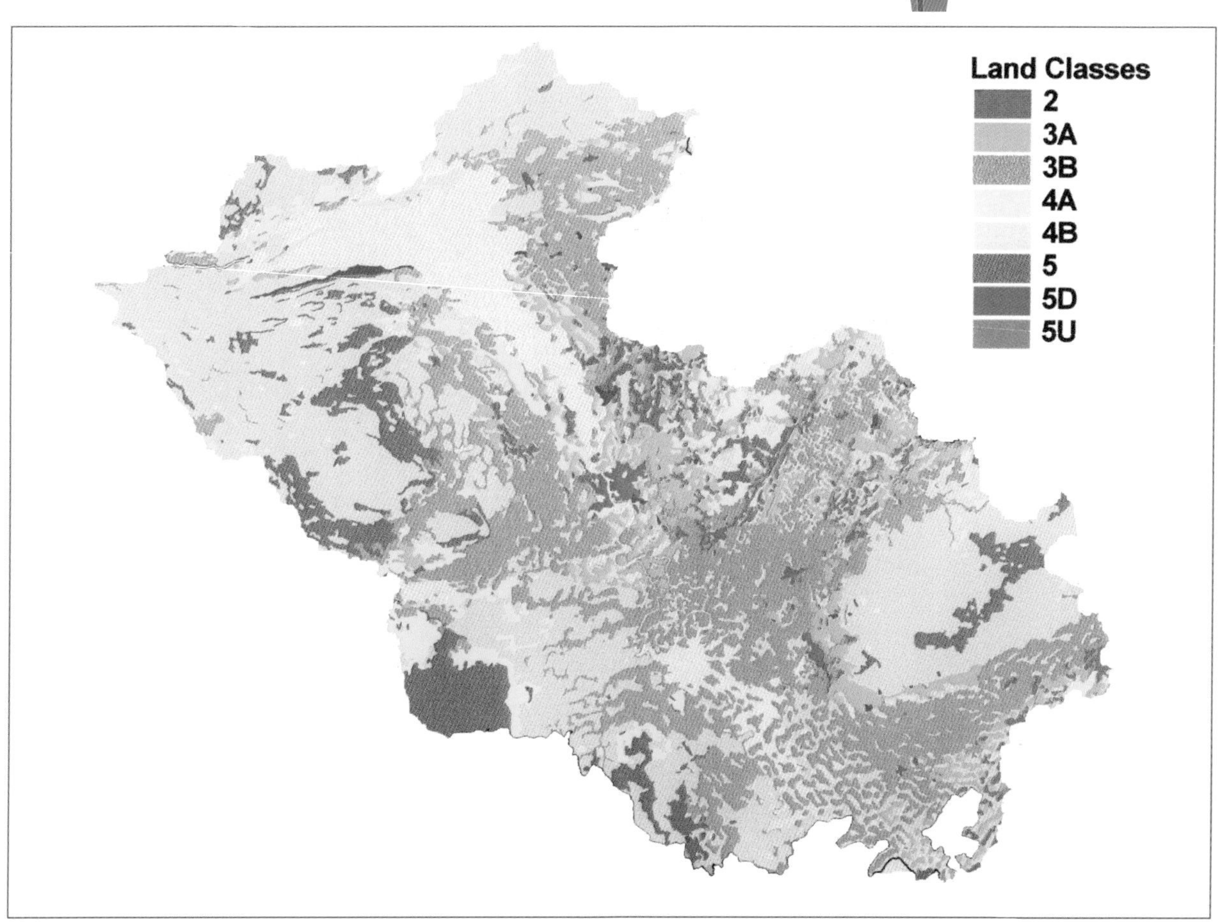

County Fermanagh Land Classification map (based on soils only) DARD 1997. 'Crown Copyright'. Reproduced by kind permission of AFBI.

Chapter 26
Vaughan's Charity

The Vaughan Trust, as Vaughan's Charity is currently known for promotional purposes, is the envy of other counties in Northern Ireland. This body, the like of which does not exist elsewhere, has contributed very significantly to the development of agriculture in County Fermanagh in the latter part of the twentieth century. The Trust has considerable income at its disposal which it uses to the advantage of the farming community through generous support for agricultural education and training, educational travel and for many other purposes which contribute to agricultural development. The Charity, which had its inception in the Will of George Vaughan Esq, was drafted over 250 years ago. George Vaughan was a married man, with no surviving children, who lived in Buncrana Castle and owned estates in north Donegal and Fermanagh. The estates in Donegal were known as Porthall and Doe Castle. The Fermanagh owned land, in the Kesh district, was called the Castlehassett estate. George Vaughan died in 1763 and left his assets and possessions to be used for very worthy charitable purposes and for the benefit of his nephew Basil Brooke. This brief history traces the changes in Vaughan's Charity over the past centuries culminating in the current scheme which has proved so beneficial to the farming community in County Fermanagh.

The Will

George Vaughan's Will was drawn up in 1753 and amended by a codicil in 1758. His estate in County Fermanagh (2,000 acres) was bequeathed to a number of Trustees who were comprised of the hierarchy of the Church of Ireland in the northern dioceses and a number of the landed gentry. The Trustees were directed to take from the rents and profits of his estate the sum of £2,000 per year. This was to be used, from time to time, to purchase additional land to add to the Fermanagh estate at Kesh. He had directed that when the income from the enlarged estate had reached £4,000 per year half of this amount was to be set aside for the maintenance of the Charity with the other half to be settled annually for the use of his nephew, Basil Brooke Esq, for life. The main provision of the Charity envisaged by George Vaughan was a school *to receive and lodge 300 boys and 200 girls, together with proper schoolroom, workhouses, and apartments for the several masters and mistresses that*

George Vaughan Esq.

Buncrana Castle.

Map of the Fermanagh Vaughan estate in 1849.

"Charitable Charter School erected and endowed by the Last Will and Testament of George Vaughan Esquire." This inscription stone was located above the main entrance door of the school. After the school was demolished it was set in the gable end of a barn in the farmyard.

A drawing of the school by Stephen Colin taken from an old photograph. This now hangs in the Vaughan Room at Enniskillen Campus of the College of Agriculture, Food and Rural Enterprise (CAFRE) - formerly Enniskillen Agricultural College.

shall, from time to time, have the care and instruction of such boys and girls, together with all proper outhouses, such buildings to be called and known by the name The Charitable Charter School, erected and endowed by the last will and testament of George Vaughan, Esquire; and in the next place, make and erect a church, and enclose a churchyard, on such place and according to such plan or model as I shall for that purpose by writing under my hand direct and appoint. A 500 acre farm was to be provided with the school.

Act of Parliament

The annual income from the enlarged estate did not rise at the anticipated rate and it was considered that it would take up to 40 years to reach the annual income of £4,000. As a consequence of this, the benefit to Vaughan's nephew, Basil Brooke Esq, and the setting up of Vaughan's Charity would have been long delayed. As a result of representations by the Trustees, an Act of the Irish Parliament was passed in 1776 which enabled half the estate to be given to Basil Brooke Esq in final settlement and the other half vested for the benefit of the Charity.

The Charitable Charter School

Shortage of finance prevented a school being established of the size envisaged in Vaughan's Will. However, a smaller school to accommodate 100 pupils, for 30 girls and 70 boys, was built at Tubrid in 1780. The purpose of the school as dictated in Vaughan's Will was for *maintaining, bringing up, educating, and instructing 300 boys and 200 girls in the said school in the several branches of linen manufacture, such as knitting, spinning and sewing for the girls, husbandry, flax dressing and weaving in which each boy is to be instructed under the care of proper masters and mistresses.* Another significant requirement of the Will was the appointment of a Church of Ireland Chaplain for the school. The Chaplain was required to be in residence. He had a superintending role regarding admissions, examinations, apprenticeships, contracts for food and the keeping of accounts. He also had responsibility *to teach and instruct the said boys and girls in the principles of the Christian religion.*

Admissions

In terms of admissions to the school, preference was to be given to the tenant families. The admission numbers for which the school was planned do not appear to have been achieved. By 1787 the intake was limited to 30 boys. In the following year 21 out of the 29 pupils were from the locality. Girls were admitted later with eight being present in 1828 and 35 by 1857. The estate at that time had been extended to comprise 4,924 acres. In 1863 there were no nominations for entry to the school. Emigration was prevalent in the area and some farms were vacant at that time.

Works undertaken

The Governors, having regard to other provisions in George Vaughan's Will, funded improvement works and other facilities for the benefit of the tenants. Buildings erected or improved included Drumkeeran Parish Church, formerly the school chapel; a dispensary in Kesh in 1823; rebuilding the mill in Kesh in 1851; provision of a police station in Kesh in 1862; and the building of a market house in Kesh in 1874. In addition, schemes were undertaken to assist tenants in improving their land and buildings.

Drumkeeran Parish church.

Financial problems

As time progressed the Governors of the school found it increasingly difficult to run the establishment as a viable economic unit. Funds to run the school depended on income from the tenants on the estate but the tenants had to contend with the famine years and depressed economic conditions for farming. By 1922 there were only 18 boys in the school. In 1930 the Governors stated that it was impossible to run the school profitably. In 1926 and again in 1932 the Governors attempted unsuccessfully to have the school adopted as a Public Elementary School by the Ministry of Education. At this time the school was being used largely as an orphanage with only three of the 73 pupils who had attended the school during the period from 1921 coming from the Kesh area. Public unrest at conditions prevailing in the school culminated in a writ being issued in January 1934 by a local magistrate, Captain T. H. Verschoyle, against the Governors of the school. A number of allegations were made against the Governors. These claimed that the Governors had not carried out the detailed wishes of George Vaughan as expressed in his last Will and Testament and, furthermore, they were responsible for mismanagement of the school. The outcome of the Court Case was the closure of the school. After certain payments were made, including the payment of £750 to Drumkeeran Church of Ireland Parish for a new rectory, the residue of the property and other resources were transferred to the Ministry of Finance and new provisions were incorporated under the Vaughan's Charity (Administration) Act 1936.

The 1936 Act

Under the new Act ten local schools received £50 per year to cover books and meals for the pupils. Female past pupils of these schools were to be awarded £20 per year to enable them to attend Enniskillen or other Technical School. Under the Act *'The Vaughan Agricultural Institute'* was established. New Trustees were appointed – two by the Ministry of Agriculture, two by the Ministry of Finance, one by the Ministry of Education, two by the Northern Ireland Rural Development Council, and two by the Ulster Farmers' Union one of whom was to represent the Young Farmers' Clubs.

The purpose of the Institute was defined as *a centre for educating students in agriculture policy and organisation and for developing interest in agricultural and rural life and inculcating the duties and responsibilities of citizenship*. The Trustees did not have access to the capital and could only deal with the income from the Trust Fund – the capital being vested in the Ministry of Finance. Plans were prepared for the buildings to serve the Institute. However, before these had advanced the outbreak of the Second World War meant that implementation had to be suspended. During the war the Institute farmland was let to neighbouring farmers and the school and outbuildings were occupied by Royal Air Force personnel. Consideration was given to the future use of the buildings at that time and it was proposed that the Institute should be used as an intermediate school but this was rejected by the Ministry of Education. The Agricultural Enquiry Committee, under Lord Justice Babington in 1943, recommended that the Institute farm should be used as a centre for grassland experiments appropriate to Fermanagh and West Tyrone and this was accepted. Provision for the new proposals was incorporated by amending the 1936 Act which became the Vaughan's Charity Administration Act (N.I.) 1954.

The Vaughan Agricultural Institute

The Trustees' responsibilities under the new scheme were defined as follows: *The Trustees shall manage the Institute as a centre for the purposes of developing and demonstrating modes of agriculture primarily suited to the conditions of County Fermanagh. The Institute may also be used as a centre for instruction and demonstration and for experimental and research purposes.* The composition of the Trustees had the same representation as in the previous Act except that the nominees of the Northern Ireland Rural Development Council were to be replaced by one representative each from the County Fermanagh Farming Society and the Ulster Agricultural Organisation Society. In 1955 the old Institute schoolhouse was demolished, some of the existing farm buildings were improved and a new Farm Manager's house was built in 1957.

Mr J. L. H. Askwith JP, Chairman of the Vaughan Trustees, and Jim Hamilton, Farm Manager, viewing the dairy herd at grass.

The dairy unit.

The poultry rearing unit.

Early farming activity

A farm manager was appointed and farming activity commenced in 1957. The first stock consisted of 30 ewes and 45 store cattle and small scale pig and poultry enterprises. The following year silage making and milk production were undertaken. The early experience of running the farm was not good. In 1960 a loss of over £1,100 was recorded. In 1963 the Ministry of Agriculture reported that the profitability of cattle and sheep was only about half of the average expectation. The financial position had not improved by April 1965. At that time, it was agreed at a meeting between the Trustees and representatives of the Ministry of Agriculture that the economic failure of the farm was due to poor management. Two farm managers had served at Tubrid during the period. It would be wrong to attribute failure of the farm business activity solely to the Farm Managers, there may have been other factors such as lack of capital and inadequate support for those with responsibility of running the farm.

The Ministry of Agriculture stated that it would support a case to the Ministry of Finance to release more funds for approved capital development and that it would second an officer who would act as Farm Manager and that the Trustees would be responsible for payment of his salary. This was agreed by the Trustees and Mr Jim Hamilton, a member of the staff of Strabane Agricultural School, was appointed Farm Manager.

Profitable farming

In 1967, for the first time since the Institute's establishment, a profit was shown. The dairy cows showed a total gross profit of £3,057 or £75 per cow with an average yield of 895 gallons per cow. The poultry enterprise, based on contract rearing of chickens, made a profit of over £1,900. Warm tributes were paid by the Trustees to Mr Hamilton and the staff of the Department of Agriculture's County Advisory Service who had worked very closely with the Farm Manager during the year. The accounts for the farm for 1968 showed a net farm income of £2,161 3s 11d which was described by the Chairman of the Trustees as *quite astonishing … Tremendous credit,* he felt, *was due to the Farm Manager and the County Advisory Staff.* The profitability of the Institute led to widespread publicity in the agricultural press. Furthermore, the Institute was widely used by the Ministry of Agriculture's Advisory Service in County Fermanagh for demonstrating to the farming community good husbandry and farm management practice. The Institute continued to run on a sound financial basis and in 1972 the net farm income was £11,078.43 which was an excellent performance judged by any standards. The success story was due to good planning, sound day-to-day management and husbandry and wise decision making by the Trustees. Stock numbers in 1972 were 77 dairy cows, 63 other cattle and a breeding herd of over 60 sows.

Future role

Consideration was given to the Institute's future at this stage. It was concluded by the Trustees that many of the purposes served by the Institute were now being carried out by the now well established Enniskillen Agricultural College and the Grassland Experimental Husbandry Centre at Castle Archdale. It was also considered that the Institute resources could be used in a different and more effective way to achieve the overall aims of the Charity. The Trustees unanimously agreed in January 1972 to recommend to the Ministry of Finance that the Institute should be wound up and the property sold. All the assets were to be invested in the Charities' Trust and were to be utilised in other ways for developing agriculture in County Fermanagh. This proposal was approved in principle by the Ministry of Finance in October 1972. The stock and equipment were sold in 1973 and realised almost £43,000. The farm was sold later. The Chairman of the Trustees, Mr J. L. H. Askwith, JP, was appointed MBE in the 1975 New Year's Honours in recognition of his services to the Institute.

Mr J. L. H. Askwith MBE, JP

Vaughan's Charity Order 1973

The 1954 Act was amended by the Vaughan's Charity Order 1973 and under it the current Vaughan Trust Scheme was authorised. The Scheme enables the Trustees to make awards which aid the development of agriculture in County Fermanagh. Awards may be made under the following headings:

1. The development of new or improved methods of agriculture;
2. Agricultural education and training;
3. Travel scholarships for young people for agricultural education and training purposes;
4. Research work of special value to the County;
5. With the approval of the Ministry of Agriculture any other purpose benefiting agriculture in County Fermanagh.

The Trustees under the 1973 Order are appointed as follows: one each by the Departments of Agriculture, Finance and Personnel, and Education. In addition to those, the Trustees appoint two others, one representing the farmers and the other representing the young farmers of the county. Since the new Vaughan Trust Scheme came into operation the Trustees have appointed the Department of Agriculture's nominated Trustee to serve as Chairman. The Clerk to the Trustees under the new Scheme has been the Senior Administrative Officer in the Enniskillen Agricultural College (later Enniskillen Campus of CAFRE)

The Trustees in 1979. Left to right (seated): Mrs A. Malone, Mr S. B. Morrow (Chairman), Mrs N. Acheson (Clerk to the Trustees). Standing: Mr N. Baxter, Mr D. Graham and Mr K. Murnaghan.

Education and travel awards

The Trustees in 2010. Left to right (seated): Miss Olwen Gormley (Chairman), Mr Brian Thomson (Clerk to the Trustees). Standing: Mr K. Murnaghan, Mr E. Rogers, Mr V. Cassidy and Mr D. Brown.

Students from Fermanagh undertaking courses in agriculture at an approved college or university are eligible to apply for assistance with travel costs to and from their place of study. As a result of awards made under the Vaughan Trust Scheme, Fermanagh farmers and students are among the most travelled and best informed in the industry. It is important that farmers and those entering the industry are aware of the production and marketing skills of competitors in different countries. Study travel awards may be given to individuals who can make a convincing case to the Trustees. However, most travel awards are given to students from Enniskillen Campus who distinguish themselves in examinations or to winners of competitions run by organisations like the Fermanagh Grassland Club or the Young Farmers' Clubs or the other farmers' organisations.

Messrs Maurice Hurst, Aghavea, and Norman Emo, Aughintra, in the Rungis meat market in Paris.

New developments in agriculture

This is an area that can be supported by the Trust if there is potential to bring benefit to agricultural development in the county. One such project was the sponsorship of drainage demonstration plots in the early 1980s. Demonstration sites were established in the county at Lisnaskea, Florencecourt, Garrison and Drumskinny, so that farmers could see the advantages of improved drainage and in particular the effectiveness of the low cost systems of mole drainage and the newly developed gravel tunnel system.

Variety of awards

County Fermanagh Farming Society, which runs the Annual Agricultural Show in Enniskillen, benefits in terms of sponsorship of prizes for livestock and other classes

Councillor Bertie Kerr, farmer and Chairman of Fermanagh District Council, who accompanied a group of farmers on a Vaughan Trust sponsored study visit to France in February 1994. Councillor Kerr is being greeted by the Mayor of Lurcy Levis.

Members of the Fermanagh Young Farmers' Clubs who gained valuable educational travel awards in 2010. From left: Trevor Wilson, Lisbellaw, 'top male Young Farmer of the Year'; Beverly Henderson, Kesh, highest marks in all competitions; Zara Stubbs, Kesh, top female 'Young Farmer of the Year'.

Work on the drainage demonstration site at Lisnaskea in progress.

confined to Fermanagh entrants. A new technique in the county for the early production of carrots using a plastic mulch on a commercial farm was supported in 1984.

Livestock improvement

Fermanagh's income from agriculture depends heavily on livestock, especially cattle and sheep. A Vaughan Trust Scheme over many years has supported the improvement in the quality of the animals produced on farms through the use of superior breeding stock. Under the Trust's Beef Improvement Scheme, an award of 50 per cent of the cost, subject to a maximum of £500, may be granted for the purchase of an approved performance recorded beef bull. A similar scheme operates for sheep in that performance recorded rams may qualify for a 50 per cent grant on the purchase price subject to a maximum of £250 or £400 where two rams are involved. Milk recording in dairy herds is also supported at a rate of 50 per cent of the costs for a two year period. All of these Livestock Improvement Schemes are supervised by CAFRE Development Advisers so that participating farmers get advice on all aspects of the management of their enterprises.

Mr Gordon Thompson, Bannagh Beg, Kesh, and Mr William Johnston, CAFRE Beef and Sheep Development Adviser discussing the merits of Mr Thompson's Charolais bull purchased under the Vaughan Trust Scheme in 2010.

In addition to these main aspects of the Trust's work, research projects or any other idea which may bring benefit to agriculture in County Fermanagh may be considered for funding.

The Vaughan Trust in the twenty-first century

In addition to previously supported measures to assist individuals and groups under the various headings the current Vaughan Trustees have expanded provision. They have initiated a raft of schemes which help to address a number of the major challenges facing Fermanagh farmers. The schemes, which are aimed at increasing efficiency and competitiveness, range from farmer training, livestock improvement, farm business management, quality assurance and the environment. The livestock improvement schemes, which offer generous financial support, cover dairying, suckler herds and pigs. Quality assurance in relation to pig production is another feature of the livestock schemes. Improved farm business management is encouraged through support for computerised accounting and benchmarking. Responsible use of fertilisers, particularly in relation to phosphorus, is a feature of the Nutrient Management Scheme.

Full details of all Vaughan Trust schemes are to be found at the Vaughan Trust website, launched in April 2010.

History

One of the projects undertaken by the Trustees, under the 1965 Order, was the commissioning of *'A History of the Vaughan Charity'* in 1985. Two very able students, Claire and Michael Jackson, a brother and sister team, undertook the task of researching the Vaughan papers and producing a detailed history, which was printed and published by William Trimble Ltd., Enniskillen. The authors now The Rt Rev Dr Michael Jackson, Church of Ireland Bishop of Clogher, and Claire Jackson, now a barrister and wife of The Rt Rev Michael Burrows, the Church of Ireland Bishop of Cashel and Ossory, in the final chapter of the book entitled *'A Final Reflection'* wrote as follows:

It almost goes without saying, at least from an outsider's point of view, the Charity as at present constituted seems far removed from that envisaged by its founder. The School is no longer in existence, the farm is no longer operative and even the land of the Vaughan estate is no longer in the hands of the Trustees.

A study of motivation, however, concerns itself less with externals. Of infinitely greater significance is the consideration of how well this motivation has been understood and carried into effect by those who have had the care of doing so. As has been revealed, throughout the development of the various aspects of the Charity, adherence to the Testator's wishes has been effected to a greater or lesser degree. With regard to the present day conception of the Charity, it is the one which in many respects comes closest to effecting Vaughan's fundamental wishes. His broad humanitarian principles are carried out by the stress laid on benefiting agriculture in County Fermanagh. The fact that the present Trustees all have strong links with Fermanagh means that the criticisms of remoteness, levelled against the Governors prior to 1934, are no longer apt. The Vaughan Trust is now very firmly based in Fermanagh; not only are the Trustees closely connected with the county, but it holds its meetings in the Agricultural College, Enniskillen, and above all its monies are employed for 'any purpose for benefit to agriculture in County Fermanagh'. Likewise full effect is accorded to Vaughan's broadmindedness and tolerance by the spectrum of people to whom the benefits of the Charity are open.

However paradoxical it may seem in view of the absence of all the external features so meticulously provided for by the testator himself, the Vaughan Charity, as conceived at present, may well be providing a truer representation of the aspirations expressed in 'The Last Will and Testament of George Vaughan Esquire'.

References:

Jackson, Claire and Michael, *A History of the Vaughan Charity.* William Trimble, Enniskillen (1985).

Minutes of the Vaughan Trust.

Ministry/Department of Agriculture's *Monthly Reports* and *Agriculture in Northern Ireland.*

Chapter 27
County Fermanagh Farming Society's contribution in the 20th century

Chapters 1 and 2 of this book traced the early development of the farming societies in County Fermanagh and outlined how they contributed to the developments which led to the introduction by Government of the Agriculture and Technical Instruction Act in the year 1900. This Act established the County Committees of Agriculture which provided an advisory service for farmers and introduced schemes for livestock and other farm improvements. The County Committees remained in existence for over 70 years by which time all their functions had been absorbed by the Ministry of Agriculture. The County Fermanagh Farming Society, established in 1836, continues to thrive and makes its own unique contribution to the development of agriculture in the county. This chapter deals with the highlights of the Society's activities up to the end of the twentieth century.

The Farmers' Challenge Cup

The Society and Show received a major boost in 1902 when Mr T. M. Hilliard of New York, whose family connections were at Trory, presented a magnificent £50 Perpetual Challenge Cup with a prize of £5 in addition to the Hilliard Prizes of £9 which had already been presented. The cup, called 'The Farmers' Challenge Cup', and prize was to be competed for by farmers of any valuation in County Fermanagh for the best cow, two year old bullock or heifer, one year old bullock or heifer and bull, bullock or heifer calf under eight months old.

All cattle in competition were to be of the Shorthorn type. The animals were required to be in the exhibitors' possession at least three months before the date of the show. This measure was intended to prevent exhibitors from purchasing cattle especially for the event. A farmer was defined as one who devoted his or her full time to the farm and who derived his or her means of living from the farm. The Society decided to offer an additional £5 to that offered by Mr Hilliard which brought the yearly prize money offered with the cup up to £10 with an entry fee of 10 shillings. The donor stated that in the event of the dissolution of the Fermanagh Farming Society the committee could dispose of the cup as its members thought fit. He did, however, suggest that in those circumstances they might consider awarding the cup to the farmer, his heirs or assigns, who had won the cup the greatest number of times or alternatively hand the cup over to the Royal Dublin Society for competition amongst the farmers of Ireland. Happily, it can be reported that the cup is still being competed for each year as enthusiastically as ever and its presentation each year is a crowning event on show day.

Mrs Ann Orr, Show Secretary, with Mr William Crawford, the winner of 'The Farmers' Challenge Cup' at the 2002 show on the 100th anniversary of its presentation by Mr T. M. Hilliard.

Mr James Crawford with his father's champion cow at the 2002 show.

Interestingly, the Fermanagh Farming Society is probably stronger now than it has ever been and the Royal Dublin Society, viewed in 1902 as a possible host for the cup in the event of the Fermanagh Society's demise, no longer holds an agricultural show.

This class was further revised in 1923 when it was agreed that the cup should be awarded for the three best Shorthorn cattle, any age, with the restriction that not more than one bull could be entered in the class. An objection was made at the 1939 Show by Mr Sandy Hilliard, Trory, (a relative of the cup donor) to the cup being awarded to pedigree Shorthorns. In 1946, following discussions with Mr Sandy Hilliard, the cup reverted to a class for the best group of Shorthorn type cattle. By 1956 the cup was awarded to the farmer deriving his/her main source of living from farming and resident in County Fermanagh who scored the highest number of points in the cattle section. In 1957 the cup was presented to the 'Championship of Ireland Dairy Cow or Heifer' at the Show and a similar class for the cup continues to the present time.

The First World War and after

During the years of the First World War limited show events were held in mid to late August. A stipulation by the Ministry of Agriculture in 1914 was that there should be special provision for registered dairy cows and their progeny and that classes for goats should be included in the Show. In 1915 the agricultural show was held as normal but there was no horse jumping event. In 1916 the agricultural show was held but no associated industrial show. However, in that year in order to cater for certain important classes normally held in the industrial show, such as crochet, needlework and flowers, these were provided for in the agricultural show. A major change in policy was made that year when the committee decided that some cattle and all poultry classes should be 'open' and not confined to County Fermanagh farmers only.

Shows were not held in 1917 and 1918 because of the war. In 1922 the Show had been planned for 3rd September. However, due to difficulty in obtaining the use of the County Hall, arrangements for the Show were cancelled. A public meeting was held in April 1923, under the chairmanship of Canon Hall with Mr W. H. West acting as secretary, to consider whether a show should be held. Arrangements proceeded and the 1923 Show was held on the Fairgreen. A general committee was appointed with Canon Hall as chairman and Mr F. R. Browne, owner of the Fairgreen, as secretary. Committees were appointed for livestock, horse jumping, and technical and industrial. At the meeting it was decided that horse jumping, riding and

Mr Edwin Bruce receiving the Hilliard Cup from the Ulster Dairy Queen at the 1969 Show. Also included from left, Mrs Carol Crooke, Show Secretary, Miss Lavinia Baird, Chairman of the Show Management Committee. Back row: Mr William Moore DL, Chief Steward, and the Duke of Westminster, President of the County Fermanagh Farming Society. The judge of the All Ireland Class and his wife are on the front right (Courtesy of Mrs Carol Crooke).

driving competitions would be held if a suitable field could be procured.

In 1924 there was a departure from the normal arrangements for the Show in that two separate events were held. The agricultural event, together with the horse jumping and driving competitions, was held on 5th September on the Fairgreen. For the first time in the equine classes, the confined sporting events were opened up to competitors from Tyrone as well as Fermanagh. A second show was held on 19th September which featured flowers, vegetables, fruit, farm produce and industrial exhibits. A dog show, for which £15 prize money was allocated, was a new feature and it was held at the latter event. The Show reverted to a one day event in 1925 and was held on 5th September. In 1927 the agricultural show moved to the County Hall grounds.

The Second World War

In 1940 it was decided not to hold an autumn show but that horse jumping with other attractions, including a sheepdog and duck driving demonstration, would be held before the end of June. The next show was held in 1945. Entry charges to the 1945 Show were fixed at two shillings with a similar charge to the horse jumping event. HM Forces in uniform were to be admitted at half price. The 1945 Show was a financial success with a profit of £779 recorded. The success of the Show was attributed to good publicity through the local press and to the support of the staff of the County Council. The shopkeepers of Enniskillen also agreed to close for a half-day for the Show to enable staff to attend. The cups won at the 1945 Show were presented at a ceremony in the County Hall at 3.30pm on 5th December by their Excellencies the Earl and Countess Granville. The Earl Granville was the Governor of Northern Ireland. The cups for the 1945 event had been supplemented when Vice Admiral Sir Edward Archdale, Bart, presented three cups which his father, the late Sir Edward Archdale, President of the Society, had won outright.

Victory Show

The 1946 event held on 4th September was billed as the Victory Show. The Society's cups and trophies were displayed in the window of Messrs J. Cooper and Company's shop window at the Diamond in Enniskillen. Mr Hayhurst, trick motorcyclist, was engaged as a special attraction at a cost of £47 1s 0d. Another special feature was a performance by the band of the Royal Irish Regiment. The Show dance was held on the evening of the Show. The Victory Show was a financial success leaving a profit of around £500.

At the Broadmeadow in the 1930s. Front row (from left) Mr Honey Archdale, ?, Colonel Clifford, Major Nixon, Miss Mary Wilson, Mr J. N. Carson, Mr William Wilson, Show Secretary, ? , Mr Henry Archdale Porter is at the back between Colonel Clifford and Major Nixon (Courtesy of Mrs Marion Maxwell).

The Duke of Abercorn with the Ulster Dairy Queen and the Dairy Princesses at the 1959 Show (Courtesy of Mrs Marion Maxwell).

The Dairy Queen and Fermanagh Dairy Princess, Miss Mona Wilson, with Mr Bill Armstrong leading the prize winning dairy cow at the 1959 show.

Mr and Mrs William Dunn being presented with the cup for grassland management in 1959 by Lady Brookeborough (Courtesy of Mr W. Dunn).

Shows in the 1950s

Obtaining a lease on the Ulster Farmers' Mart Company property, located on the former Fairgreen, in 1951 gave the show a fresh lease of life. The Mart not only provided facilities but also granted valuable prize money. At this time the Ministry of Agriculture's educational exhibit became a regular feature at the shows. In 1953 championship spoons and medals were presented in different sections of the show to commemorate the Coronation. In 1954 the Society learned that it would once again have the use of the County Hall. The County Hall had been leased to Messrs Taylor Woods (nylon factory) in advance of their move to the new factory in Derrychara. The 1956 event, held on 29th August, was regarded at that time as the best event ever held by the Society and it left a profit of £449. A new feature in the agricultural show was a class for Landrace pigs and tug-o-war was a new introduction at the horse jumping ground. The 1957 show received a very considerable boost when the Mart presented a prize of £50 for the champion dairy cow of Northern Ireland and £50 was received from the Northern Ireland Pigs Marketing Board for a bacon carcase competition. Another major attraction which was repeated in the following years was the visit of the Ulster Dairy Queen and five Dairy Princesses who also attended the Show dance.

The Governor of Northern Ireland, Lord Wakehurst, and Lady Wakehurst, attended the 1958 Show. They were entertained to lunch in the Minor Townhall and his Lordship was presented with a suit length from Lisbellaw Woollen Mills. The weather was appalling for the Show and profits were reduced to £100. A new competition for grassland management, which ran for a number of years, was introduced in 1959 with 'open days' being held on winners' farms.

At the 1959 Show the Dairy Queen and Dairy Princesses are pictured with Alderman Dr W. F. Bryson, Mayor of Enniskillen, Lady Brookeborough and Mr Henry Archdale Porter. Mr William Wilson, Show Secretary, is seated in front (Courtesy of Mrs Marion Maxwell).

The 1960s

The steady progress made during the previous decade was consolidated in the 1960s. A very considerable well-earned honour was conferred on one of the Society's long serving members in 1960 when Captain The Hon John W. Brooke was appointed captain of the Irish International Horse Jumping Team.

Captain The Hon John W. Brooke and his wife, The Hon Mrs Rosemary Brooke, with one of their favourite show jumpers in 1960 (Courtesy of Viscount Brookeborough).

Later in the year Miss O'Reilly, Ulster Dairy Queen, was invited to present the cups at a social gathering. That year was also noteworthy in that the Ministry of Agriculture banned the showing of poultry at any show in Northern Ireland as a Fowl Pest precautionary measure. Tractor driving competitions and weight judging were introduced in 1966. The tractor driving event was expanded into an International event in 1967 when the YFC and Macra na Feirme were participants. Another major attraction at the Show that year was the *All Ireland Baby Beef Calf Championship.* The social and entertainment aspect of the Show had been expanded at this time to include two show dances – one on the Tuesday night and the other on the evening of the Show.

The 1970s

A public address system was employed for the 1973 Show. Mr Bill Wilson was invited to give the commentary, a service which he continued to provide into the twenty-first century.

Miss Philomena O'Reilly, an administrative officer in the County Agricultural Executive Office in Enniskillen, was crowned the Ulster Dairy Queen in 1965 and her attendance at the Show brought much pleasure and pride to those present (Courtesy of Mrs Bronagh Reilly).

Cups for all members of the family. Mr and Mrs Jack Veitch of Drumlone, Lisbellaw, with their daughter, Doris, and sons Derek and Kenneth, at the 1964 Presentation of Cups ceremony (Courtesy of Mrs M. Veitch).

Mr Bill Wilson with his prize winning exhibit at the Show towards the end of the century.

The availability of the assembly hall in the new Further Education College in 1974 was a big boost for the display of children's work, needlework, flowers, cookery, fruit and eggs. Swine classes, which had been suspended earlier due to an outbreak of Swine Vesicular Disease, were not revived in 1975 due to lack of interest by exhibitors.

Livestock and associated Classes

In 1900 the agricultural classes catered for cattle, sheep, swine, poultry and butter. Horses were very important in the first half of the century and classes for them featured strongly at the Show. The only cattle breeds mentioned in the 1919 Show Schedule were Shorthorns. Again there were two main sections depending on whether an exhibitor's Valuation (Poor Law Valuation) was under or over £35. All sheep classes were for long-wool breeds. No breeds were specified for swine. There were four breeds for poultry – Black Minorca; Leghorn; Faverolle and Rhode Island Red.

There was considerable interest in the 1920s in improving the output from dairy cows. Cow Testing Associations were established in the Kinawley, Gardiner's Cross and the Monea and Springfield areas. The chairman of each of these associations namely Messrs H. Breen, W. Livingstone and J. Cathcart (junior) respectively were members of the Farming Society's management committee.

In 1925 there were 19 showing classes for equines varying from the 'best ass' to 'saddle or harness mares' and to that for a 'heavy draught mare or gelding'. Cattle classes featured Shorthorn and Aberdeen Angus breeds, both pure-bred and crossbred, in 27 different classes.

Milk recorded classes

In the 1927 Show schedule there were classes for dairy cows which had been milk recorded. Judging not only included conformation but also milk yield and milk quality were considered. In so far as milk yield was concerned one point was awarded for each 100lb milk during a 45 week lactation. Butter fat was rewarded with 15 points for every one per cent of fat. Conformation of the udder and other general animal characteristics each qualified for a maximum of 100 points. There were three milk recorded classes. An open class and a confined class existed for participants in a Fermanagh Cow Testing Association. The confined class was limited to those farmers with a Valuation of £25 or less. There was a specific class for cows tested by Monea and Springfield Cow Testing Association.

Monea and Springfield Milk Recording Association silver medal (Courtesy of Mr S. Meehan).

In the sheep section there were classes for both long and short-wool breeds. In the pig section Ulster and York breeds were featured. Weight judging of a beef animal was also a feature.

By 1936 there were classes for pure-bred Shorthorns and again classes confined to farmers whose valuation was under £20. Milk Recorded classes were a continuing feature. These classes, one for cows yielding 600 – 800 gallons and one for cows yielding over 800 gallons, were limited to cows on the Ministry's or Department's (Irish Republic) Register and milk recorded by a Fermanagh Cow Testing Association. They were designed to encourage a dual purpose animal of Shorthorn type, and besides giving credit for the milking properties due consideration was given to the size, constitution, symmetry, and quality of the animals. The Cow Testing Associations were disbanded in Northern Ireland in 1939.

New breeds

Ten years later there were classes for Ayrshires as well as for the previously mentioned breeds. Milk recorded classes had disappeared by 1945 but a new class for ensilage had appeared. Advertising by the Shorthorn, Aberdeen Angus and Hereford breed societies publicising the merits of each breed was a feature in the 1946 show catalogue. The year 1946 was also significant in that there were classes for Ayrshire and Friesian cattle. Pig classes in 1946 catered for both Large White York and Ulster breeds. Advertising was a continuing feature for Shorthorns in the 1952 catalogue claiming that: *they were the only breed which provides both an economic supply of milk and an economic carcase of beef.* Sheep breeds in 1952 included Border Leicester, Suffolk and Blackface. Wessex was included in the pig breeds that year but the Ulster breed had disappeared from the catalogue.

In 1956 Herefords, as well as Aberdeen Angus, featured in the beef classes and classes for sheep included those for Border Leicester, Suffolk, Black Face and Cross-bred.

Mr Albert Lucy, Cullen, Monea, with his prize winning Hereford bull at the 1963 Show at the Fairgreen site (Courtesy of Mrs E. Dickson).

A Show in progress on the Fairgreen site.

The pig classes now incorporated a class for a pig of bacon weight most suitable for curing into 'Wiltshire' sides of bacon. Friesians were in favour in 1957 and special prizes were offered to the Society by the British Friesian Society. The 1957 Show was significant in that it included the *Championship of Ireland Dairy Cow or Heifer* class and the award of the Hilliard cup. Bacon carcase competitions were also a feature of the 1957 Show and this would become an annual competition at each show until the late 1990s.

The Dairy Queen and Dairy Princesses with the winner of the bacon carcase competition in 1959.

A 'one-day wonder'

In 1962 Mr Henry Archdale Porter suggested that the 'All Ireland Dairy Cow Classes' should incorporate milk records as in the 1930s. He said that at present a one-day wonder could take all the prize money. In 1964 forty-five per cent of livestock entries were recorded as coming from County Fermanagh whereas eighty per cent of other entries were from the county. An appeal was made in 1972 by the Charolais Club to have pure bred classes for the breed included in that year's show. The Show committee decided that there would not be sufficient support for pure breds but suggested classes for 'up grade' cattle of that breed.

Milk recorded classes reintroduced

The value of milk recording, together with good conformation, acknowledged by the Society as far back as the 1920s, was once again included in 1980. In that year a class with valuable prize money, sponsored by the Vaughan Trust, was introduced for Fermanagh farmers whose cows were milk recorded under the Department of Agriculture's Milk Recording Scheme. The class was for cows of any breed, pedigree or non pedigree, in calf or in milk. The cows in the class were to be judged not only on conformation but also on milk and butter fat yield. Sadly, as was the case in previous efforts by the Society, the class for milk recorded cows was dropped for the 2000 Show due to lack of entries.

Continental breeds

In the 1970s Continental breeds of cattle joined the native breeds of beef cattle on Northern Ireland farms and classes for the new breeds were introduced at agricultural shows

By 1977 beef cattle classes for Simmental featured at Enniskillen followed by the other Continental breeds, Charolais, Limousin and Belgian Blue. These breeds were joined by Blonde D'Aquataine towards the end of the century.

The 1980s Shows were significant in that suckler cow classes were introduced and the show hosted finals for the Coopers Animal Health Hogget Chamionship in 1985. In 1986 that company's Irish Shows Association All Ireland Sheep Championship for the Ile de France breed was also hosted. Texels had joined the other sheep breeds in 1986 and in the 1990s the Beltex breed was featured. The 1990s also saw the development of a Young Handlers' class.

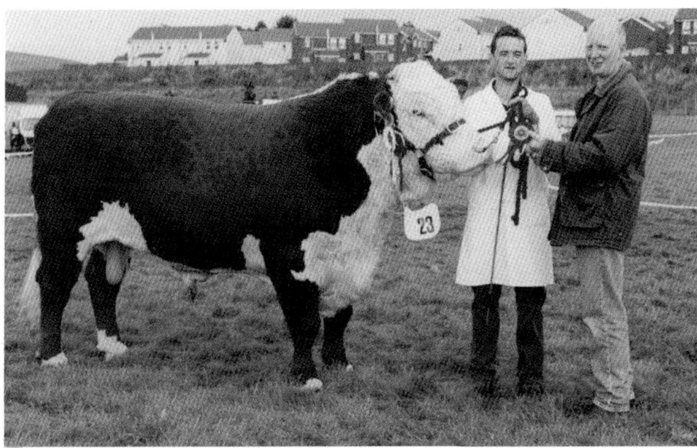

Prize winning Hereford at the 2000 Show owned by David Wilson, Magheraveely. The class was sponsored by Erne Veterinary Group which was represented at the Show by Mr Ivan Henderson.

Killadeas Barney, owned by Stuart and David Bothwell, was the 2007 champion Charolais at Enniskillen Show, champion at the Northern Ireland Charolais show at Fintona, champion at the Perth Sales and the 2008 overall male champion at the Royal Show in England. David and Stuart (Junior) are pictured at Enniskillen Show with Clive Richardson (Richardsons Butchers) who sponsored the Class.

Limousin champions owned by Crawford Brothers, Stephen and Raymond. The 2000 class was sponsored by the Ulster Bank represented by Mr Robert Scholes, Manager of the Enniskillen Branch and Mr Stephen Smith, Senior Agricultural Manager with the Bank. The Crawfords have enjoyed tremendous success with their Limousins. Their bull, Sauvingnon, was the overall male champion of the breed at the Paris Show in 2007. Sexed semen from this bull is breeding top class progeny in many countries.

A champion Simmental owned by Mr Frank Kelly, Ballyreagh, Tempo, and shown by Mr Robert Forde, Mullyknock, at the 2000 Show.

A champion cross-bred ewe owned and shown by Mr George Knox, Mullinroddy, Kesh. The class was sponsored by the Vaughan Trust. Mr Stanley Lytle, Chairman of the Vaughan Trustees, congratulates George on his success.

The Society depends heavily on sponsors and income from trade exhibitors to help with the running costs of the Show. Lord Anthony Hamilton, Chairman of the Committee of Management, receives a sponsorship cheque from Mr Cecil Morton of Fermanagh Creameries at a 1990s Show.

Mr Sean McGeehan with his prize winning Limousin and the Judge of the class. Mr Ian Crawford (right) of Farm Care Products sponsored the class.

Industrial classes

The classes in the home industries section over the years have been appropriate to the needs and fashions of the time. In 1908 classes included house joinery including the making of furniture, farming utensils, basket making, horse shoeing, brick making, boot making including a class for the 'neatest patch on a half worn boot', needlework, sprigging, knitting, crochet, lace, art, photography, wood carving, fretwork, embossed leather work, walking sticks and painting. It also included a comprehensive School Childrens' Section, cookery and laundry classes, honey, wax and hives, vegetables, fruit, flowers, and agricultural produce including root crops, butter, hay and flax.

Many of these classes remain and cater for a range of age groups. In the shows during the last decade of the twentieth century the industrial section was probably stronger than at any previous time. Extensive vegetable and fruit classes still exist. There are classes for eggs and honey. Cut flowers and pot plants, flower arranging for children and adults are all features that enjoy great support. Cookery classes for both adults and children attract very keen competition. Art and photography together with the long established classes for sprigging, embroidery and knitting are still as popular as ever.

There is keen competition each year in the School Childrens' Section. The cups and other trophies are presented each year on a special evening in a local hotel. Mrs Anderson, wife of the guest speaker at the 2001 Prize Giving, presenting the awards to very proud exhibitors. Sam Galloway from Lisbellaw Controlled Primary School received the Collum Shield. Back row from left: Rachel Morrison from Kilskeery Independent Christian School, Gareth Donaldson from Tempo Controlled Primary School and Laura Kettyle, Lisbellaw Primary, all received cups.

Anniversary

The year 1985 marked the 150th anniversary of the Show's establishment. A cavalcade through the town indicating progress in agricultural development over the years was a special feature.

Mr John James Robinson, Tower Beg, Garrison, participated in the cavalcade with Jane Morrow's pony, Cara, equipped with pardogs.

The 1990 event was the first Show with a vintage agricultural machinery display which continues each year to attract considerable interest. A cookery demonstration was a further attraction that year as was the Northern Ireland Baking Championships. Racing pigs, which raised £750 for a charity, were an attraction in the same year.

A number of significant events took place in 1999. A decision was made that in future the Show would be held during the first week in August. A food hall was a new feature. A sponsors' evening in advance of the show was held in the Killyhevlin Hotel. This sponsors' event is now held in advance of the Show at Enniskillen Agricultural College or as it is now called - CAFRE's Enniskillen Campus.

The Millennium

Millennium year was marked in a number of ways. There was a partnership link-up between Fermanagh Farming Society and the Belturbet Show Committee. Each Society's show that year was well attended by members from the other Society. Twelve members from the Fermanagh Society attended a dinner hosted by Belturbet during the year. At the Enniskillen Show there was the Millennium Dairy Heifer class sponsored by Fermanagh Creameries.

The Horse Show

Horses were probably the most important animals on the farm until tractors and cars replaced them as main sources of power for farm work and transport during the Second World War and the years that followed. Not surprisingly horses featured strongly in the showing classes up until that time. For example, in 1919 there were 11 classes for horses compared to 15 for cattle. The equine classes reflected both agricultural and saddle and harness categories. Classes for agricultural horses remained an integral part of the agricultural show right up to 1982 but were transferred to a separate horse show in succeeding years.

Horse jumping was a popular attraction over the years and was an integral part of the Farming Society's activities although at times it took on a life of its own. For example, in 1903 there is reference in the minutes to the horse jumping and driving, which had previously been a separate organisation, being integrated into the Farming Society. In 1927 when finances of the Society were strained the horse jumping committee decided to hand over its credit balance of £3, equipment and cups worth £110 to the Society, provided that body would undertake the organisation of the horse jumping each year. The jumping events normally took place on the afternoon of the agricultural show but from time to time there were departures from

From left: Mr Peter Johnston; The Duke of Westminster, President of the Society; Miss Lavinia Baird, Chairman of the Management Committee; Mrs Carol Crooke, Show Secretary; and Mr Ronnie Smith. Peter Johnston was the owner and Ronnie Smith the rider of the horse that won a show jumping competition in 1977 (Courtesy of Mrs Carol Crooke).

this arrangement. For example, in 1936 the horse jumping event was held in May whereas the agricultural show was held in August.

A significant development in the Horse Show event was its move from the Broadmeadow in 1975 to St Angelo Airfield at Rossahilly. The Horse Show reverted to the Broadmeadow for the August 1976 fixture. In 1977 and succeeding years the Horse Show was held at Castlecoole at the kind invitation of Lord Belmore. The Show went back to Rossahilly for 1981 but returned to Castlecoole in 1984 and in 1985.

The opening of the Society's new show grounds at Lackaboy with its purpose built 'double bank' in 1994 offered exciting new opportunities for the Horse Show. However, over the years, as horses ceased to have the same pivotal role as utility farm animals, there was a slow but sure divergence of the horse events from the main agricultural show. This divergence became increasingly evident within the committees that managed each event.

Canon Alfred O'Connor did sterling work as Chairman of the Horse Show Committee during the 1980s and early 1990s. He and Mrs O'Connor are receiving a retirement presentation from Lord Anthony Hamilton, Chairman of the Committee of Management.

Relationships between the Committee of Management and the Horse Show Committee became strained in 1999 due to the financial drain on show finances arising from the running of the horse show. The outcome was a total separation of the two events. This brought to an end the long established Horse Show and jumping event as an integral part of the Fermanagh Farming Society's activities. An independent horse show committee was established and thereafter Enniskillen Horse Show was held at Necarne Equestrian Park at Irvinestown.

The Showgrounds

The provision of suitable accommodation for the various show events provided a significant challenge over the years. In the early days of the Society the show was held in the Market Yard or Butter Market. The old gaol yard and the adjacent County Hall were chosen as the location in the early years of the twentieth century.

The Market Yard in 1900 (now Dickies' shop and yard premises). (Courtesy of the National Library of Ireland).

Concern was expressed in 1919 when the Council proposed to lower the wall around the showgrounds at the old gaol. Over the next few years an effort was made to find a permanent home for the show and consideration was given to a number of possible sites. No progress was made and it was decided to hold the 1923 show and horse jumping events on the Fairgreen which the owner, Mr F. R. Browne, Lakeview, Enniskillen, had promised free of rent. In subsequent years further consideration was given to the acquisition of a permanent site. Those investigated included the Castle Barracks, Celtic Park, the Broadmeadow, and the main barracks (now the police station). In 1930 the Broadmeadow had been offered to the Society for £1,600 but the committee decided in favour of the Fairgreen which was offered by Mr F. R. Browne at a rent of £10 per year.

Mr Jack Thompson, Cleans, Springfield, with his prize winning dairy cow at the 1964 Show. The cow is being led by the Ulster Dairy Queen and Mr William Wilson, Show Secretary, is following (Courtesy of Mr Jack Thompson).

The Broadmeadow.

In October 1933 a major decision was made by the Society when it entered into an agreement with the Enniskillen Urban Council to rent *the enclosed and drained ground on the Broadmeadow* (where Forum is today) with the proviso that the Society could erect a grandstand and hold fund raising events if so desired. A lease of the Broadmeadow for 35 years was negotiated at an annual rent of £17 per year. A grandstand, seating 230 people, was erected by the Society which as well as being used for the horse jumping event was let out to responsible organisations for other events on the understanding that half the proceeds would be given to the Society. Corinthians Football Club had the use of the grounds as a playing pitch.

The Fairgreen

The need for a permanent showground for the agricultural event became an issue again in 1947 when the Fairgreen had been sold to the Ulster Farmers' Mart Company Ltd (the Mart). In the meantime, the Mart had offered the use of the Fairgreen for the show on the same terms as Mr Brown had let it on former occasions. In a reciprocal gesture the Society offered all the assistance it could give to the Mart in its effort to get licences etc for the new mart building. This proved to be the beginning of a very long and happy relationship with the Mart which still exists today. In 1948 there was still concern about the lack of a permanent exhibition hall for the industrial exhibits. The County Hall, which had traditionally been used for industrial and other exhibits, had been leased to the firm of Taylor Woods Ltd. For the 1949 show Messrs T. P. Topping, John Cathcart and Sons, and Enniskillen Milling Company granted the use of part of their premises for the industrial and produce classes. Problems in 1950 associated with the showing of attested cattle evaporated when the Mart offered their new buildings and yard for the Show at whatever rent the Society was prepared to pay. The Mart subsequently gave free use of the buildings and in addition presented a cup to the Society.

Real progress and security were reported in 1951 when the Society obtained a twenty-five year lease on the buildings and grounds of the Mart and that secured a home on a medium term basis for the agricultural and industrial show. The lease was due for review in 1976 and arrangements were made with the Mart for a twenty-two year lease extension.

Problems at the Broadmeadow

While progress had been made with the agricultural show, rising costs in relation to the maintenance of the Broadmeadow facilities including the grounds, grandstand and perimeter fencing presented a problem. Things came to a head in 1965 when the lease was due to expire. Costs to the Society of maintaining the Broadmeadow complex at that time were estimated at £250 per year including rent, rates and maintenance. In 1968 the jumping programme on the Broadmeadow was suspended for the year because

Work in progress on the new showgrounds at Lackaboy in 1993.

of drainage problems. At the same time Captain John Brooke, member of the management committee, proposed that the Broadmeadow be abandoned by the Society and that the Borough Council should be asked to take over the grandstand at a valuation agreed between the parties. Follow-up negotiations with the Council were successful. There were no horse events at the Broadmeadow during 1969 but they continued in succeeding years until 1974 when there was a very poor attendance at the event due to bad weather. A recommendation that the horse event should be moved in future years to St Angelo Airfield, Rossahilly was accepted and the next horse jumping event was held at the airfield on Saturday 25th June 1975. This brought to an end the long established tradition of holding the horse jumping event on the afternoon of the agricultural show.

Lord Anthony Hamilton, Chairman of the Committee of Management, with Mr Johnston Erwin, Show Secretary, arranging for the move to Lackaboy.

Move to Lackaboy

In the early 1990s Enniskillen town was developing rapidly and the Mart at Fairgreen was experiencing difficulties with its activities due to the increase in urbanisation. Dunnes Stores wished to establish in the town and had identified the Mart site at Fairgreen as a potentially good site for their new store. Negotiations between Dunnes and the Mart company were successful and the Mart decided to develop a new livestock mart and auction centre on its property at Lackaboy on the Tempo Road. In negotiation with the Mart the County Fermanagh Farming Society obtained the freehold of five acres of land adjacent to the proposed new mart and auction centre at Lackaboy. This was a most generous gift by the Ulster Farmers' Mart and demonstrated its total commitment to the welfare of the Fermanagh farming community. Jointly, the Ulster Farmers' Mart and the County Fermanagh Farming Society were able to take advantage of a grant under the EC INTERREG programme for the developments at Lackaboy. The five acres acquired by the County Farming Society required extensive reclamation and drainage together with a substantial security boundary fence. The comprehensive improvement work was undertaken by Prunty Contracts of Newtownbutler.

The resulting field surface is of playing field quality and is ideal for the showing of livestock under all weather conditions. The Farming Society also built a general purpose house on the field which proves invaluable for storage of equipment and for catering purposes on show day. The total cost of the work on the new showgrounds was of the order of £150,000 and this amount qualified for a 50 per cent grant under the above mentioned scheme. The first agricultural show at the new facilities was held in 1994. In addition to the new show grounds the Farming Society obtained a lease, for show purposes, on the new mart and auction facilities for a period of twenty-five years with a further 10 year option. In addition, the Farming Society has the exclusive full-time use of an office in the new mart building.

Management of the new show field presented a challenge. Keeping the grass cut and managed throughout the year was a major consideration. The ideal solution came in September 2000 when Rangers Football Club requested the use of the field for a 'mini soccer school' which involved the coaching of children from four to eleven years of age. They undertook to keep the grass cut during the period when soccer was being played. When not used for football the field would be grazed by sheep owned by one of the directors of the Club. This arrangement continues and is most satisfactory. Not only does the Society have the field well maintained and receive a reasonable rent but more importantly, the field is used by up to 100 boys and girls on a very regular basis.

Aerial photo of mart and show field.

Mr Stuart Johnston, President of the The County Fermanagh Farming Society, with Mr Harold Bothwell, Tattyknuckle, Fivemiletown, and his champion Holstein cow at the 2001 Show.

A feature of annual interest is the judging of the most appropriately dressed gentleman and lady at the show. The winners in 2002 were Mr Acheson Aiken and Mrs Aileen Scott. They received their prizes from the judges Mr Billy Crooke and Mrs Carol Crooke, former Secretary of the Show.

The Ministry of Agriculture, and its successor the Department, has had an educational exhibit at the show each year from the post-war period. Mr Connor Maguire, Agricultural Adviser (left), is in conversation with Mr Eric Johnston from Cooneen at a Show in the early 1990s.

Management of the Society

Responsibility for managing the Fermanagh Farming Society's affairs rests with the Committee of Management. This body is elected by members of the Society at the annual general meeting. The size of the Committee of Management has varied over the years. In the early years of the century it was quite a sizeable body but since 1971 it is now comprised of 20 members, two of whom are appointed by the Young Farmers' Clubs in County Fermanagh. The Committee is headed by a Chairman and two Deputy Chairmen. There are committees appointed by the Management Committee which report to the Management Committee on the various aspects of management of the Society's affairs. These committees deal with livestock classes, industrial classes, finance, vintage event, and grounds management. Day to day management of show affairs is the responsibility of the Secretary which is a remunerated position and appointed by the Committee of Management. A Treasurer is appointed from within the membership of the Committee of Management. As well as the Committee there is the honorary position of President of the show – an appointment which is made each year at the annual general meeting.

The Society's contribution

The Fermanagh Farming Society was established in 1836 for the purpose of improving the standard of farming and rural enterprise in County Fermanagh. It achieved this objective by planning an agricultural show and a home industries exhibition each year. In this way it enabled the general public to see the very best standards of livestock, agricultural produce, fruit, flowers and a whole range of items manufactured in the cottages and yards of the residents in the county. The intention was that everyone would be encouraged to improve the quality of everything that was being produced. Evidence of the success of the event in the early years was reported by the Earl of Erne's Agent in 1844 when he stated that cultivation was improving due to the agricultural societies including the Fermanagh Society.

The Society also achieved a great deal more than agricultural improvement especially in the area of social development of the rural population. The Society brought together a wide range of people who undertook the organisation of the events. In the nineteenth and early twentieth centuries these included the aristocracy and landlords, the tenant farmers, small holders, church figures, the local council, the business people, serving and retired army and police officers and the teaching profession. The shows provided a marvellous forum where town and country people could mingle and they provided a social gathering and entertainment opportunity for a very wide range of people. A show dance provided further opportunities for town and country to meet in a social environment. Among

the main attractions for entertainment in the early years was the horse jumping which was a regular feature each year at the show. Throughout the twentieth and up to the present time the Society has enjoyed financial support from Government. Right from the formation of the County Committee of Agriculture in 1901, under the Agriculture and Technical Instruction Act, the Society has received a subsidy to encourage its work. For example in 1925 a subsidy of £35 was received in support of the Society's educational work and the provision of facilities for the Agricultural Instructors. This support from Government continues today with an annual financial contribution from the Department of Agriculture and Rural Development.

The Society has been well served over the years by excellent secretaries and willing stewards. The stewards assist with every aspect of running the show including manning the entrance gates, organising the competitions and manning the displays. The qualities required include diplomacy, firmness and good judgement at all times.

Mr Michael Murphy with Violet Bell in light hearted mood on Show day. Mr Murphy is a show stalwart who keeps the public informed, through a lively and well informed commentary, of progress in the livestock showing classes.

The Committee of Management in 2008. Lord Anthony Hamilton, JP DL, Chairman, front row centre with from left: Mrs Hazel McDonald, Sam Morrow OBE, William Graham, Vice Chairman, Seamus Gunn. Second row from left: Cecil Morton, Mrs Melanie Little DL, Mrs Heather Crawford, Secretary, Miss Ruth Reid, Edward Rogers. Back row from left: Derek Quinton, Robert Scholes, Tom Palmer MBE. Missing from the photograph were Miss Maisie Guy, Miss Margaret Henderson, Mrs Ann Orr and Mr Douglas Graham.

The show could not exist without its sponsors and advertisers. These bring valuable sources of funding which, together with other income, has enabled the Society to remain in a strong financially viable position.

Mr Douglas Graham JP, Vice Chairman.

The Show, each year, provides an opportunity for the best animal breeders in the country to compete against each other. The general farming community has the opportunity of seeing and inspecting the very best livestock and the most up-to-date farming equipment and supplies. At the same time it provides a forum for the general public to see agriculture at its best. The home industries and the wide variety of trade stands provide interest for young and old from both town and country.

The dog and pet shows create keen competition and widespread public interest. Bygone days are not forgotten with vintage machinery and rare breeds of livestock and poultry displays. The one hundred classes for school children provide a tremendous opportunity for creativity.

The Society which has served County Fermanagh and the wider community so well for more than 170 years is in a strong position to meet the challenges in the foreseeable future.

References:

Minute books of the County Fermanagh Farming Society.

Files of *The Impartial Reporter* and *Fermanagh Herald* held in Enniskillen Library.

Photographs, unless otherwise acknowledged, were supplied by Fermanagh Farming Society.

Business in full swing for the trade exhibitors in the Mart building at the 1998 show.

Chapter 28
Farmers' organisations

Farmers, like other members of society, have found it advantageous to come together to form groupings for competition, social engagement, and for furthering their business interests. Farming societies and other organisations have played a significant role in furthering these interests over the past two centuries. One such body was the Enniskillen and Irvinestown Union Farmers' Club. This body, which was in existence since the 1850s, appears to have been primarily interested in ploughing matches. Their sixty-first ploughing match was held at Makeny, in a field owned by Mr Irvine Stewart, in early March 1913, with classes for swing and chill ploughs. Prizes were also presented for the best pair of horses and the best turned out team. After the ploughing match three horse races took place. It was customary after such events to have a dinner and to make the presentations and propose toasts. The dinner was held in the Commercial Hotel under the chairmanship of Major C. C. D'Arcy Irvine.

The Ulster Farmers' Union

The Ulster Farmers' Union (UFU) was formed in 1917. This was a difficult time for farming. The 1914-18 War was raging on land and sea. Fifteen to twenty ships carrying desperately needed supplies, including food, were being sunk each week crossing the Atlantic. The production of food at home took on a new significance. Compulsory Tillage became a feature and Government regulations covered nearly every aspect of farming. An article in the *Belfast Newsletter* of 17th November 1917 articulated the difficulties being faced by farmers at that time. It stated: *Farming has become a controlled industry and the farmer's complaint is that the orders under which he has to work his land and market his produce have been made without due consideration to the difficulties he has to contend with and his just claims as the producer.*

An organisation was therefore clearly needed to represent farmers' interests. Associations had been formed to negotiate prices on behalf of milk, pig and flax producers with those who purchased these commodities. The Ulster Farmers' and Flax Growers' Association developed from the above associations. It held its first Annual General Meeting in Belfast on 17th October 1917 and appealed for branches of the organisation to be set up in every district. Support for this development was considerable culminating in a well attended meeting in the Ulster Hall in Belfast on 14th December 1917 when it was decided to form the Ulster Farmers' Union to unite all existing farmers' organisations. This body would act as a strong central organisation representing all farming interests in negotiation with Government. An Executive Committee was set up in 1918. It reported to the first Annual General Meeting of the Union that 70 Branches were affiliated with the Union in the nine counties of Ulster. Two of these branches were in Fermanagh. One of the early decisions by the Union was the adoption of a non-sectarian policy. Mr A. A. McGuckian of Cloughmills, County Antrim, a leading Irish farmer, commented on this particular policy at the time. He stated: *as a non-political organisation, called into existence by the stress of economical considerations and in the midst of a population where various elements have unfortunately been taught to regard each other with suspicion, the Ulster Farmers' Union has done a useful service by uniting all farmers with a view to attending their own businesses. Through the Union enthusiastic men have found a common platform on which to meet their neighbours all over the country and a new outlook for their abilities.*

Mr A. A. McGuckian [*From A. A. McGuckian - A Memorial Volume,* **edited by Professor A. E. Muskett (1956)**].

The Union was pursuing the interest of farmers vigorously in 1918. It sent a delegation to Dublin in January of that year to point out the serious position of farmers due to the very high price of feedingstuffs and of labour, making it unprofitable to produce pork or beef. Following the signing of the Peace Treaty, the Union Council sent a resolution to the Prime Minister in London seeking *to ensure for the agricultural industry government assistance to make the country as nearly as possible self-supporting in food.* The aim of the Union was to secure a guaranteed price for all farm produce based on cost of production plus 5 per cent on the value of land, buildings and working capital.

Sir Basil Brooke's support

In November 1919 Sir Basil Brooke took the chair at the Colebrooke Branch of the Union. In addressing the members present he said: *Every person who subscribed to the Union has been rewarded a hundred times over and everyone who does not do so is a blackleg. Every man who does not join the Union is working against his own interests and should not receive the benefits thereof.* He urged the members to get hold of every man who was not a member already and bring him to the meetings and when he realised the benefits he would soon become a member. The meeting was also addressed by Mr Martin, Secretary of the UFU. He dealt with the main issues facing farmers principally in relation to inadequate prices for produce. Fixed prices for potatoes and pork were being demanded and the price being given for flax was not acceptable. Mr Martin also promoted the case for milk recording pointing out that cows yielding 600 gallons were needed.

One of its earliest and most commendable activities was to establish a weekly newspaper in 1920 called *'The Farmers Journal'*. In 1922 it became a monthly magazine and continued as such until 1970 when increasing costs of production and posting to members became too great to be covered by advertising income. From that time onwards *'Farm Week'* and later the *News Letter* have carried the Union news.

Negotiating body

Agreement in 1922 was reached with the Government for Northern Ireland, set up after partition, that the Ulster Farmers' Union would be the body which would represent farmers in discussions with the Ministry of Agriculture. The economic depression of the 1920s had an adverse impact on Union activity. In 1926 it was reported that many branches were inactive and the Union headquarters organisation was in financial difficulties but survived through the generosity of some of its leading members. The Union received a major boost in October 1930 when the National Farmers' Union Mutual Insurance Society was adopted as the Union's Insurance Society. Since then the income from this Insurance Agency for Branch and Group Secretaries has helped to recompense them for the work carried out for the Union. Sir Basil Brooke MP was President of the Ulster Farmers' Union in the 1930/31 year.

He gave an address about the work of the Union and 10,000 copies of his address were printed for distribution among the farming community to promote the work and activity of the Union. This campaign was successful and by 1933 the Union had expanded to 119 Branches.

Sir Basil Brooke (Courtesy of Viscount Brookeborough).

Throughout the development of agriculture in Northern Ireland during the century the Ulster Farmers' Union has had a considerable input in terms of advice into the development of Ministry of Agriculture policies. This has been significant in relation to the formulation of Ministry of Agriculture farm improvement schemes and in initiating marketing strategies for agricultural produce and also in the determination of commodity prices. Throughout the organisation's life it has had effective representation from County Fermanagh in its headquarters organisation.

County organisation

Mr T. D. Wilson was appointed Organiser for Tyrone and Fermanagh in 1922. By 1953 Fermanagh had 30 Branches of the Union. These were Boho, Brookeborough, Bellanaleck, Ballinamallard, Garvary, Corryyglass, Colebrooke, Cashel, Clabby, Derrygonnelly, Garrison, Irvinestown, Killadeas, Killesher, Kinawley, Kesh, Ederney, Letter, Dernasesk, Lack, Lisnaskea, Lisbellaw, Mulleek,

Newtownbutler, Roscor, Rosslea, Springfield, Teemore, Tedd, and Tempo. The Branches normally met in the local school or hall and each had its own Chairman and Secretary. As time passed it was found to be more satisfactory to organise the Branches into Groups and follow the pattern established in North West Derry in 1950. The grouping enabled full-time Group Secretaries to be appointed whose responsibilities included the organisation of local meetings and the collection of Union membership subscriptions. The Group Secretaries also had the agency for the National Farmers' Union Mutual Insurance Society.

Group Secretaries

In the 1950s Mr B. Armstrong and Mr W. J. Crawford served as Group Secretaries for Fermanagh North and the post was held by Mr George Foster in 1964. Mr John Brady followed Mr Foster in office. Union activity expanded considerably in the period that followed. Mr Claudie Stinson and Mr Crawford Breen were both appointed Group Secretaries in 1969. Mr George Eames succeeded Crawford Breen who retired in December 1985 and Mr Richard Trimble joined as a Group Secretary at the same time. Claudie Stinson retired in September 1994 and his role was then undertaken by Mr Albert McClelland. When George Eames retired in December 1999 Mr Richard Henderson was appointed.

Mr Claudie Stinson, Senior Group Secretary (centre), discussing the winter programme with from left: Mr Richard Trimble (Group Secretary), Mr Robert Jones, UFU Technical Officer, Mr George Eames (Group Secretary) and Mr Jim Hamilton, UFU Technical Officer (Courtesy of Mr Albert McClelland).

The Bellanaleck Branch

Bellanaleck Branch of the Union, formed in 1938, was very active over the years. The founding Chairman was Mr George Cathcart who made an outstanding contribution to farming politics during his lifetime. George became a founding member of the Northern Ireland Milk Marketing Board in 1954 and was President of the Ulster Farmers' Union in 1963. He also gave valuable service outside

Mr Crawford Breen, Group Secretary 1969 – 1985.

Mr Richard Trimble, Group Secretary, with Messrs William Warnock, DARD, John Courtney, DARD, and John Rutledge, Derrylin.

Mr Derek Thornton, Tonywall, Derrylin (centre), active UFU member, with Mr David Brown MRCVS (left), Divisional Veterinary Officer, and Mr Cormac McKervey BAgr, then DARD Agricultural Development Officer and now Head of Agriculture at the Ulster Bank.

Mr Albert McClelland, Senior Group Secretary, with Messrs William Rea, Tullynagowan, Brookeborough, and Graeme Melville, Senior Agricultural Development Officer, DANI.

agriculture, both at county and provincial level. He was Chairman of Enniskillen Rural District Council for a number of years and was also a member of Fermanagh County Council. In addition, he served as a member and eventually as Chairman of the Northern Ireland Fire Authority. He served as a JP and was appointed OBE in the 1979 New Year Honours. The Bellanaleck Branch was also exceptionally well served by its long serving and very efficient secretary Mr James Murphy. For a number of years James contributed an article to *The Farmers' Journal,* The Ulster farmers' Union monthly magazine, under the title of *'Bellanaleck Calling'* which dealt with the issues facing Fermanagh farmers. Another regular Fermanagh contributor to *The Farmers' Journal* during the 1960s was Mr P. T. O'Reilly from Kinawley who wrote a feature article entitled *Down in Fermanagh.*

Mr George Cathcart OBE JP (Courtesy of Mrs Marion Maxwell).

Social and educational activities

The Union has also performed a valuable social function. Many Branches and County Committees of the Union held entertainment functions like socials and concerts. Annual dinners, to which the ladies were invited, were also a regular feature over the years. The Farmers' Union dinner dance in Enniskillen continues to be a very well attended function. Outings of educational and social value were also organised. In the days before cars were in common use many Branches organised bus trips to events like Balmoral and Dublin Spring Shows. The Union has a pavilion at Balmoral Show where members can meet to discuss farming issues and to receive hospitality at the annual show.

Bellanaleck Branch members at a meeting in the 1980s.

Mr Claudie Stinson, Senior Group Secretary (right) discussing the programme with the Lisnaskea Branch Chairman, Mr John Johnston, Carrickmacusker, and the speaker at the meeting, Mr Sam Morrow, County Agricultural Executive Officer.

Branch and Group meetings of the Union over the years have been excellent venues for the transmission of information and advice to members. For example, during the 1980s the County Agricultural Executive Officer and his Deputies addressed practically every Branch of the Union each year on important agricultural matters.

Fermanagh leadership

County Fermanagh provided many outstanding leaders for the agricultural industry and the Union over the years. One of its early Presidents was Sir Basil Brooke MP who played such an important role in promoting the value of the Union to the farming community in 1930/31. Sir Arthur Algeo CBE JP from County Antrim, but whose roots were in Fermanagh, served as President of the Union on no less than four occasions stretching from 1946/47 to 1963/64. Mr Harry West MP who, like Sir Basil Brooke, would eventually become the Northern Ireland Minister of Agriculture, served the Union as its leader during 1955/56. Mr George Cathcart, OBE, JP was President in 1962/63, Mr Mervyn Loane CBE, who farmed at Seskinore, County Tyrone, but again like Sir Arthur Algeo had his roots in Fermanagh, was President in 1981/82. Mr Harold Hamilton MBE from Kesh was President in 1986/87 and went on to become Chairman of United Dairy Farmers Ltd. Mr Ronnie Farrell from Lisnaskea, was President in 1989/90 and Mr Douglas Rowe from Rosscreenagh, Letter, Kesh, served in the Union Presidency post in 2000/02.

Mr Harry West, President 1955 – 1956.

Mr Douglas Rowe, President 2000 – 2002, in conversation with the DARD Minister, Mrs Brid Rodgers and Mr John Gilliland, UFU Vice President.

Mr Harold Hamilton MBE, President 1986 – 1987.

Over the years representatives from Fermanagh served on the various committees at headquarters and on the Executive. Membership of the Union was open to both men and women. Miss Mary Wilson MBE from Lisbellaw was a particularly active member serving as Secretary of the Fermanagh County Committee of the Union for many years. She was also, for a time, Chairman of the Union's Central Poultry Committee and through her Union connections was a member of the Northern Ireland Milk Marketing Board.

Mr Ronnie Farrell, President 1989 - 1990.

The Young Farmers' Clubs

The person responsible for establishing the Young Farmers' Clubs of Ulster (YFC) was Mr W. S. Armour MBE MA BLitt, a native of North Antrim. Mr Armour became Editor of the

Northern Whig newspaper and in an article published on 30th August 1929 he advanced the case for an organisation for the rural youth. He had knowledge of the YFC in England and promoted the case for a similar movement in Northern Ireland stating: *in an effort to fill the blank in young Ulster countryman's life, and as a hope for the creation of a rural community spirit.*

The Executive of the Ulster Farmers' Union recommended in October 1929 that Branches of the Union should encourage the formation of Young Farmers' Clubs. The Young Farmers' Clubs movement was formed in 1930 at a meeting organised by Mr W. S. Armour, supported by Mr Humphrey Jamison, General Secretary of the Ulster Farmers' Union and Mr Harold Barbour of the Ulster Agricultural Organisation Society. Several Branches of the Union had formed Junior Members' Clubs. The Ulster Farmers' Union provided office accommodation for Mr Dick Kimber who had been brought from England to establish the new organisation for young farmers. The Carnegie Trust funded the YFC for the first few years of its organisation and the Union took responsibility for administration of the funds. The YFC became an independent organisation in 1937. The organisation served as an excellent training ground for young farmers and others with an interest in rural affairs. Apart from agricultural training in topics like stock judging and other farm based activities, the encouragement of members' public speaking skills has always been an important aspect of YFC programmes. This equipped members to take an active part in public life. Many Presidents of the Ulster Farmers' Union had their early training in the YFC movement.

The YFC has been active in Fermanagh over the years. In the autumn of 1934 a series of meetings was held in Fermanagh, which was the only county in Northern Ireland at that time in which there were no Young Farmers' Clubs. Derrylin gave the lead. At a meeting in the Countess of Erne Public Elementary School it was decided to form a Club and officers were elected. Mr H. M. Irwin JP, a member of the Fermanagh County Committee of Agriculture, presided at the meeting which was attended by about 50 young farmers. Mr Irwin said that it was one of the best objects with which he ever had the privilege of being associated. He said the whole point of the Clubs was for the benefit of the youth, young ladies and young gentlemen. They had to realise that the future was theirs. He said that they had to endeavour to become better men and better women and get more out of the land and improve on what their fathers and grandfathers had done.

Mr R. M. Chambers, Organiser of the Young Farmers' Clubs, then addressed the meeting and thanked Mr Irwin and Mr D. T. Ritchie, Agricultural Instructor, and several other gentlemen in the district for their support in encouraging the movement. Mr Chambers stated that there were currently 40 Clubs in Ulster. The speaker explained that while the object of the movement was mainly educational, the Clubs had introduced variety into the meetings by organising debates and competitions. After a question and answer session it was

Mr Michael Graham, centre, discussing grassland management with (facing camera): Messrs Michael Murphy, Ballyreagh; Connor Maguire and Alan Warnock, Agricultural Development Advisers, and Harold Hamilton, Agharainy, Kesh, in 1994.

agreed to form a Club. The following officials were elected: President – Mr James Emo, Aughintra; Secretary – Mr James Breen, Mullaghgarrow; Assistant Secretary – Miss Henrietta Breen, Stragowna; Treasurer – Mr Arthur Rutledge; two members of Committee – Miss Ethel Willis, Drumbroughas, and Mr William Magee, Druminiskill. Over 20 submitted their names for joining the Club.

In 1934, Mr D. T. Ritchie, County Instructor in Agriculture, had established Clubs in Derrylin, Aghadrumsee, Mullaghmeen, Gardiner's Cross and in 1938 there were active Clubs in Colebrooke and Clabby. The war years obviously had an effect and by 1947 the only Clubs of the movement existing in Fermanagh were at Lisnaskea, Cavanaleck and Cashel. In 1978, Garvary, Kesh, Lisbellaw and Lisnaskea were all active and that remained so until the end of the century. Fermanagh has produced two Presidents of the YFC movement. Mr Noel Baxter served from 1977 to 1979 and Mr Michael Graham, when he was Farm Manager at Enniskillen Agricultural College.

Mr Noel Baxter.

Northern Ireland Agricultural Producers' Association (NIAPA)

NIAPA was formed in 1974 as an amalgamation of farmers' action groups which had their origins mainly in the Less Favoured Areas (LFAs) in the west of the Province.

The initial groupings consisted of suckler and sheep farmers whose incomes were being devastated and who felt isolated. These groups had a fragmented approach but a common aim, which was to maintain and improve the income of the family farm. Therefore, a natural progression

Mr Gabriel O'Keefe, Chairman of NIAPA, presenting the 'NIAPA Young Farmer of the Year' cup to Sean Bradley at Balmoral Show in 1986.

was to concentrate efforts and form a representative body to articulate views and aims. The initial motto of the organisation was the "The voice of the Family Farmer".

NIAPA was organised and managed on a totally voluntary basis from its inception until 1988 when it began to employ full time professional staff. Its role over time has evolved and now membership encompasses all farm sizes, commodities and comes from all counties of the Province.

One of the founding members of NIAPA was the late Mr Gabriel O'Keefe from Newtownbutler. He was a council member from the organisation's inception and Chairman from 1984-1989. It was during Gabriel's term as Chairman that plans were laid and came to fruition to employ staff and develop the organisation into a full time professional body. Indeed Gabriel worked tirelessly for NIAPA and the community from its origins until his untimely death in December 1992.

References:

MacLurg, Alastair, Ulster Farmers' Union – *The History of its first Seventy Years 1917 – 1987.*

Files of *The Impartial Reporter, Fermanagh Herald* and *Fermanagh Times.*

Information supplied by Northern Ireland Agricultural Producers' Association.

Chapter 29
Fermanagh Grassland Club

In 1959 staff of Imperial Chemical Industries (ICI), working in County Fermanagh, and the Department of Agriculture's Advisory Service in the county, introduced a Grassland Competition for farmers, which was adopted by the County Fermanagh Farming Society as an integral part of its agricultural show programme. This competition attracted quite an interest in the farming community and 'Open Days' were held on the winning farms. At a meeting of the judges after the 1963 competition, Mr Alan Tisdall, a well known farmer and quarry owner, from Lisnaskea, suggested the formation of a grassland club.

Mr Alan Tisdall.

An advertisement appeared in the local press inviting any farmer interested in the formation of a grassland club in Co Fermanagh to attend a meeting to be held on 13th November 1963 at 8pm in the Imperial Hotel in Enniskillen. It was explained that the purpose of the club was to stimulate interest in grassland production and management. Forty farmers responded to the advertisement and the decision was made to form the Fermanagh Grassland Club at that meeting. This marked the formation of what continues to be one of the most successful farming societies in Ireland.

Inaugural meeting

Mr J. T. Kernohan OBE BAgr, Secretary/Manager of the Royal Ulster Agricultural Society and former Treasurer and Past President of the British Grassland Society and founder member of the Ulster Grassland Society, was the guest speaker at the Club's inaugural meeting which was held in the Imperial Hotel, Enniskillen, on 14th January 1964. Mr Kernohan in his address said: *"I am very pleased to be present on this first evening of your Club, and I would take the opportunity of congratulating the founders of this significant development in your county and to hope that this will be a most effective organisation and of considerable benefit to members. No doubt in these days of reduced margins, increased competition and higher quality standards, an organisation that can provide enlightenment and spread information more widely, deserves the support of all concerned."*

Committee membership

The office bearers appointed were Mr Alan Tisdall, Chairman; Mr Robert Houston BAgr, Deputy County Agricultural Officer; Vice Chairman; and Mr Robin Stevenson BAgr, one of Ministry of Agriculture's Agricultural Advisory Officers in County Fermanagh, Secretary. The committee appointed was: – Captain R. O. Hermon, Irvinestown; Messrs Eric Hassard, Churchill; William Moore, The Coagh, Enniskillen; David Elliott, Maguiresbridge; Robert McFarland, Tamlaght; and John Bailie BAgr, Castle Archdale Experimental Husbandry Farm.

Since then a committee and office bearers have been elected each year at the annual general meeting and a programme of monthly meetings, competitions and a Club outing are organised. The standing of the Club is such that it can attract to its meetings the very best speakers on the various aspects of grassland production and associated farm management. Furthermore, commercial firms and the banking institutions are keen to be associated with the Club in its competitions and offer generous sponsorship and other services. In addition, the Ministers with responsibility for Agriculture in Northern Ireland have been regular speakers at the Club's annual dinners and prize presentations over the years.

The first farm visit for members was to the well run unit of Mr Eric Hassard at Churchill, Derrygonnelly, on 28th March 1964. The small farm carried 18 cows on 25 acres together with pig and poultry enterprises.

Annual dinner

The Club held its first annual dinner in February 1965 in the Imperial Hotel, Enniskillen, under the chairmanship of Mr Robert Houston. Mr Harry West MP, Minister of Agriculture, was special guest. The Minister warned that in the near future the less efficient farmer might have to give up farming. He said that at present there was a surplus of eggs, milk and pigs and because of this it was becoming more difficult to sell these products at economic prices. He said beef was still in great demand and this was where grassland farmers could score in the future. He went on to say that because of over-production of products net farm income tended to fall. Production should be matched by increases in customers but they could not look to a rapidly increasing population. It seemed as if there were too many farmers trying to get a living out of an almost fixed income to the farming industry and it appeared as though less efficient farmers would, in their own interests, have to give up farming. He said it was a great problem and the Government did not want to force anyone out of agriculture. He added: *"We must face reality. Farmers nowadays should look on their farms as businesses and not so much as farms."* Mr West expressed his pleasure at the good relations which existed between Ministry of Agriculture officials and farmers. He said a confidence had sprung up which could only bring good to the agricultural industry, and he hoped this bond would be strengthened. He also highlighted the change in the attitude towards grass which was now rightly regarded as a crop.

Mr R. H. Houston BAgr.

Mr John Murray CB (centre), Permanent Secretary of the Department of Agriculture, addressed the Club during Mr Albert Bruce's (second left) term as Chairman in 1995. Mr Alan Warnock (left), Secretary, and Mr Connor Maguire (right), Treasurer, are accompanied by Mr Pat Mohan.

Cups and prizes were awarded at the dinner to the winners of the Club's first silage making competition. The Tisdall Cup for first prize in the over 200 tons class went to Mr Derek Emo. Second and third prizes went to Mr Bernard McGirr and Mr Basil Little respectively. The Hermon Cup for first prize in the under 200 tons class was won by Mr Jack Robinson, with second and third prizes going to Mr David Fawcett and Mr Michael Murphy. The judge for the competition was Mr Vincent Courtney BAgr, Deputy County Agricultural Officer in Tyrone.

New Secretary

Mr Sam McEwen, the Ministry of Agriculture's Agricultural Advisory Officer in south-west Fermanagh, was appointed Honorary Secretary/Treasurer of the Club at the start of the 1965 winter programme in succession to Mr Robin Stevenson who had gone to the United States on a Kellogg Scholarship. The Club's membership had grown to 60 by this time.

Noted speakers

The years 1965/66 saw the first speakers from the Irish Republic visit the Club. Dr Dan Browne from Moorepark Research Station in Cork amazed members when he informed them that cows were out to grass by early March at Moorepark. Mr Paddy O'Keefe, editor of the Irish Farmers' Journal and Mr John Mulqueen from the Agricultural Research Institute in County Leitrim also addressed meetings of the Club that year. Mr Mulqueen's visit led to the building up of a great relationship between himself and Club member Mr Joe Pat Prunty, drainage contractor, of Lettergreen, Newtownbutler. Messrs Mulqueen and Prunty were instrumental in developing the gravel tunnel drainage system which has brought untold benefits to County Fermanagh and much further afield. This system was a forerunner which led to the now famous playing field development known as 'Prunty Pitches'. The basis of these pitches involves laying a system of collector drains and gravel tunnel drains over which a layer of sand is spread; this provides the seed-bed for the grass turf mixture. The result is, in effect, an 'all weather' pitch for field sports, such as, gaelic football rugby and soccer.

Competition winners

Two members in the early years brought great credit to the Club and the County. Mr John Ferguson of Blaney won the 'David Brown Farmer 65 Competition' in 1965. This was followed the next year by Mr Eric Hassard of Tully, Churchill, winning the 'BBC Farmer of the Year' against very stiff competition from the other five counties.

Throughout the 1960s the main emphasis within the Club was on how to grow more grass by improving soil conditions through the use of lime, fertiliser, drainage, and then reseeding which led to great improvements throughout the county. In the 1970s, the emphasis moved to improving silage quality by earlier cutting and wilting and improving fermentation by the use of additives. From the mid-1980s Government policy saw a change of emphasis towards protection of the environment coupled with more efficient food production.

Over the years annual competitions among members have been a feature of Club activities. The competitions have included silage making, grassland and farm management. The environment also featured in the competitions. The Club has been fortunate in that it has been able to attract generous sponsorship for its competitions from banks, fertiliser and meal companies and other organisations that supply the farming community with requisites.

Mr Ronnie Farrell, Lisnaskea, winner of an environmental award. This competition was judged by Dr Harry Gracey (right), Countryside Management Division, Department of Agriculture and Rural Development. This Club competition was sponsored by the Bank of Ireland. Mr Hugh Mannix, Manager of the Bank's Enniskillen Branch, is on the left.

'The Troubles'

The Club provided a marvellous service throughout 'The Troubles' in that it had a cross-community membership and brought people together with a common purpose. However, Club activities did not escape unscathed. Mr John Wallace BAgr, County Agricultural Executive Officer in County Tyrone, was the invited guest speaker for the annual general meeting planned for 13th December 1971. Mr Wallace and Mr Sam McEwen, Honorary Secretary, were enjoying a pre-meeting meal in the Imperial Hotel in Enniskillen when a bomb went off in the hotel but fortunately neither was injured. Needless to say the annual general meeting was adjourned.

Minister addresses the Club

Mr Harry West, Minister of Agriculture, was the guest speaker at the February 1971 annual dinner of the Club. Mr West's address was as follows: *"As a Fermanagh man I am only too aware of the problems faced by Fermanagh farmers in trying to achieve maximum output in this region of heavy soils and high rainfall. However, my Ministry's Grassland Experimental Centre at Castle Archdale has carried out considerable work directed to the development and investigation of practical methods of increasing production under Fermanagh conditions. Early work at the Centre studied methods of improving grassland output and it was clearly shown that high yields of grass can be obtained under our conditions. Recently there has been a greater emphasis on the problems associated with grass utilisation and more emphasis was now being placed on the development of complete grassland farming systems, particularly for beef production. This type of work, which was very commercially orientated, was intended to be of direct interest to farmers in the area. For example, the Centre was examining among other things, the feeding, management, and economics of a beef breeding herd, making the maximum use of grass and silage. I know only too well that our major problem in Fermanagh is our long wet winter and, indeed, the possibility of very wet spells in summer. If under these conditions one is to achieve intensive stocking, provision must be made for insurance in the form of large quantities of conserved grass, preferably in the form of high quality silage and this would be intended primarily to allow for the long winter housing period, it should always be remembered that circumstances could arise when it might have to be used even during the normal grazing season during a particularly wet period. I think farmers should not overlook the increasingly high capital requirement not only for stock but also for silos, housing and equipment. Careful planning is essential if the optimum use is to be made of highly expensive capital and when doing such planning farmers should always bear in mind the possibility of using an agricultural contractor, for example for silage making."*

Rt Hon H. W. West MP PC (Courtesy Mrs M. West).

Mr West concluded by commending the Club on its progress from 1963. He said: *"It is most encouraging to know that this degree of enthusiasm for better grassland management exists among County Fermanagh farmers and it augurs well for the future prospects of grassland farming in the county."*

Direct Rule Minister's visit

Mr Peter Mills MP, the Parliamentary Under-Secretary of State with responsibility for Agriculture in Northern Ireland, was the guest speaker at the Club's dinner on 13th February 1973. Earlier that day, under heavy snow conditions, Mr Mills, accompanied by Mr Sam Morrow, Deputy County Agricultural Officer, visited farms in the Border area. In his speech at the Club's dinner Mr Mills stated that he was pleased to see that such a Club existed with the objectives of *"promoting and stimulating a greater interest in grassland production, management and utilisation in County Fermanagh."* Mr Mills in his address when commenting on the prospects for agriculture on entry to the Common Market stated: *"I think most farmers in County Fermanagh will gain more by concentrating on milk and beef from their grassland".* He went on to state: *"To me it is gratifying to know that levels of grassland production on the leading farms in your county compare favourably with those elsewhere in Northern Ireland. I do feel that your Grassland Club through its meetings, discussions and competitions has had and will continue to have a most useful role to play in raising the standards of grassland in the county".* In conclusion Mr Mills stated: *"making the most of the opportunities which lie ahead in the fields of milk, beef and lamb production depends on the full exploitation of the ability of your land to produce an abundance of grass. I am quite confident that your Club has an important part to play in the continued development of grassland farming in County Fermanagh and I wish you every success in the future."*

The Chairmen

Throughout the life of the Club it has had a new Chairman each year. This policy has ensured that the Club has been led with enthusiasm throughout its life. Most of the Chairmen have been farmers who have given distinguished service. The Ministry of Agriculture's senior staff in Fermanagh have also served in a leadership capacity. The County Agricultural Officer, the Deputy County Agricultural Officers, the Divisional Veterinary Officer and Principals of Enniskillen Agricultural College, all have had the honour of serving as Chairmen of this distinguished Club.

The Secretaries

Mr Sam McEwen served the Club with distinction as Honorary Secretary from 1965 until September 1973,

Mr George Black, Chairman in 1989, cutting the 25th anniversary cake. Included are Messrs Alan Warnock, Secretary, Edward Rogers, Vice Chairman, and Connor Maguire, Treasurer.

when he was transferred to County Antrim on promotion to Deputy County Agricultural Executive Officer. His successor, as Secretary of the Club, was Mr Norman Shirley BAgr, a Department of Agriculture Adviser in Fermanagh, who again served faithfully until his transfer to a lecturing post in Greenmount Agricultural College in 1975. Another Department Adviser, Mr Alan Warnock BAgr, was appointed in his place as Club Secretary at that time. Over the years the success of the Fermanagh Grassland Club has been determined by the quality of its programmes. This has mainly been the responsibility of the Chairman and Committee who are elected at each year's annual general meeting. However, the Committee and members of the Club would agree that the driving force behind the expansion and success of the Club has been due, in large measure, to the excellent service provided by its Secretaries. The longest serving of these has been Alan Warnock. There is no doubt that the growth and expansion of the Club since 1975 has been largely attributable to the enthusiasm, foresight, popularity and organising ability of Alan.

The Treasurers

The success and sustainability of any organisation depends on its finances. The Fermanagh Grassland Club has been well served over the years by dedicated and committed Honorary Treasurers. For the first 26 years of its life, the Club's Treasurers were members of the Ministry/Department of Agriculture's Advisory staff in County Fermanagh. From its foundation in 1963 until 1970 there were joint Secretary/Treasurers, the posts being filled successively by Mr Robin Stevenson and Mr Sam McEwen. From 1970 until 2001 the officers fulfilling this important role were: Messrs David Todd BAgr (1970-73), John McIlmoyle BAgr (1973-75), Rayner McKinley BAgr (1975-81) and Connor Maguire BAgr (1981- 2001). At the beginning of the new century Mr Maguire was succeeded in the post by Mr Cormac McKervey, who like his predecessors in office, is another Queen's University graduate in agriculture and is the Ulster Bank's Senior Agricultural Adviser in Northern Ireland.

Mr Matt Dempsey, Editor of The Irish Farmers Journal, guest speaker at a Vaughan Trust sponsored Club meeting with Messrs Stanley Lytle (right), Chairman, and Mervyn Gould, Kinawley.

Vaughan Trust support

The Club received a great boost in 1976 when it gained generous sponsorship for its competitions from the Vaughan Trust. This funding enabled prize winners to travel quite widely to see good farming practice in other countries. A condition of these awards was that the travel award winners would give an illustrated talk to Club members on their return. This has proved to be a tremendous benefit in widening members' horizons and attitudes. The Vaughan Trust's support also extends to the sponsorship of an annual Club meeting to which the general public is invited. This enables the Club to engage the very best speakers, including those from Great Britain, which would otherwise put a strain on Club finances.

Full attendance at a Vaughan Trust sponsored meeting in Enniskillen Agricultural College.

Visitors

The Club has played its role in hosting visiting grassland enthusiasts including visits by members of the Ulster Grassland Society in 1970 and again in 1991. On 10th May 1991 the Society held its summer outing on two farms in Fermanagh. In the morning the venue was the farm of Mr Louie Lynch at Drummerwinter, Rosslea. Here the 150 acres of difficult land were carrying a 75 dairy cow herd and a sheep enterprise. Emphasis was placed on low cost production maximizing output from grassland. The merits of different drainage systems and particularly the value of gravel tunneling were demonstrated. In the afternoon the members of the visiting society were hosted by Mr and Mrs J. B. McGuckian at their Lisgoole Abbey Estate outside Enniskillen. The Farm Manager, Mr Denzil Johnston, conducted members around the estate where 160 suckler cows, maintained in three separate herds according to calving date, were kept on high producing permanent pastures and short-term leys. Emphasis was placed on the production of quality silage for over-wintering.

The BBC's agricultural correspondent, Mr Richard Wright, (centre) guest speaker at a Club meeting in conversation with Mr John Fay (left), at the time Vice Principal of Enniskillen Agricultural College, and Club member Mr William Graham.

The British Grassland Society included County Fermanagh in its programme of visits in Northern Ireland as part of its summer tour to Ulster in 1997 and again in 2009. Detailed arrangements for these visits were co-ordinated through the Fermanagh Grassland Club.

Well informed farmers

The Fermanagh Grassland Club continues to make a valuable contribution to the development of farming in the west of the Province and currently has a membership of around 200. In recent years, the Club has attracted as members an increasing number of farmers from County Tyrone and indeed from counties in the Irish Republic, particularly County Cavan. The Club's contribution to development is not simply limited to the information

Discussion is important. Messrs Albert Foster (right) and Timothy Carson (centre) in discussion with Mr Trevor Gilliland of the Plant Breeding Station, Crossnacreevy.

gained from speakers by those attending meetings nor indeed by what is seen on farm visits arranged by the Club. A valuable aspect of Club activity is the discussion that takes place among members at meetings or on outings.

All of this helps to reassure individuals of the value of particular innovations and gives confidence in implementing new practices and developments on the home farms. Visits to farms or other places of agricultural interest are features of each year's programme of activities. These provide an excellent opportunity for the membership of the Club to see best farming practice.

Keen interest is being shown by members on a farm visit.

The Club continues to enjoy the enthusiasm of its members which has characterised its activity from the time it was established in 1963.

References:

Records of the Fermanagh Grassland Club.

Files of *The Impartial Reporter* and *Fermanagh Herald* held in Enniskillen Library.

Photographs supplied by the Fermanagh Grassland Club.

Chapter 30
Post War Farming

In May 1945 when the war was over with Germany (but not with Japan) the Fermanagh County Committee of Agriculture was calling for the abolition of the Tillage Order. However, there was no relaxation in relation to the area required for tillage in 1945 beyond that achieved for the 1944 cropping season. Some further relief was gained in 1946 and in 1947 when the tillage quota in Fermanagh was dropped to 25 per cent and to 20 per cent respectively. When the tillage quota was reduced in 1946 the Ministry stated that it was not to be regarded as an indication that times of scarcity were past. Rationing of animal feeding stuffs would continue. The Ministry advertised in March 1947 encouraging farmers to plough 'night and day'.

Ware potatoes in 1946 varied in price depending on variety between 102 and 107 shillings per ton. The minimum price for pigs was 24s per score (20 lbs) and for eggs 3s per dozen. A Calf Rearing Subsidy was an encouragement for livestock farmers. A temporary grant of £4 per sow was introduced in 1946.

Agricultural development in the post-war period was encouraged through the introduction of a number of schemes aimed at encouraging investment on farms in order to increase production and improve efficiency. The first of these was the Hill Farming and Livestock Rearing Land Improvement Scheme. At this time the County Committee of Agriculture was requesting the Ministry to restore its pre-war powers in relation to the employment of staff and associated matters. This request was not granted.

Hill Farming and Livestock Rearing Land Improvement Scheme

This scheme was introduced in 1946. A 50 per cent grant was available on a range of improvements including: farm buildings, roads, bridges, the provision of electricity and water supplies, livestock pens, silos, fencing, grids, drainage, reclamation, shelter belts, machinery, liming and manuring. The Scheme was at first limited only to hill sheep farms but in 1951 its scope was extended to include all livestock rearing land in upland areas. It closed for new applicants on 6th November 1963. This Scheme was not popular in County Fermanagh primarily because of its very complex nature and also the requirement to put a comprehensive development plan together at

A well developed hill farm near Benaughlin.

application stage. Furthermore, the eligible land as defined in Fermanagh at that time contained mainly very small farms whose owners could not take advantage of the Scheme. Hill Sheep Subsidy at the rate of 7s 6d per ewe was available to hill farmers at that time. Hill Cow Subsidy was also introduced then.

The 1947 Agriculture Act

The most important development in securing a reasonably stable future for agriculture was the passing of the 1947 Agriculture Act. The guarantees under the war regulations assured a reasonable stability of prices up to the end of June 1948. The new Agricultural Act was aimed at providing assurance beyond that time. The experience of the two wars within a relatively short time span made the Government realise the need to be reasonably self sufficient in so far as a food supply was concerned. Dr Scott Robertson, Permanent Secretary of the Northern Ireland Ministry of Agriculture, in a broadcast on BBC radio on 30th December 1946, gave the background to the new Act. He stated that the introduction of a Bill into the British House of Commons sought to make permanent the guarantee of assured markets and minimum prices for the principal items of our agricultural produce (the existing war guarantees). The farmer will know in future for three or four years ahead the minimum price he will receive for his beef, mutton, milk, pigs and eggs. He will know from eighteen months to two years ahead the minimum price he will receive for his crops. He hoped that 1947 would be the last year of compulsory tillage. Milk output in Northern Ireland during the war had increased from 40 to 70 million gallons per year. He looked forward to 100 million gallons per year being produced. He went on to stress the virtues and potential of grass and silage and the need for mechanisation and electricity on the farm.

The Bill, *inter alia,* had the purpose *of sustaining a stable and efficient agricultural industry capable of producing such part of the Nation's food supply as in the National interest it is desirable to produce in the United Kingdom, and of producing it at minimum prices consistently with proper remuneration and living conditions for farmers and workers in agriculture and an adequate return on capital invested.* An integral part of the Bill was the continuation of the system of Annual Price Reviews into the condition and prospects of agriculture. These reviews were carried out involving representatives of the three UK agricultural departments and representatives of the three farmers' unions. Following these reviews prices were fixed in advance. The continuation of grants for liming in Northern Ireland was part of the Bill.

Agricultural Expansion Programme

In August 1947 the Agricultural Departments of the United Kingdom announced, in a joint statement, a programme designed to increase agricultural output over the next four years. In so far as Northern Ireland was concerned minimum prices for livestock and livestock products were guaranteed. The prices represented a considerable increase over the previous ones. For example, the price of oats would increase from 19s 2d in 1947 to 20s 6d per cwt in 1948 and 1949. Potatoes in 1947 were increased by 23s per ton over 1946 prices and 10s 6d per ton in 1948 over the 1947 prices. As further encouragement, there was an acreage payment of £8 in 1947 increasing to £10 (for the first 10 acres) in 1948. Milk would have a guaranteed price of 2.6d per gallon above current prices. A guaranteed price of 98s 3d per live cwt applied to fat cattle. For the twelve months beginning in April 1948 the average price guaranteed for eggs was 4s 0d per dozen.

Harvesting by scythe was still common on very small farms in the 1940s. The Rev W. F. Maitland, Rector of Clabby Church of Ireland Parish, on a pastoral visit to the Kerrigan small holding in Camgart in September 1948. Miss Cissie Kerrigan has the scythe and Mrs Minnie Credden was tying and stooking the sheaves of oats.

In addition to the commodity price guarantees, there were new subsidies. These included a Ploughing Grant of £4 per acre for grassland of three years old or over; a Calf Rearing Subsidy of £4 per steer calf and £3 per heifer calf of approved types if reared to twelve months old.

End of Compulsory Tillage

In October 1949 the Minister of Agriculture, the Rev Robert Moore, announced that there would be no tillage quota for the coming season but he appealed for more oats to be grown. In 1949 the price of oats varied from 20s 6d per cwt to 21s 8d depending on the month of the year. Flax Subsidy for the 1950 crop would only be payable if the prices paid by the spinners in the markets were less than the Standard Growers' Prices fixed by the Ministry of Agriculture. In the meantime, further measures were introduced by Government to boost agricultural production and improve efficiency. Cows and heifers attracted a subsidy of £10 per head under the Hill Cow Subsidy Scheme. Despite the new opportunities farmers,

like others, had to cope with shortages of certain items. For example, petrol supplies were still a problem in 1950 and farmers had to make application to the Petroleum Officer in Belfast by 1st May for a supply of petrol for agricultural purposes.

Guaranteed price for milk

Under the Agriculture Act of 1947 guaranteed prices were assured for the main agricultural commodities including milk. Under the Act prices each year were subject to negotiation between the UK Government and the farmers' unions. This process had started during the war and had been placed on a permanent basis in 1945. The Annual February Price Review from 1947 was to become an important fixture in the farming calendar for years to come. In so far as milk was concerned the guaranteed price applied to an agreed quantity of milk. If production exceeded the Standard Quantity then the industry sold the surplus milk to the processors at the best price possible. The price obtained for the total milk supply was then averaged and producers were paid accordingly for their supplies. The Standard Quantity for Northern Ireland was initially set at 93 million gallons. By 1956 production in Northern Ireland had increased to 106 million gallons for which the amount produced above the Standard Quantity received only the manufacturing price obtained from processors. This had the effect of reducing the price to producers by two pence below the guaranteed price. By 1964 milk production had reached 124 million gallons which was 27 million gallons over the Standard Quantity.

Milk Regulations (NI) 1951

These regulations under the Northern Ireland Milk Act of 1950 came into operation on 1st November 1951. They were designed to ensure the maximum degree of cleanliness at all stages of production and distribution. The regulations specified that a producer must have a byre and dairy conforming to the Ministry's requirements. These requirements were a development of those that had been in force since 1934. Producers held a licence on condition that they took the precautions necessary for clean milk production. In the case of Grade A milk producers, all milk had to be bottled on the farm where it was produced. Grade A producers had TB free status and the farm bottling was aimed at avoiding contamination that could arise if the milk was bottled at a creamery. All other milk for human consumption had to be pasteurised. The Milk Act of 1950 stipulated that only pasteurised or Grade A (TT) milk could be sold to the public for liquid consumption.

In the meantime the use of milking machines was gaining some ground. Milking machines were being promoted as a labour saving device in a feature in the Ministry of Agriculture's *Monthly Report* in 1947. It was suggested that a two-unit plant could be operated to milk 30 cows with the use of only one man.

Decontrol

The war-time regime for the purchase of all fatstock by the Ministry of Agriculture, on behalf of the Ministry of Food, continued until decontrol in July 1954. Prices

Milk producers in 1948 who attended the 50th anniversary of the establishment of Derrygonnelly Co-Operative Dairy Society. Front row (Included from left): Messrs W. Ferguson; R. G. McCullagh, Manager of Springfield Creamery; Bertie Anderson; Percy Bell, Ministry of Agriculture; Courtney Hood, Ministry of Agriculture; Eddie Hassard, George Ferguson, Thomas Nixon, Geoffrey Rogers, Chairman; Fred Fawcett, Manager; James Johnston, Ulster Agricultural Organisation Society (UAOS); John Wilson, William Crooke, Edward Corrigan, Wilson Wadsworth, William Roberts, Miss Lucy Cassidy. Second row (Included from left):Messrs Fred Acheson, Albert Acheson, Acheson, William Rutherford, Archie Cathcart, Eddie Abercrombie, Bobby Acheson, Robert Hamilton, ?, Jason Donaldson, ?; ?;?; ?, Bobby Byers, Patrick Dolan. Third row (from left): Harry Donaldson, Eddie Kerr, William Brown, John Flanagan, ?, ? Armstrong, ?, Wood, ?, Davy McBrien, ?, Tommy Robinson, James Saunderson, ?, ? Ferguson, Sandhill; David Hamilton, ?, Ernie Donaldson, ?, Bob Ferguson, ? Johnston, ?, Tommy Nixon, ?????.
(Courtesy of Mr Basil Fawcett).

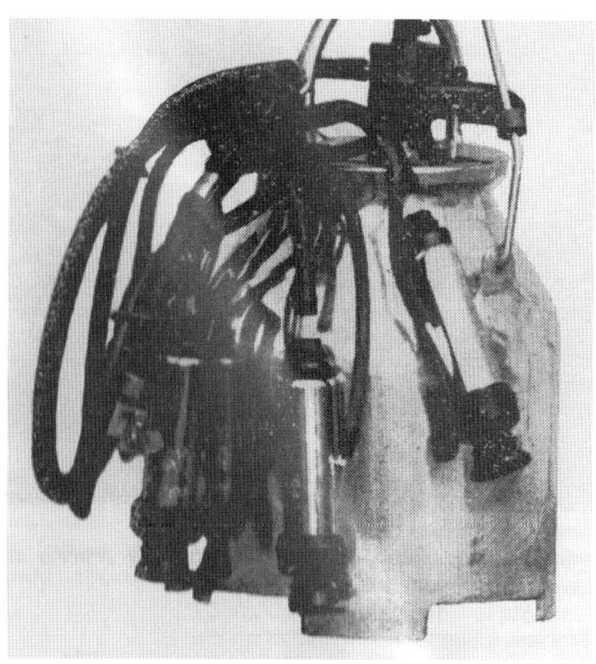

Milking machine unit.

Creamery Management Conference (c1950). Back row (from left): Messrs Andy Crawford (Irvinestown Creamery), James Dunlop (dairy engineer), Percy Bell (Ministry of Agriculture), James Johnston (UAOS, and formerly of Termon Creamery), Jack Crawford (County Antrim), R. G. McCullagh (Springfield Creamery). Front (from left): Messrs W. J. Simpson (Leckpatrick, formerly at Kesh Creamery), W. A. V. Saunderson (Ministry of Agriculture). (Courtesy of Mr Robin McCullagh).

The acquisition of a new Ferguson tractor from 1947 onwards was a great boon to the self carter who previously transported his milk to the creamery by horse or donkey. Before link or transport boxes became common, farmers made platforms from wood supported by timbers running over the cross bar of the three point linkage and under the rear axle. This beautifully restored Ferguson tractor belongs to Mr Malcolm Finney.

Messrs Patrick McGurn (left) and Patrick Burns taking milk to Derrygonnelly creamery in 1953.

Plan of Springfield Creamery circa 1948 (Courtesy of Mr W. Dickson).

before decontrol were: steers, heifers – 133s 2d per cwt gross weight; fat sheep and lambs – 2s 10½ per lb dressed carcase weight; fat pigs – 54s 3d per score dead weight; milk – average 3s 2.2d per gallon and eggs – average 4s per dozen. After decontrol the industry had to adjust to finding a market for its own produce. In November 1956, the Ulster Farmers' Union welcomed the announcement of the British Government regarding a proposed new support system for farming. In introducing the new measures the

The Springfield Creamery Management Committee, staff, milk producers and guests at the 50th anniversary celebrations (c 1948).
Included in front row were: Messrs J. R. Brownlee, J. A. Reid (chairman – 6th from left), R. G. McCullagh(manager – 7th from left), G. Gowan, Courtney Hood (Ministry of Agriculture), Percy Bell (Ministry of Agriculture), W. A. V. Saunderson (Ministry of Agriculture), J. Thompson, J. Ellis, R. Plunkrtt, B. Gamble.
Included in second row from left: Messrs J. Cathcart, T. Bothwell, D. Carson, W. Brown, T. Fawcett, W. Graham, J. Kells, J. E. J. Fawcett, J. Gallagher.
Included in back row: Messrs P. Duffy, A. Nixon, Ms Hilda Beattie, Mr M. Irvine, Mrs W. Abercrombie, F. Fawcett, M. Burns, I. Elliott, A. Kennedy, G. Little, J. Johnston, S. Buchanan, G. Rogers.
(Courtesy of Mr R. McCullagh).

British Minister of Agriculture, the Rt Hon D. Heathcoat Amory, said that the objective was to find a system of forward guarantees that would give more positive help to the industry in its planning for the future. He said the Government's long term policy was to support and assist the industry to achieve maximum economic output. He said he was confident that the assurances offered would enable farmers to go forward with renewed confidence. The Government was anxious to see still further increased production of beef, mutton, lamb and home-grown feedingstuffs. The main provision of the proposals was that the guaranteed price of each commodity would be maintained each year at not less than 96 per cent of that of the previous year. This applied to crops, livestock, and livestock products. There was a special provision in the case of livestock and livestock products which stipulated that in any period of three years reductions in the guaranteed price of a particular commodity would not together exceed nine per cent. This replaced the minimum prices for livestock and livestock products provided for in the 1947 Agriculture Act. The introduction of the Farm Improvement Scheme which offered grants of one-third of the cost, to encourage the provision of permanent fixed equipment and long-term improvements of land, was aimed at modernising farms in all parts of the United Kingdom.

The Annual General Meeting of Derrygonnelly Creamery in 1955. From left: Mr Fred Fawcett, Manager; James Johnston, Secretary UAOS; Mr Geoffrey Rogers, Chairman of the Committee; Mr George Cathcart, member of the NI Milk Marketing Board (Courtesy of Mr Basil Fawcett).

The Remoteness Grant

The UK Government's guarantees regarding prices for agricultural produce applied to the industry as a whole rather than to the individual farmer. Northern Ireland farmers believed that they would be worse off than their British counterparts due to higher transport costs arising from their geographical position. As a result of strong representations from the Ulster Farmers' Union, supported by the Northern Ireland Ministry of Agriculture, a concession was granted. In March 1954 the Northern Ireland Minister of Agriculture, the Rev Robert Moore, made the following announcement: *With the return of free markets farmers in Northern Ireland will find themselves at a disadvantage in having to market much of their produce in Great Britain. The United Kingdom Government does not expect Northern Ireland producers to carry the whole burden of a greater degree of price differential than that borne by other distant producers on the mainland. A financial adjustment would be made between the two governments. A grant, the amount which will be determined annually, is to be placed at the disposal of the Northern Ireland Government to assist the agricultural industry in the Province.*

This support became known as the Remoteness Grant. The fund was based on the amount by which the average price of fatstock in Northern Ireland fell short of the prices being obtained in the three most northerly counties of Scotland. In 1957 the grant was set at £1 million for the next five years. In 1962 the Grant was renewed and fixed at £1.25 million. In 1965 it was further increased to £1.75 million. The Grant was used in Northern Ireland for a wide variety of purposes mainly for projects for which other Government funds were not available. One such scheme, which was of particular significance to County Fermanagh, was the Beef Breeding Herd Subsidy which was introduced in 1961. The aim of this subsidy was to encourage suckled calf production and to reduce the amount of milk which had to be marketed. As a result of increased milk production producers were receiving up to 5d per gallon less than the guaranteed price simply because the amount of milk being produced exceeded the quantity to which the guaranteed price applied (known as the Standard Quantity).

Agricultural Development Scheme

Until 1949 the Land Improvement and Water Supplies to Farms Schemes had been operated on funds voted by Parliament each year and accordingly had not any real permanency. Under the Agriculture Act of 1949 the schemes were placed on a more permanent basis. A new scheme called 'The Agricultural Development Scheme' was introduced. As well as the items covered by the Land Improvement and Water Supply Schemes, silos, farm sewage disposal systems, and machines for generating electricity (where a mains supply was not available) became eligible under the new scheme

A disused water pump house. Under the Water Supply Scheme, grants were available for sinking wells, installing pumps (normally petrol engine driven) and piping to a water storage tank for distribution.

Mr Edwin Hetherington (right), seen cutting turf in the old fashioned way in the early 1970s, was the Ministry of Agriculture Officer who was in charge of farm water supply installations in County Fermanagh in the post war period. The author is filling the turf onto a turf barrow.

Marginal Land Scheme

This Marginal Land Scheme, introduced in 1943, applied to Fermanagh and certain districts in West Tyrone. The scheme offered financial support for improvements which were likely to increase or maintain output of food or fodder which would have been uneconomic without assistance. It applied to those farmers who owned less than 50 acres of arable land. Grants under the Marginal Land Scheme were available for small scale silo construction from 1943. Silos of 14, 25, 40 and 60 ton capacities, depending on the size of the farm, qualified for a 50 per cent grant on construction costs. Under the Scheme a grant of 50 per cent of the cost of fertilisers, limited to phosphates for grassland, and half the cost of phosphates and grass-seed when putting land back to grass, was available on farms where the arable acreage did not exceed 50 acres. As a concession for 1944 under the Tillage Order, farmers in Fermanagh were required to cultivate at least 30 per cent of their arable land (a reduction from 45 per cent in the previous year) provided they applied a certain amount of fertiliser. They

were required to apply phosphatic fertiliser (8 cwt basic slag per acre or equivalence in ground rock phosphate or semsol) to an area of their grassland equivalent to one-sixth of the arable area. It was also a requirement to apply 6 cwt per acre of special potato manure to land planted with potatoes. A 50 per cent grant was available to cover the cost of the fertiliser (apart from that sown on the potato crop) and of an approved grass-seed mixture when land was being sown out to grass. The Fermanagh seeds-mixture was formulated at that time and consisted of 26lb ryegrass, 6lb timothy, 2lb Alsike clover and ½lb wild white clover. The grass-seed cost 32 shillings per acre and there was a grant of 16 shillings. Tributes were paid by the County Committee of Agriculture to Mr W. T. McClintock and Mr T. Moore, Deputy County Agricultural Executive Officer, for their good work in developing this scheme. Area Officers of the County Staff of the Ministry attended meetings at villages throughout the County to explain the scheme.

In County Fermanagh grant amounting to £20,000 was paid out under the scheme in respect of fertiliser applications in 1949. In addition £7,000 was earned for reseeding. Other significant income to the County that year was £36,000 under the Hill Cattle Scheme and between £900 and £1,000 on Hill Sheep. Calf Subsidy attracted £117,605.

An establishing reseed.

By 1951 the Marginal Land Scheme had been extended to cover a 50 per cent grant on fertiliser applied to grassland, sowing land down to grass, the potato crop, and the oat crop. There was a limitation as far as grassland was concerned in that the 50 per cent grant on fertiliser only applied to half the total grassland farmed. In order to qualify for grant aid specified quantities of approved fertilisers and seeds mixtures were required to be used. For example, potatoes received 6 cwt per acre of Special Potato Manure (1 part sulphate of ammonia, 4 parts superphosphate and 1 part muriate of potash), oats 3 cwt per acre of the same mix and grassland 4 cwt per acre again of the same mixture or equivalent. In the 1956/57 season the rate of grant was increased to 85 per cent and in the following year it was reduced to 75 per cent. The scheme initially applied only to farms with not more than 50 arable acres. Later, it was extended to farms with more than 50 acres providing the Ministry was satisfied that the land was of such a nature that it could not, without special treatment, be reasonably productive either in regard to crops or the grazing of livestock.

Radio Broadcasts

In January 1948, Mr McClintock made two broadcasts on BBC's *Radio Ulster* in which he explained the problems of farming marginal land. He emphasised the need for improved grassland and said that three blades of grass should be grown where one grew before. He explained the benefits of the Marginal Land Scheme which encouraged proper fertilising, the use of good seeds mixtures and appropriate pasture management. Utilisation of the grass presented problems due to the heavy nature of the soil. He explained that it was very expensive and not cost effective to carry out conventional tile and stone drainage. Mole drainage, where soil conditions were suitable, offered a low cost alternative. The Ministry had provided a mole ploughing service in County Fermanagh which was introduced in February 1948. Under the scheme the Ministry carried out mole ploughing for farmers on land which had been previously assessed as suitable at a cost to the farmer of £3 per acre. Two hundred applications for mole draining were received in 1948. Mr McClintock also publicised the newly introduced Housing on Farms Scheme which offered grants for the improvement of farm dwellings.

'God-send' to Fermanagh

In February 1952, Mr J. E. J. Fawcett JP DL, at a meeting of the County Committee of Agriculture, described the Marginal Land Scheme as 'a God-send to Fermanagh'. That meeting was attended by the Minister of Agriculture, the Rev Robert Moore and Professor Ronald Baskett, the new Permanent Secretary of the Ministry of Agriculture. Professor Baskett commented that Fermanagh had a relatively small number of poultry. Members responded to this comment by stating that this was due to the lack of satisfactory housing. The members appealed to the Minister to have poultry housing included as an eligible item in the Marginal Land Scheme. This was the right time to raise this issue as poultry housing was becoming much more important due to the adoption of the deep litter system of keeping hens. Miss McCombe, the Poultry Advisory Officer in the county, was promoting this system of poultry keeping by giving lectures on that method of keeping hens.

Grants for farm buildings

The County Committee's appeals for the inclusion of farm buildings as eligible items under the Marginal Land

A deep litter house, erected under the Marginal Land Scheme, on the farm of Mr Johnston Elliott JP, Drumconnis, Ballinamallard.

A hayshed built under the Marginal Land Scheme.

Despite the decline in tillage in the county there was enthusiasm to maintain ploughing skills through membership of the Fermanagh Ploughing Society. Mr Mervyn Dunne, Dring, Ballinamallard, formerly of Roscor, Kilskeery, was exercising his skills as a horse ploughman at a competition in 1956. Mr Eddie Crean is holding the horses while Mr Bertie Crean adjusts the plough. The two fine strong horses are Bob on the left and Prince on the right (Courtesy of Mrs Eileen Wilson).

Scheme were answered in August 1953 when the Ministry announced that grants would be available for new or the reconstruction of poultry houses, piggeries and calf houses. The maximum grant for any one building would be £100 with a farm maximum of £150. The extended scheme met with immediate success and 482 applications from farmers had been received within one month of its announcement. In October 1953 it was reported that in County Fermanagh 290 applications had been made in respect of poultry houses, 219 for piggeries and 197 for calf houses. It was estimated that the work on these facilities would cost £120,000 and would attract £60,000 in grant. While the response was good it was considered that there were not enough applications from the poorer areas of the county. At the end of the year £85,000 had been paid out in grant in respect of 1,097 buildings.

Haysheds

In October 1955 the County Committee argued for the inclusion of haysheds as an eligible item under the scheme and in due course the request was granted. The County Committee was informed in July 1956 that the numbers of applications for the various buildings under the Marginal Land Scheme were as follows: 189 calf houses; 95 piggeries; 234 deep litter poultry houses and 513 hay sheds. At that time it was stated that there were 350 silos in the county. Mr McClintock estimated that around 15,000 tons of fertiliser were applied to Fermanagh farms in 1957. The Marginal Land Scheme for buildings closed for applications on 31st May 1957 with claims for payment having to be submitted by 31st December 1957. It was replaced by the UK Farm Improvement Scheme. The Marginal Land Scheme which offered grants for fertilisers and seeds came to an end for purchases made after 30th June 1959.

Disappointment

Members of the Fermanagh County Committee of Agriculture, at its meeting in October 1959, expressed their disappointment at the discontinuation of the Marginal Land Scheme. It was stated that an eligibility requirement under the newly introduced Hill Farming Scheme would be a limiting factor. That eligibility requirement was that the income from milk or beef must be less than 40 per cent of the farm income. In addition, the new scheme would apply only to the designated hill areas of the county rather than the marginal land area which was a further limitation. The new scheme would therefore not be an effective replacement for the Marginal Land Scheme. Mr William Swan commented at a meeting of the County Committee in March 1961 that the Marginal Land Scheme was one of the greatest benefits farmers had ever received in County Fermanagh. Its discontinuation represented a disastrous blow to the county. Mr Swan said he had been speaking to traders who

told him that their fertiliser sales were down by a third. Mr J. L. H. Askwith said that 19,000 tons of fertiliser had been applied in the last year of the Marginal Land Scheme and that only 12,000 tons had been applied in the first year of the new scheme in Fermanagh. A delegation from Fermanagh County Committee of Agriculture met the Northern Ireland Minister of Agriculture on the subject but failed to get the scheme continued.

Mr West, Minister of Agriculture, referred to the success of the Marginal Land Scheme at an 'Open Day' at the Grassland Experimental Husbandry Farm in April 1967. He said that under the Scheme, during the period 1953 to 1958, farmers in Fermanagh and West Tyrone received £1,500,000 in grant aid.

The Silo Subsidies Scheme

The value of silage as a cheap winter food for cattle was being fully appreciated and farmers were encouraged to conserve winter fodder in this form. In 1956 a Bill in Westminster had been introduced under which grants of 50 per cent were offered for the construction or reconstruction of silos. The grant for silo construction became available under the Silo Subsidies Scheme from 19th November 1956. Grant aid was limited to a maximum of £250 per farm.

A silo with dimensions of 45 feet by 20 feet.

Farm Improvement Scheme

The UK Agriculture Act, 1957 came into operation on 1st September 1957. Part II of the Act enabled the UK Minister of Agriculture, Fisheries and Food to pay grants of one-third of the cost of making long term improvements for the benefit of agricultural land. This was the first scheme to introduce the concept of standard costs. Participants in the scheme had the choice of applying for works on the basis of either standard or actual costs. Standard costs were laid down by regulation and when claiming grant on this basis receipts were not required. Standard costs became very popular because, generally, they were reasonably generous and form filling and bureaucracy for the farmer were reduced to a minimum. The items of improvements

The 1950s witnessed a great interest in ploughing with tractors. Mr Bill Wilson, tractor champion of the field at the 1956 Fermanagh Ploughing Association event, congratulates Mr Mervyn Dunne, who won the horse section. Also included (from left) are Messrs Roland Hurst and John Fallis (Courtesy of Mr Bill Wilson).

eligible included: farm buildings and yards, farm sewage disposal systems, roads and bridges, stock handling facilities, fencing, cattle grids, reclamation, hedge removal, and filling in of ditches.

A grant-aided byre and dairy for 16 cows on the farm of Mr Johnston Elliott, Drumconnis, Ballinamallard.

In November 1965 silos were included as an eligible item under the Farm Improvement Scheme and this brought to an end the Silo Subsidies Scheme. Some of the original items, like fencing and farm sewage provision, attracted an additional one-sixth grant which brought the grant on these items up to 50 per cent. Drainage continued to be an eligible item under the Agricultural Development Scheme attracting a 50 per cent grant.

References:

Records of the County Agricultural Executive Office.

Files of *The Impartial Reporter* and *Fermanagh Herald* held in Enniskillen Library.

Ministry of Agriculture's *Monthly Reports.*

Chapter 31
The 1960s

The 1960s ushered in a new era in farm development. The importance of grass as a crop and the value of silage as a low cost quality winter feed were now recognised by the most progressive farmers. Mixed farming was still a feature of agricultural production. Guaranteed prices had contributed to expansion to such an extent that in some commodities over-production was leading to marketing and pricing difficulties. The potential for increased beef production was realised. The recognition of the farm as a business, and the need for increased efficiency of production, all contributed to the significant developments in agriculture during the 1960s. There was a realisation that small farms had particular problems and that there was some potential for farm amalgamation and the prospect of alternative employment for those who gave up their farms in the process. The provision of good agricultural education as a foundation for a prosperous agricultural industry was now a Ministry of Agriculture priority. Fermanagh was to the fore in pressing for an agricultural college to be based in the county. These efforts were rewarded when Enniskillen Agricultural College was built and opened for students in 1967.

The small farmer

Throughout the decade the problems associated with small farms featured prominently in Ministry of Agriculture policies both in Britain and in Northern Ireland. On 12th November 1958 Mr John Hare, British Minister of Agriculture, referred to the future introduction of the Small Farmers' Scheme. He said: "*We have diagnosed the needs of the small farm as being first advice and assistance in drawing up proposals for giving a new look to the farm business, and an initial boost of working capital which could get the proposals under way.*" Many small farms had found things difficult and there were those who said the economic tide was flowing against the small farm and it was useless to try and preserve them. To that suggestion he replied: "*The countryside, indeed the whole country, would be immeasurably the poorer. Agriculture is more than a mechanism for producing food, more even than a means of livelihood for so many workers. It is a way of life. The pride in independence which leads the small farmer to work all hours and accept a frugal life is something well worth preserving. And indeed in many areas the whole social life will break down if we let the small farmer go under.*"

The Small Farmers' Scheme

This was a United Kingdom Scheme which came into operation on 1st April 1959. Its objective was to inject capital into small farm businesses so as to enable them to increase their economic efficiency and their profitability. Grants, amounting to a maximum of £1,000, were paid to eligible farmers who carried out a planned programme of improvement over a three to five year period. Those farmers who were not in a position immediately to take advantage of the main scheme could qualify for the Small Farmers' Supplementary Scheme from 1st July 1959 which entitled them to grants in excess of the normal rates for fertiliser, lime, ploughing and for the cleaning of sheughs. From that date the special subsidy payable for fertilisers purchased by occupiers of farms with more than 50 acres was withdrawn, as was the special subsidy for grass seeds and fertilisers purchased by occupiers in the Marginal Land Areas of Fermanagh and West Tyrone.

Fermanagh's concerns

The Fermanagh County Committee of Agriculture, under the chairmanship of Captain John Brooke, discussed the proposed Small Farmers' Scheme and its limitations in the county. The new scheme had a qualified welcome. Whilst it was regarded as an honest attempt to help small farmers it was concluded that for the majority of cases in Fermanagh it would have serious limitations. There was concern that only an estimated 2,700 of the county's 8,000 farmers would benefit due to the acreage limitations and the size of eligible farm businesses as determined by standard man-days. To qualify under the Scheme the farm business needed to be within the range of 250 to 450 standard man-days and to have an area of between 20 and 100 acres. The other issue was that in order to earn the grant substantial capital was needed. Under the Scheme grassland ploughed up could qualify for the £7 ploughing grant and if it was put through a three year crop rotation under the Small Farmers' Scheme it could qualify for an additional £27 per acre. There was a renovation grant of £9 per acre for cutting rushes and applying lime and fertiliser. An 85 per cent grant was available for reclamation, subject to a maximum payment per plan of £100. A grant of £1 per chain (22 yards) was available for cleaning sheughs. A business grant of £6 per acre, subject to a maximum payment of £360, was also available. There was a maximum payment per Scheme of £1,000. The new scheme was widely publicised to farmers through meetings at centres throughout the county with follow-up press reports. The scheme closed for applications on 31st December 1965.

In March 1961 the County Committee of Agriculture was still concerned about the value of the Small Farmers' Scheme. Comparisons were made with the Marginal Lands Scheme which had proved very popular. Mr George Cathcart, a member of the County Committee, warned that the Scheme could prove to be a millstone around the neck of a farmer with limited resources. He claimed that there were 3,500 farmers who previously enjoyed the benefits of the Marginal Land Scheme who would not benefit from the Small Farmers' Scheme. Another member, Mr Paddy Gallagher of Tullyrosmearn, Garrison, said that the small farmer in his area was the man with 40 acres who had six suckler cows and that less than 10 per cent of farmers in the area would benefit under the Scheme as their businesses were too small.

Minister's visit to the County Committee

In March 1961, Mr Harry West, Minister of Agriculture, on a visit to the Fermanagh County Committee of Agriculture, informed members that a total of 881 Small Farmers' Schemes had been approved in Fermanagh and a further 153 were awaiting approval. In addition, a further 2,396 had successfully applied under the Supplementary Scheme. He also said that Fermanagh had a higher percentage of potential qualifiers for the scheme than any other county.

Mr Harry West, Minister of Agriculture (Courtesy of the Belfast Telegraph).

At the meeting Mr William Swan stated that it was a tragedy when the Marginal Land Scheme came to an end. He could foresee a large proportion of Fermanagh going back to the conditions of 30 years ago. Mr J. L. H. Askwith referred to the serious drop in fertiliser use since the end of the Marginal Land Scheme. Mr George Cathcart again emphasised that many farmers who enjoyed the benefits of the Marginal Land Scheme were now outside the scope of the Small Farmers' Scheme.

In April that year, Mr West informed a wider audience of the plight of the small farmer. When addressing the Ulster Unionist conference he said the small farmers in Northern Ireland *are having a very difficult time.* He was referring particularly to those farmers whose holdings and businesses were too small to qualify under the Small Farmers' Scheme.

Concern for the small farmer

The Minister addressed the small farmer issue at a meeting of the Fermanagh County Committee of Agriculture in March 1965. He said: "*I need hardly say in present company that the small farm and low incomes are a problem in this part of the world. Many of the farms in County Fermanagh are uneconomic, and the question is therefore posed of how to alleviate the position. There can be only limited success in tackling the problem of increased production, as this can lead to over-production. We must therefore concentrate on other methods of increasing farm incomes. I propose to outline three methods:-*

1. *The possibility of lowering costs of production, thereby raising margins of profits;*
2. *Improvement of marketing; and*
3. *Continuing to make careers outside agriculture more attractive, so as to encourage small farmers and their families who had difficulty in making a living on the land to leave agriculture and take up alternative employment. This has the double attraction of providing the farmer who has given up the land with a better source of income and enabling other farmers to buy up their land and create larger more viable units.*

It is well known that some farmers have larger margins of profits than their smaller brothers. How can the smaller man be helped to lower his costs?"

Mr West said his Ministry was pursuing various courses towards finding the possible answers through:

1. farm advisory work through which they hoped to encourage the keeping of records thereby enabling decisions to be based on fact rather than fancy;
2. agricultural education;

3. **research into both the technical and management aspects of farming, and also into food processing; and**
4. **helping the farmers to make the best use of the improvement schemes which were available.**

Employment opportunities

Mr West in referring to alternative sources of employment for those leaving the land stated: "*I have already said that we are trying to find more jobs outside agriculture for the small farmer who wants to leave farming. But there is no question of forcing people out of agriculture against their will. We must face facts, however, that other industries, which can expand more quickly than agriculture, create a demand for labour and attract people from the land. In the last ten years about 10,000 farmers have left the land for this reason. This enables the average size of farms to be increased through amalgamation, allowing the total income to be spread over fewer people, raising the average income per farmer. This trend will continue, as the stepping up of industrialisation continues.*"

In response to a question from Mr George Cathcart, Mr West pointed out that that there was a very great problem of the elderly farmer retaining control until his son became too old to marry. Very often the son did not get a free hand until middle life. Increasing the size of the holding was one answer.

Misunderstanding

Mr West's comments on the problems of small farms were misinterpreted in some quarters. The Minister, subsequently, clarified the position. At a meeting in Ballinamallard in early April 1965 he stated that some people had gained the idea that it was the Government's policy to force the small farmer out of business. He said: "*Some have even suggested that this is my plan as Minister of Agriculture. I am sorry that my previous statements have been misinterpreted in this way. Nothing could be further from the truth.*" He went on to explain that that Government policy had two main aims: to help every farmer, large or small, to achieve the highest possible income; and to create the maximum of alternative employment in industry for those who felt they could earn a better livelihood there than in farming. He said with reference to those leaving the land: "*I must emphasise that it is the farmers themselves who make this choice and that their reason for leaving agriculture is to earn a better living. Our figures show that over the past ten years approximately 1,000 farmers have left agriculture for industry each year – and they have done this entirely of their own free will.*" With regard to the potential for intensification on farms Mr West stated that they could only produce economically as much as they could sell on the market. He said that the market for both pig and poultry products was in danger of being over-supplied. There was already an over-production of milk to such an extent that Northern Ireland farmers were receiving five pence per gallon less than the guaranteed price. He pointed out that no sensible Government could be expected to take steps to produce additional quantities of foodstuffs that could not be sold. Mr West assured his audience: "*Again may I emphasise, with all the power I can command, that there will be no question of forcing any farmer out of the industry against his will. I will continue to do everything I can do to ensure that the agricultural industry will support as many people as possible on a rising standard of living.*"

Farmers' concerns

In November 1965 a meeting, which was sponsored by the Boho Branch of the Ulster Farmers' Union (UFU), was held in Enniskillen Townhall. The meeting, with 150 present, was attended by UFU members from throughout the county. Lord Brookeborough and Mr Harry West, Minister of Agriculture, were in attendance. Mr Ceely Irwin, Secretary of the Boho Branch of the UFU, explained that the meeting was called to discuss two issues of concern to farmers namely the need for milk quotas and the Government's proposals to help the small farmer. Mr Irwin proceeded at length to enumerate the difficulties being faced by small farmers. These included: non-viability for improvement schemes; small milk producers going out of business (he quoted that there were 20,000 milk producers in N.I. in 1960 but by 1965 the number was down to 17,000) and stock reduction through the implementation of the Tuberculosis and Brucellosis eradication schemes. Mr Irwin claimed that the under the Government's economic plan 20,000 small farmers were being induced to sell their farms. He also stated that farmers were losing sixpence per gallon under the guaranteed price system due to over-production. He advocated a milk quota system based on 1960, 1961 or 1962 levels so that producers would get the full guaranteed price for their milk.

Mr West opened by saying: "*I have never said I am against a milk quota.*" He then explained that if the UFU came to him with a scheme he would discuss it with them. He said it was a problem for the industry and that the Ministry could not be expected to force a milk quota system against the wishes of the majority of producers in the country.

With regard to the small farmer issue, Mr West said surveys had shown that quite a number of farmers were working for a weekly income less than that of a farm labourer. He said that a farmer who struggled on getting less money than a farm labourer was being unfair to himself and his family. His son could not be expected to carry on in the same way; he has to find something better. Mr West then explained his proposals for helping the small farmer who wished to retire from farming. A man under 65 years would receive a resettlement grant, and a man over 65 would get a pension. Under the proposed Amalgamation Scheme a farmer buying a small adjacent farm, to make his existing farm larger, could qualify for a grant.

Lord Brookeborough spoke in support of Mr West's work for farmers. He referred to progress made in farming in recent years and said that Mr West was a Fermanagh man who was in sympathy with farmers and he did not think they could get a better Minister. Lord Brookeborough stated that Mr West enjoyed his complete confidence.

Lord Brookeborough.

A Family Farm with a Future

Despite the concerns expressed about the future of the small farmer there was optimism in some quarters. Mr Sam McEwen, Agricultural Advisory Officer, in County Fermanagh, had reported in 1967 on the success achieved by Mr Thomas McKeogh and his family who farmed at Killee, Coa, Ballinamallard. Mr McEwen in a feature article in *Agriculture in Northern Ireland* explained how dairy cow numbers had been increased from 13 in 1964/65 to 25 in 1967. The number of laying hens on the farm had been increased from 720 to over 1200 in the same period. Plans existed to expand the dairy herd to 30. Developments planned for the farm included the installation of cow cubicles and the building of a new silo. Mr McKeogh emphasised the need to keep abreast of modern developments, hard work, co-operation with neighbours and making use of the results from farm management accounts.

Minister of Finance's views on the small farmer

Mr Herbert Kirk, Minister of Finance for Northern Ireland, when speaking at a meeting of the Fermanagh Junior Chamber of Commerce in May 1968, stated that the movement towards larger farm units was the result of the economic forces not only in this country but throughout the world. He said this movement would continue whether we liked it or not. With regard to the economic development of Fermanagh Mr Kirk said: "*Firstly we look to the development of agriculture; increased mechanisation*

The Murphy dwelling and farmyard at Ballyreagh in the 1960s. The farm has developed steadily from that time.

leading to greater productivity and ability to compete on the market. I should add that we hope for the growth of processing industries based on farm products." The Minister said that Fermanagh reflected in miniature one of the basic conditions of the Northern Ireland economy – the gradual change from an agricultural to an industrial community. He went on to say that because of the rather wet climate and the heavy soil of the area, the land in Fermanagh was mainly under grass and was used for the production of beef and milk. Fermanagh produced about one-seventh of the milk and one-sixteenth of the pigs in Northern Ireland. Individual farms tended to be small holdings with poor land. Many were not large enough to give their owners a reasonable livelihood.

Mr Kirk pointed out that there were two possible solutions to the difficulties. First, through co-operation which gained some of the advantages of larger scale operations. He said that the Ministry of Agriculture encouraged co-operation by giving up to 90 per cent of the establishment costs involved in some cases. The small farmer could adopt more intensive methods, for example the greater use of fertiliser to increase yield. Mr Kirk said: "*Neither of these presents a total solution, the only realistic step is amalgamation of smaller farms which involves a move from agriculture to some other form of industry by a number of farmers.*"

The Minister then went on to deal with possible alternative employment for those giving up or not going into agriculture. He referred to the success of the Government in attracting firms to County Fermanagh like Slack and Parr Ltd., Standard Telephones, Sir Richard Arkwright and Ulster-Swift. The Minister then stressed the tourism potential of the county. He said: "*This county has the potential to become a major centre of tourism, with its beautiful lakes and landscape, its forests, its fishing and other sports. It is worth remembering that tourism benefits not only those directly engaged in the industry, but also local commercial interests which attract more business.*"

Minister's good news

Mr H. W. West, as well as dealing with the sometimes contentious issue of the small farmer, also brought very welcome news with him to the meeting of the County Committee of Agriculture in March 1965. He announced that there was to be a new agricultural college in Enniskillen and also that a veterinary laboratory was to be established at Omagh. The laboratory was to be a centre for investigation of animal and poultry diseases. Carcases could be brought there for pathological examination. These announcements were warmly welcomed by the members.

The farm as a business

Whilst the issues surrounding the small farmer were being debated in the early years of the decade, progress was being made in improving the standard of management on farms. By 1963 there was a new awareness that farms should be treated as businesses. It was realised that there was more to successful farming than good crop and animal husbandry. Messrs Liversage and Mawhinney of the Economics and Statistics Division of the Ministry of Agriculture (they were also lecturers in the Faculty of Agriculture in Queen's University, Belfast) had developed a new system of keeping farm management accounts in the mid 1950s. Under this system, costs were classified as direct or indirect. Direct costs (later known as variable costs) were those that could be attributed directly to a particular enterprise on the farm. For example, dairy meal would be charged to the dairy herd. Indirect costs, on the other hand, were those that could not be easily allocated to a particular enterprise. A good example of an indirect cost would be farm labour or farm fuel. Using this system of accounting, it was possible to identify the financial contribution of each enterprise on the farm to farm income. Furthermore, it was also possible to assess accurately the physical performance of each enterprise. For example, average milk yield per cow and also the amount of meal that was used to produce each gallon of milk could be calculated. Similarly, in the case of a pig enterprise the average number of pigs produced each year per sow and the amount of meal required was easily determined. This financial and physical information was regarded as vital in making sound farm management decisions.

Farm management classes

The Ministry of Agriculture's Advisory Staff commenced a series of farm management classes in March 1963 where the new method of keeping farm records was taught.

Mrs Moore of Tirraroe keeping the farm accounts.

These classes were continued in subsequent years. The first classes in County Fermanagh were held in Derrygonnelly, Teemore, Ballinamallard and Brookeborough. The classes on the new approach to farm accounting were backed up by press articles such as the one written by Mr Robert Houston, the Deputy County Agricultural Officer, entitled *'Farm Business – Profit or Loss'*.

Farm Management Standards

Each January from the early 1960s the Ministry of Agriculture's Economics and Statistics Division published Farm Management Standards. The information on which these standards were based was obtained from the results on a wide range of farms where staff of the Economics and Statistics Division of the Ministry assisted farmers in keeping detailed accounts. The standards were produced to help farmers in interpreting results obtained from the accounts for their own farms. Gross Margin standards for the main enterprises were presented. Yields, prices and certain input costs associated with four different levels of Gross Margin, 'Excellent', 'Good', 'Moderate' and 'Poor', were shown. By studying the results from their own farm management accounts farmers were able to identify those enterprises which contributed most to farm incomes. Furthermore, they were able to compare the performance of each of their enterprises with the published standards and identify any that were performing poorly. The physical information contained in the accounts such as milk yield, meal fed, price received for products, when compared to the published standards gave a clue as to where husbandry and management weaknesses occurred and to the remedial action required.

For the year 1967/68 a Gross Margin of £100 per dairy cow was regarded as 'Excellent'. This was associated with a milk yield of 1,000 gallons per cow and a meal usage of 2.75 lb per gallon of milk. 'Poor' performance was associated with a yield of 600 gallons a meal usage of 4 lb per gallon of milk.

Suckler cows on lowland showed a Gross Margin of £45 in the 'Excellent' category with a stocking rate of 1.5 acres per cow equivalent. In the 'Poor' category £15 was recorded as the Gross Margin.

Rearing and fattening pigs showed an excellent Gross Margin of £6 5s 0d per pig associated with 2.0 litters per year and 19 pigs weaned per sow per year and with feed costs of £62 per £100 of gross output. 'Poor' performance showed a £2 10s 0d Gross Margin per pig with 13 pigs weaned per sow per year and feed costs of £83 per £100 of gross output.

Laying hens gave an 'Excellent' gross margin of 13s per hen per year with 250 eggs per hen. A Gross Margin of 1s represented 'Poor' performance with an egg yield of 195 per hen.

Beef breeding cows

Standard	*Excellent*	*Good*	*Moderate*	*Poor*	*Your farm*
Gross margin per acre	£30	£22	£14	£8	
Gross margin per breeding cow . .	£45	£35	£25	£15	
Acres used per cow equivalent . .	1·5	1·6	1·8	2·0	

Sheep

Lowland flocks

Standard	*Excellent*	*Good*	*Moderate*	*Poor*	*Your farm*
Gross margin per acre	£25	£18	£12	£8	
Gross margin per ewe	£8	£6	£4 10s. 0d.	£3	
Lambing percentage .	150	140	125	115	
Acres used per cow equivalent . .	1·6	1·7	1·9	2·0	
Gross margin per cow equivalent . .	£40	£30	£23	£15	

The published Gross Margins and Physical Performance figures for dairy cows and cattle rearing or fattening in 1968.

Farm Business Recording Scheme

The keeping and use of accounts for farm management purposes was regarded to be of such importance that the Ministry of Agriculture introduced a Farm Business Recording Scheme to encourage farmers to keep accounts. A grant of £90 per year, for a three year period, was available to all farmers whose businesses were in excess of 250 standard man-days. The aim of the scheme was to encourage farmers to keep business management accounts which would assist them in increasing the efficiency of their farming operations and in making business decisions in relation to the running of the farm. The scheme opened on 1st November 1965 and closed to new entrants on 14th May 1972.

Small Farm (Business Management) Scheme

The next schemes were aimed at small farmers so as to enable them to improve their farm businesses through better farm management and husbandry practice. On 1st September 1965, the Ministry introduced two schemes to encourage farmers to keep accounts and improve their farm businesses. The Small Farm (Business Management) Scheme, which replaced the Small Farmers' Scheme, was open to farms with businesses between 20 and 125 acres and with a labour requirement of between 250 and 600 standard man days. Farm account keeping was an integral part of the scheme. A maximum grant of £1,000 was available under this scheme for items of improvement that would increase the efficiency and profitability of the farm enterprises. A three year development plan was prepared for each eligible applicant. Grants were available to participants who undertook development plans amounting to £8 10s 0d per acre of crops and grass and £150 over the three years for keeping the farm accounts.

These schemes provided an excellent opportunity for the Ministry of Agriculture's Advisory Officers to give well informed advice to individual farmers. This advice was based on the information gained about the efficiency of the enterprises and the farm business as a whole from the results of the farm accounts. The Ministry also provided trained Farm Accounts Assistants at the Ministry offices to help farmers with their record keeping and analysis of the accounts.

Mr Derek Noble and his Ministry of Agriculture Agricultural Adviser, Mr Alan Warnock.

The Agricultural Trust

This body was established in 1964 and was partly funded from the Remoteness Grant. Mr Harry West, Minister of Agriculture, in presenting the case for the Trust said that the idea was to ensure that everything possible was done to increase the volume and variety of outlets for Ulster farm produce. Mr West said: *"There have been times when my Ministry's research or investigations indicated that a certain commercial development would be practicable, economical and beneficial to our farmers but yet several years might pass before a commercial firm appeared to take up the idea."* He continued: *"It will be the responsibility of the Trust to ensure that no such opportunity is missed or unduly delayed in future."* One outcome of the Trust's activities benefited Fermanagh in particular and that was its contribution in having the gravel tunnel drainage system accepted as an eligible method of drainage qualifying for grant aid. After the gravel tunnel drainage system had been assessed as a good system of field drainage at Castle Archdale further extensive field trials were conducted on a wide range of commercial farms in Fermanagh and West Tyrone. The farmers who undertook this trial work received funding equivalent to grant aid from the Trust. These farm trials showed beyond doubt the value of this method of drainage under heavy land conditions.

Gravel tunnel drainage.

Farm Amalgamations and Boundary Adjustments Scheme 1967 and the Farm Structure (Payments to Outgoers) Scheme 1967

The introduction of this scheme was referred to by Mr West, Minister of Agriculture, at the meeting of farmers in Enniskillen in November 1965. It came into operation in 1967. The Amalgamation and Boundary Adjustments Scheme provided 50 per cent grants towards the costs of a wide range of expenses arising from the amalgamation of small farms. Remodelling works such as new buildings, necessary to take advantage of the enlarged holdings, qualified for the generous grant aid. The aim was to form farms big enough to provide full-time work for a farmer and one other man. Similar grants were available for the transfer or reshaping of farms to give them more satisfactory boundaries. The Outgoers' Scheme, on the other hand, provided for the payment of grants to owner occupiers and tenants who gave up their farms for amalgamation. This part of the scheme was referred to as the 'Golden Handshake' and its purpose was to make the transition from farming less painful. For outgoers under 55 years of age a lump sum was available amounting to £1,000 for a 10 acre farm increasing to £2,000 for farms of 110 acres or over. For those outgoers over 65 years of age an annuity of £200 for a 10 acre farm increasing to £275 for a farm of 110 acres or above was payable. Payment to outgoers could take several forms depending on the outgoer's age. Farmers who were less than 55 years of age could get a sum of £1,000 plus £20 per acre (excluding the first 10 acres) up to a maximum of £3,000. Individuals of 65 years and over could get an annual income of £250 plus £10 per acre (excluding the first 10 acres) up to a maximum annuity of £450. Those aged between 55 and 65 years had a choice of the lump sum or the annuity. The payment to outgoers was an incentive to farmers who were either selling their farm or leasing it for a minimum of twelve years to another farmer. Both the outgoer and the amalgamator had to satisfy their own set of conditions under the Scheme before the outgoer could obtain the 'Golden Handshake'. This scheme was revised with effect from 1st September 1973 when the outgoers' grant was increased to a maximum payment of £3,000 or £450 of an annuity depending on age. Approved amalgamators qualified for a payment of £12.50 for each acre the amalgamated farm exceeded the area of the largest unit of land involved in the amalgamation.

The amalgamator in an approved scheme could also obtain a Government loan if required to finance the purchase of the land. In March 1968, Major James Chichester-Clark, Minister of Agriculture, told the Fermanagh County Committee of Agriculture in Enniskillen Agricultural College that while 500 applications had been received in Northern Ireland only 36 were from Fermanagh. The scheme proved to be of considerable benefit to a limited number of farmers. It appeared that most beneficiaries were those who, for particular reasons, were in the process of giving up farming and who had a willing neighbour or relative prepared to expand their properties. However, the scheme failed to have a major impact because of the small farmers' attachment to the land and the lack of available well paid alternative employment. Many small farmers who were unable to earn a satisfactory income from their small farms were not prepared to give up their heritage. Instead many managed to get employment in a variety of jobs such as bus drivers, postmen, and workers in local factories. At the same time they were able to retain their holdings and became part-time farmers.

Grassland improvement schemes

Whilst major resources were being devoted to the small farmer problems, other schemes were introduced which applied to a wider range of farmers and aimed at grassland improvement. The Grassland Renovation Scheme which ran from1st April 1963 for a three year period had a big impact in Fermanagh. Mr Harry West, Minister of Agriculture, pointed out at the 'Open Day' at Castle Archdale Experimental Husbandry Farm in April 1967, that Fermanagh farmers had received £37,000 out of a total of £40,000 paid out in Northern Ireland.

Improved grassland.

The scheme covered such operations as fertilising, liming and weed control and associated operations. The Hill Land Improvement Scheme introduced in 1967 offered a 50 per cent grant on grassland improvement such as re-seeding, reclamation, fencing, shelter belts, out-door shelters for cattle and sheep, farm roads and provision of a water supply. Drainage attracted a grant of 60 per cent (including a 10 per cent supplement from the Agricultural Development Scheme). This scheme, whilst most welcome, had limited application as it applied only to the designated hill land in the county.

Oats was still an important crop in Fermanagh in the 1960s. A restored binder and Massey Ferguson 35 are harvesting oats at a demonstration.

Developments in cattle housing

Very significant developments took place during the 1960s in relation to cattle housing. Difficulties were arising on farms due to a shortage of straw bedding particularly since farmers were withdrawing from cropping in favour of all-grass farming systems. Farm units were getting larger and as a consequence of the cost of farm labour higher outputs per man were required. Pressure was also mounting on the need to control farm effluents. Two major developments in cattle housing involved the introduction of cow cubicles and slatted floors. County Fermanagh farmers were well to the fore with these developments. Slatted floors were a relatively new development in Northern Ireland in 1961. One of the earliest users of the system was Mr Alan Tisdall at Farranaconaghy, Lisnaskea. He built two self feed silos and a cattle court, each of which had a slatted floor. The project was grant-aided under the Ministry of Agriculture's Experimental Farm Buildings Scheme. The new beef unit worked very satisfactorily.

Mr John Ferguson's farm at Blaney was also at the forefront of development. His farm was used as the site for a major three-day farm demonstration organised by the meal firm Silcocks in October 1961. Mr Robert H. Houston, Fermanagh's Deputy County Agricultural Officer, participated in that event. The demonstration was attended by 1,000 farmers from all parts of the Province. Mr Ferguson had changed his cows from the Shorthorn

breed to Friesians in 1956. His 35 milk recorded Friesians, which were brucellosis-free, were averaging 1,000 gallons per cow. A feature of particular interest was a new slatted court for the cows which was under construction. This was one of the first such sheds in County Fermanagh. It was of two-storey construction with space under the slats for mechanical cleaning out. Emphasis was placed on the use Mr Ferguson had made of soil nutrient testing, fertilising, drainage, reseeding and reclamation. In 1963 Mr Ferguson was the runner-up in the *'David Brown Farmer of the Year'* competition and in 1965 he won the event.

Tisdall's beef house. The feeding face of the silo showing the tombstone barrier in position. The slatted area extended 38ft up the silo.

Cubicles for dairy and beef cattle

Cubicles were a major advance in cattle housing. They reduced the need for bedding. Furthermore, dairy cows were easier to keep clean which was a big advance in terms of hygienic milk production. Mr Michael Murphy, Ballyreagh, Tempo, was one of the pioneers of this method of housing dairy cattle in Fermanagh. His farm was the location for a silage and farm demonstration in 1963. Mr Murphy had 35 dairy cows averaging 930 gallons per cow on 16 cwt of meal per cow. Mr Murphy had adapted his previously straw bedded cattle court by installing cubicles. The cows were milked in a milking parlour.

Mr Alan Tisdall announcing the results at the YFC Ploughing Match at Donagh in 1945.

Mr Michael Murphy MBE JP of Ballyreagh, with his son, Michael, and the cup they won for grassland management in the 1960s.

Blaney Lodge.

Fred Elliott's cubicles.

Mr Robert L. Thornton's cubicles for fattening heifers.

An early tank and slurry pump on the farm of Mr S. Crowe, St Angelo, Enniskillen.

One of the first farmers in Fermanagh to use cubicles for beef cows was Mr Fred Elliott of Mullaghbane, Florencecourt. His new cattle court with a self-feed silo, built during the winter of 1964/65, incorporated cubicles for 30 beef cows, together with calving boxes and a calf creep. The cubicles were grant aided under the Ministry's Experimental Farm Buildings Scheme. A feature article in Agriculture in Northern Ireland, describing Mr Elliott's new buildings, was written by his Agricultural Adviser, Mr Sam McEwen.

In 1966, again in *Agriculture in Northern Ireland,* Mr McEwen described the experience of Mr Robert L. Thornton of Derryhowlaght, Bellanaleck, in using cubicles for fattening heifers.

Cubicles reduced or eliminated the need for straw bedding. This meant that dung and urine had to be dealt with as a slurry rather than as farmyard manure stored in a manure pit or midden. Before the widespread adoption of slatted dunging passages with tanks underneath, passages were scraped out with the dung and urine being stored in underground tanks. Slurry was removed from the tanks and spread on the land using slurry tankers.

An early model of slurry tanker in use on a Fermanagh farm.

Pig housing

Developments in livestock housing were not limited to cattle only. Intensification of pig production was taking place. An innovation during the 1960s was the introduction of sow stalls. This was an economical way of housing, feeding and managing dry sows and in time the system was adopted on many intensive pig farms.

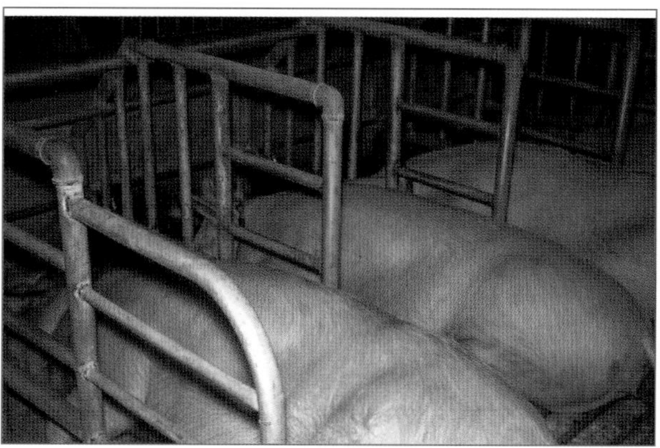

Sow stalls.

However, this level of intensity of housing sows was not favoured by all producers. A more welfare friendly method of housing dry sows was by using sow kennels. This method involved bedded covered lying areas with outside runs for exercise and feeding.

William Swan's sow kennels.

Pig fattening houses also received attention. Many modern efficient pig fattening houses were built in the county during the decade. Two such units were constructed on the Colebrooke Estate farm. High standards of construction and insulation were employed so as to ensure maximum feed efficiency. Slatted dunging passages and underground slurry tanks ensured minimum labour inputs.

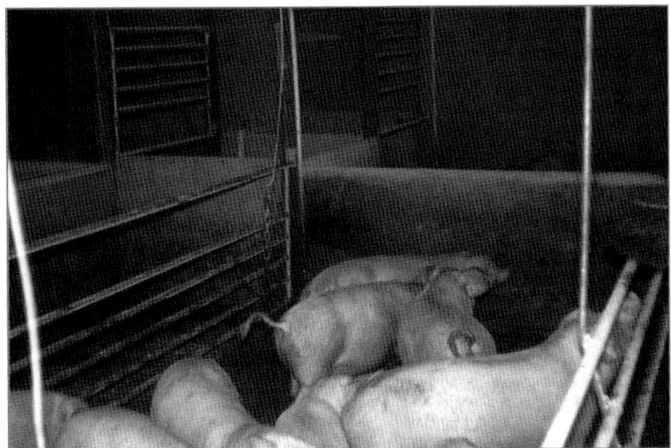

The Colebrooke pig pens.

Boost for suckled calf production

The introduction of the Beef Breeding Herd Subsidy (funded from the Remoteness Grant) in 1961 gave a considerable boost to suckled calf production. This gave farmers under lowland conditions encouragement to keep cows for the sole purpose of producing and rearing calves which were suitable for beef production. Further encouragement to this enterprise was received in 1966 when the Beef Cow Subsidy, which applied throughout the UK, was introduced into Northern Ireland.

Hill cows.

Economics of farming in the 1960s

A major factor in determining farm incomes is the price obtained for produce. The guaranteed prices for commodities announced in March 1960 were: fat sheep 3s 3d per lb; steers and heifers 157s 0d per live cwt; fat pigs 45s 10d per score (20 lbs); eggs 3s 11.15d per dozen; barley 28s 9d per cwt; potatoes 260s per ton. The guaranteed price for liquid milk, other than for Grade A licence holders, varied from 3s 8d per gallon in December and January 1961 to 1s 11d in May, June and July. Grade A milk commanded substantially higher prices. For example, in May, June and July the guaranteed price was 2s 7d per gallon which was 8d higher than the other category. The guaranteed prices for beef and sheep, like milk, varied according to the time of year. April and early May marked the peak for beef prices at 173s 0d per live cwt and also for sheep at 43½d per lb dressed carcase weight.

Guaranteed prices were related to a certain level of production. In the case of milk in Northern Ireland the volume of milk to which the guaranteed price was related was known as the Standard Quantity. By 1964 the volume of milk produced in the Province had increased to 124 million gallons which was 27 million gallons in excess of the Standard Quantity. This excess resulted in producers receiving 5d per gallon below the guaranteed price.

A threshing outfit used in the 1960s. Mr William H. Elliott, Tempo, is forking the straw and Mr Cyril Ferguson, Clabby, is feeding the thresher.

The Price Reviews

The Annual Price Review report for 1961 indicated that too little beef was being produced and as a consequence the guaranteed price for beef was raised by 10 shillings per cwt (157 shillings per cwt in 1960). On the other hand, milk was being over-produced in that the volume produced considerably exceeded the Standard Quantity to which the guaranteed price (3 shillings and 1.45d per gallon in 1960) was linked. This meant that farmers were receiving less per gallon than the guaranteed price.

At the end of the decade (1969/70 Price Review) the lowest standard price for beef was 201s 6d at the end of September and the highest at 23rd March was 224s 6d. Milk prices, as determined by the Milk Marketing Board for Northern Ireland, varied from 26.86d in September to 42.17d per gallon in March. The Annual Price Review report for 1971 made reference to forthcoming significant changes in the system of agricultural support and to the industry having experienced unprecedented production cost increases. The Minister, the Rt Hon P. H. O'Neill, DL, MP, when referring to the increase in guaranteed prices, was hopeful that they would give Northern Ireland farmers confidence and encouragement to increase production of beef, sheep, pigs and milk. The guaranteed price for eggs had been reduced by 0.5p per dozen to 16.5p (now expressed in decimal currency). The guaranteed prices for the other commodities of particular interest to Fermanagh were: milk 22.1p per gallon (an increase of 2.5p) but that was accompanied by a reduction of the 'Standard Quantity' in Northern Ireland of one million gallons; cattle £12.35 per cwt (an increase of £1.22); sheep 22.3p per lb (an increase of 2.8p) and pigs £2.93 per score (an increase of 7p). The increased prices were intended to meet the increased costs facing the industry.

Efficiency gains

During the 1960s there was considerable development on farms encouraged by various Government schemes. Better agricultural education and intensive advisory work on the major aspects of crop and animal husbandry led to greater output and better farm business management. As a consequence of the these developments, and reasonable price stability for produce, improved efficiency gains on farms enabled successful farmers to absorb a substantial proportion of their increased costs. During the period 1960 to 1970/71, the cost of feedingstuffs bought by farmers increased by 42 per cent while wages paid to farm workers increased by 85 per cent. During the same period the increases in prices received by farmers were 19 per cent in respect of milk, 30 per cent in respect of pigs and 57 per cent in respect of fat cattle. The price received by farmers for eggs had fallen by about 20 per cent in the same period.

References:

Ministry of Agriculture's *Monthly Reports* and *Agriculture in Northern Ireland.*

Files of *The Impartial Reporter* and *Fermanagh Herald* held in Enniskillen Library.

Records of the County Agricultural Executive/Development Office.

Chapter 32
The Common Market

Mr Harry West, Minister of Agriculture, speaking at the Fermanagh County Committee of Agriculture in October 1971 expressed his views on the prospects for agriculture if Britain joined the Common Market or European Economic Community (EEC). He said it was difficult to be precise and that there was a lot of speculation. He thought that within the EEC there was a greater degree of prosperity. Beef production appeared to have a favourable future, pigs might not do so well and milk production had a fair prospect. He said industry stood to gain a lot in the EEC.

Prospects

Mr West, when speaking about the outcome of the February 1972 Price Review, said that he had no doubt that the substantial increases in Guaranteed Prices would encourage an expansion in production. He said that would be particularly true of milk, beef and sheep – all enterprises which can be based largely on the output from our grassland. The Minister said: *"I hope farmers will take full advantage of these increases and of our favourable climate by going all out to increase production from grassland, both as grazing in summer and as high quality silage and hay in winter. This is the best way to prepare for U.K. entry to the EEC".*

Rt Hon H. W. West MP PC.

He also referred to increased prices for cereals and increased prices for pigs. He hoped that the better price for pigs would encourage expansion again. He went on to say that the increase in the guaranteed price for pigs together with the raising of the middle band (the number of pigs to which the guaranteed price applied) should give pig producers the confidence to increase production again. With regard to egg production, Mr West said producers could no longer expect encouragement from the Price Review and must rely instead on their own efficiency and on the marketing ability of the egg packers, aided by the minimum import prices. He said that while there was no need for egg producers to panic there was no encouragement to expand production.

Map of the EEC in 1973.

EEC entry

The United Kingdom (UK) joined the EEC or Common Market on 1st January 1973. The EEC Common Agricultural Policy (CAP) replaced the price guarantees that had been established under the UK's 1947 Agricultural Act. There was a five-year transitional period for price harmonisation. A well-attended information meeting in relation to the Common Market was held in Enniskillen Agricultural College in April 1972 under the chairmanship of Mr Tom Moore, Chief Inspector, Ministry of Agriculture, and a former Deputy County Agricultural Executive Officer in Fermanagh. Mr W. G. Malcolm, Deputy Secretary in the Ministry, explained the background to the EEC. He said that the basic principle was freedom of marketing. Goods could move freely across Member States' borders. Agricultural support would depend on tariff protection from cheap foreign imports. Support buying within the EEC would put a floor in the market by buying and storing surplus stocks. The Annual Price Review would be replaced by prices determined in Brussels after consideration of farming economic conditions in the ten Member States. He predicted that as a result of entering the Common Market, UK agricultural output would increase by seven per cent. He concluded by saying that Northern Ireland could contribute to increased production by making better use of grassland.

Low food prices

Mr Tom Stainer, an economist with the Ministry, stated that the EEC policy was aimed at low food prices for the human population and reasonable incomes for farmers. Target prices would be set by the EEC and farmers would get these prices when supply and demand for products were in balance. Deficiency payments, which had been the pattern of support for farm products since 1947, would end. Farm income from now on would become almost entirely dependent on market returns. Marketing would therefore take on a new significance.

Opportunities

Mr Tom Larmour, Deputy Chief Inspector of the Ministry, dealt with the opportunities and problems for Northern Ireland farmers in the new regime. Higher priced feeding stuffs would result from increased cereal prices. Pigs and poultry, which depended on bought-in feeding stuffs, would therefore require the greatest possible efficiency in production and marketing. With regard to beef and milk production, Mr Larmour predicted favourable prices, with a potential for a 25 per cent expansion in production by 1975 and a shortage up to 1980. He indicated that to take full advantage of the opportunities for beef production, farmers would need to expand the suckler herd by 25 per cent over the next two years. He said that with brucellosis-free status, and the meat plants up to EEC standards, Northern Ireland beef producers had a very real opportunity for expansion. He concluded by stating that while there were these opportunities there would also be increased competition from other countries.

Less Favoured Areas

Prior to entry to the Common Market, part of County Fermanagh was classified as 'hill land' qualifying for Hill

Speakers at the meeting in Enniskillen Agricultural College. Left to right: Mr Tom Moore, Mr Tom Stainer, Mr Tom Larmour, Mr Gerry Malcolm, Mr Ronnie Martin, Deputy Chief Veterinary Officer, and Mr W. T. McClintock, County Agricultural Executive Officer.

Cow Subsidy and other associated benefits. The subject of extension of the area in the county eligible for hill subsidies was raised by Mr George Cathcart when the Fermanagh County Committee of Agriculture met the Minister of Agriculture in March 1969. Mr Cathcart stated that one-third of Fermanagh came under the 'hill land' classification, another third could be classed as 'livestock rearing land' and the remaining third as 'reasonable agricultural land'. Mr Cathcart felt that the rearing land should be brought under the Hill Scheme and thereby benefit from Hill Cow and Hill Sheep Subsidies and the higher rate of grant on the use of fertiliser. He was informed that the Ministry had already stretched the definition of hill subsidy land as far as possible. On entry to the Common Market the previously defined 'hill land' in the UK was classified as 'Less Favoured' or 'Disadvantaged' and therefore qualified for preferential treatment under EEC rules. Farmers in Fermanagh, supported by the Ministry's County Agricultural Executive staff, believed that the new EEC definition of Less Favoured Areas was much wider than 'hill land' as previously applied in the county. They believed that the Less Favoured Area should include all or most of Fermanagh.

Mr George Cathcart OBE JP.

Approach to Minister

A delegation from the Fermanagh County Branch of the Ulster Farmers' Union (UFU) in 1974 made an appeal to Mr Peter Mills, Parliamentary Under-Secretary of State for Agriculture in Northern Ireland.

Mr Peter Mills, Parliamentary Under-Secretary of State.

The delegation was comprised of Mr Robert L. Thornton, County Chairman of the UFU, Mr George Cathcart, The Earl of Enniskillen, Mr P. C. Falconer, Mr David Fawcett, Mr William Rea and Mr William Swan. These Fermanagh men were accompanied to the meeting by Mr Wallace Perry, President of the UFU at that time, and Mr Percy Richardson, an official at UFU headquarters. The delegation made the claim that Fermanagh suffered from natural handicaps like poor soil quality, steep sloping land, poor climate and a short growing season. Part of the argument was that Fermanagh previously qualified for special assistance under the Marginal Land Scheme and, furthermore, it was surrounded by areas in the Irish Republic that were classified as 'Less Favoured' under the EEC definition. Other points made included Fermanagh's remoteness from the markets, small farm and herd sizes and the lowest stocking rate of any county in Northern Ireland. The appeal to the Minister was successful. Subsequently, 92 per cent of the county was classified as a Less Favoured Area (LFA) in 1975 under EEC Directive (75/268/EEC). This was a great boost to the county as detailed in the previous chapter. Farmers within the area qualified for Compensatory Allowances on breeding cows and sheep. They also qualified for higher rates of grant under capital grant and development schemes. A further advance was made in 1985 when almost all of County Fermanagh (99 per cent), apart from a very small area near Brookeborough and another small area beside Fivemiletown, was admitted as a Less Favoured Area. The additional seven per cent was classified as a Disadvantaged Less Favoured Area with the former area (92 per cent) redefined as a Severely Disadvantaged Area.

Benefits of the Common Agricultural Policy

The UK's formal accession to the EEC after the five-year transition period occurred in 1978. During this period, UK prices for agricultural products were brought up to EEC levels. The UK system of price guarantees was replaced by measures under the Common Agricultural Policy. Intervention buying was a feature of the EEC regime. When there was overproduction of a commodity intervention buying took place and this action upheld prices. The excessive stocks of the main commodities, in time, would become known by such titles as 'butter mountains' and 'grain mountains'. These intervention stocks were released for sale when commodities were scarce or were sold off at reduced prices to countries outside the EEC. Prices within the EEC were maintained by placing tariffs on imports of agricultural produce. This approach gave farmers confidence in that it put a floor in the market for the main agricultural products.

The designation of Less Favoured Areas (LFA) status for almost the entire County under the EEC Directive brought great benefits to County Fermanagh. Hill Livestock Compensatory Allowances were introduced from January 1976 as part of the EEC Directive to help farmers in the LFAs. Their purpose was to supplement the income of farmers in the LFAs to take account of the permanent natural handicaps affecting farming activities. The objective was to ensure the continuation of livestock farming in these areas, thereby helping to maintain the population in the hills and uplands and to conserve the countryside. These Allowances replaced the Hill Cow and Hill Sheep Subsidies, which had been part of the UK support system for farming. In addition to the direct benefits to livestock producers, capital grant and development schemes undertaken in these areas attracted higher rates of grant.

Decimalisation and Metrication

Part of the process of preparing the UK for EEC entry involved the introduction of decimalisation and metrication. Pounds, shillings (20 to the pound), pence (12 to the shilling and 240 to the pound) would disappear in favour of pounds and pence with 100 pence per pound. The change from pounds, shillings and pence (£ s d) to pounds and pence (£ p) took place on 15th February 1971.

Metrication was the next phase and the agricultural industry changed during the year 1975/76. Milk was purchased from farms in litres for the first time in October 1976. Livestock weights from then were officially expressed in kilograms. Acres and yards were replaced by hectares and metres respectively. Fertiliser nutrients were expressed in kg per hectare rather than units per acre.

New opportunities in Fermanagh

The 1970s were characterised by very considerable progress in agricultural development despite the problems of the collapse in beef prices in 1974 coupled with a number of poor seasons. Opportunities and encouragement were presented to farmers on entry to the Common Market through comprehensive and relatively generous capital grant and development schemes. New techniques of low cost drainage systems were developed and there was a new appreciation of the role grass could play in reducing the costs of milk and meat production. The need for livestock improvement through breeding and husbandry was fully appreciated. The designation of a significant part of Fermanagh as a Less Favoured Area gave agricultural development a new impetus. It was against the background of accession to the EEC, that the Department of Agriculture launched a Province-wide initiative to prepare farmers for making the most of the opportunities that lay ahead. It was intended that there would be a series of campaigns, over the next number of years, aimed at improving grassland output and reducing costs of production.

Mr H. W. West urges boost for Farmers' Incomes

When Mr Harry West was elected leader of the Ulster Unionist Party he did not forget the interests of the farmers. Mr West, in a public statement in March 1979, said that the EEC Agricultural Policy and Regional Aid were of particular interest to Northern Ireland. He said that the basic aim of the Common Agricultural Policy was to ensure the security of food supplies at stable and reasonable prices to the consumer, to make farming more efficient by boosting productivity, thereby improving farmers' incomes and bringing them more into line with those of other sectors. He went on to say that the security of food supplies to a nation or a community cannot be ensured by a rigid management of the agricultural industry that will trim production to the exact requirements of the market. He said: *"It is impossible to manage the weather and all the other uncontrollable factors entailed in farm production. It is most disturbing to find certain people with great responsibilities in these matters, but with an apparent lack of practical knowledge, speak as if the agricultural industry can be halted when market requirement has been met. The guarantee of a secure supply of food requires, as an insurance against uncontrollable factors, a certain tolerance in production which must of necessity bring surpluses which must be held to a minimum in order to eliminate the unnecessary expenditure of public money."* Mr West continued: *"That there has been great extravagance and bad management cannot be denied but the result of these unfortunate happenings, which are quite outside the control of the United Kingdom farming industry, have brought a demand from Mr Silkin, the British Agriculture Minister, that*

for this year, and every year from now on, farm prices should be frozen until there is no more surplus. If this is really what he means it is a most irresponsible statement. Farm costs during this year have risen by 11 per cent. But if this policy were to be adopted, the agricultural industry would be expected to carry this increase and continue to produce a secure supply of food for the nation despite the fact that other sections of the community, with even less responsibility, are compensated for an increase in costs. This apparent over-production and waste has some of its origins in the absence of the implementation of the concept of free trade between member countries. The lack of monetary stability and currency problems of member nations has bedevilled the CAP more so than any other factor." He concluded by saying: *"The European monetary system, if it comes to fruition, could create the degree of currency stability so urgently needed to offset many of the present problems."*

Reform of the Common Agricultural Policy (CAP)

Under the leadership of an Irishman Ray McSharry, European Commissioner for Agriculture, the CAP Policy was reformed during 1992. The object of the reform was to limit rising production levels within the European Community (EC) while at the same time adjusting to the trend towards a more free and competitive agricultural market. Intervention prices for cereals and beef were reduced by 29 per cent and 15 per cent respectively over a three-year period from July 1993. Compensation by means of premia payments were made to offset the reduced prices. The concept of 'set-aside' for cereals was introduced, with the objective of withdrawing land from agricultural production. Limits were placed on stocking levels for livestock. The agreement also contained a commitment to environmental protection becoming an integral part of the CAP.

Lord Arran.

The Parliamentary Under-Secretary of State with responsibility for agriculture in Northern Ireland, Lord Arran, when commenting on the Reform stated: *"I believe this is a good settlement for Northern Ireland, particularly in relation to our vital livestock enterprises. In the beef sector in particular, the shift in support arrangements provides the opportunity for the industry to trade competitively in real markets and reduce the unhealthy dependence on intervention."*

Reform of livestock schemes

The schemes affecting livestock were naturally of particular interest to Fermanagh farmers where most income is generated from those enterprises. Meetings were held at many centres throughout the county where County Agricultural Development staff explained the details of the CAP Reform and its implications for Fermanagh farmers.

Under the reforms, the Beef Special Premium Scheme (BSP) commenced in January 1993. Payments, amounting to 60 ecu (European Currency Units) or £49.13 per head in 1993 rising to 90 ecu or £73.70 per head in 1995 and thereafter, were made at two stages in the male bovine's life – 10 months and 23 months. There was a headage limit of 90 animals per age group per year per holding. An Extensification Supplement (30 ecu or £24.56 per head) was payable on eligible animals up to the 90 headage limit at both stages of the BSP. A Deseasonalisation Premium (60 ecu or £49.13) was also payable to encourage slaughtering between 1st January and 30th April.

The Suckler Cow Premium Scheme (SCPS) under the new regime also applied from 1st January 1993. Its purpose was to help maintain the incomes of specialist beef producers at a satisfactory level. Rates of payment were: 70 ecu or £57.32 per cow in 1993 increasing to 120 ecu or £98.26 in 1995 and thereafter. In addition to these payments, there was the potential for a national top-up of 25 ecu or £20.47. Quotas for suckler cows were also allocated in the autumn of 1993, with 1992 being made the reference year. As in the case of beef cattle, an equivalent Extensification Supplement was also payable. The Extensification Supplement was payable on eligible animals under BSPS and SCPS where stocking rates were under 1.4 LU per hectare.

The Sheep Annual Premium Scheme (SAPS), like the other schemes, applied from January 1993 and quotas were involved which were based on sheep numbers paid on in 1991. Payments under this scheme were intended for those sheep meat producers who retained flocks of breeding ewes. The purpose of SAPS was to compensate producers for the difference between market prices and the price fixed by the EC. There was a headage limit (1,000 ewes in the Less Favoured Areas and 500 ewes in lowland) for payment of full Premium.

With milk production which was already subject to quotas,

there was an increase in quota of 0.6 per cent given for the 1993/94 year but this was accompanied by a reduction in the intervention return for butter of three per cent in 1993 and by two per cent in 1994/95. Dairy cows were taken into consideration when calculating stocking rates on farms relating to Extensification Supplements for BSPS and SCPS.

IACS

Part of the CAP reform was the introduction of the Integrated Administration and Control System, commonly known as IACS. The purpose of IACS was to control the potential for fraud across the EC support schemes. IACS consisted of a computerised database, field identification, animal identification, yearly submission by farmers and an integrated checking and inspection system. This new system was to be fully operational by 1st January 1996. Penalties for late or inaccurate applications were severe.

Agenda 2000

The final review of the Common Agricultural Policy of the twentieth century was carried out in 1999. It set the policy framework for the years 2000 to 2006. The revised policy divided the CAP into two 'pillars' – production support and rural development. Rural development was considered important, as agriculture alone could not guarantee jobs and growth. It was stated that economic renewal and stabilising the rural population had a central role to play in safeguarding the vitality of rural communities. Environmental considerations, which had received consideration and protection in the 1992 reform, were strengthened in Agenda 2000. When the CAP was first established, it was a time of food shortages but food production was now no longer so strategically important. There was now an increasing focus on how food was produced and a greater emphasis on the relationship between farming and the environment.

References:

The Department of Agriculture's *Agriculture in Northern Ireland.*

Files of *The Impartial Reporter* and *Fermanagh Herald* held in Enniskillen Library.

Alexander, Derek W., and Drake, Michael, *Breaking new ground – Fifty years of change in Northern Ireland agriculture 1952 – 2002.* Glenfarm Holdings Limited, Blackstaff Press, Belfast (2002).

Chapter 33

Farm support measures after entry to the Common Market

The United Kingdom joined the European Economic Community on 1st January 1973. In the succeeding years, new support measures gradually replaced those which had been in existence in the United Kingdom in one form or another since the introduction of the 1947 Agriculture Act.

Farm and Horticulture Development Scheme (FHDS)

Britain's entry to the European Community brought significant changes to the UK's system of capital grants. Agricultural policy was determined by the terms of EEC Directive 72/159 on farm modernisation. The FHDS, introduced on 1st January 1974, provided grants for capital expenditure on those farms where the income per labour unit was less than the national average in non-agricultural activities (the comparable income), and where a development plan was submitted to show that within six years the farm income would reach the comparable income with the implementation of the plan. In 1975, nine applications were received in Fermanagh. In 1976, applications reached 150 with a slightly increasing number of applications being received each year reaching 177 in 1980. The amount of grant attracted by the scheme in County Fermanagh in 1979 was £1,242,890. The scheme was replaced in 1980 by the Agriculture and Horticulture Development Scheme (AHDS) which had similar aims.

Farm Capital Grant Scheme (1973) [FCGS 1973]

Following entry to the EEC, the national governments of member States could provide national aids for capital investment on farms not subject to farm development plans. In response, the UK reintroduced the Farm Capital Grant Scheme (1973) (FCGS 1973). The original scheme remained open to hill farmers. The new scheme opened for applications on 1st January 1974.

EC Less Favoured Directive (75/268)

Under this Directive, the FHDS and FCGS (1973) were amended to provide for higher rates of grant for Less Favoured Land.

Rates of grant in 1975

Under the FCGS (1973) in the Less Favoured Areas (LFAs), drainage attracted 70 per cent grant. Roads, stock handling facilities, fencing and grassland improvement works each gained a 50 per cent grant. The rate of grant aid for silos, livestock housing and waste storage systems was 30 per cent and for milking equipment 20 per cent. Rates of grant for silos, livestock housing and manure storage under the Farm and Horticulture Development Scheme (FHDS) at 40 per cent were 10 per cent higher than under the FCGS. Machinery and livestock purchases under the FHDS qualified for a 15 per cent grant.

Labour efficient cattle housing.

A modern silo.

Agriculture and Horticulture Development Scheme (AHDS)

Following a review of the administration of the schemes, the FHDS and the FCGS (also the HCGS - the Horticulture Capital Grant Scheme) were simplified and a new replacement scheme (AHDS) came into being on 1st October 1980. Detailed variations of these schemes were introduced from time to time to cope with particular emergencies such as Foot and Mouth Disease and flooding. Under these schemes, a comprehensive range of grants was available to support investment and provide better incomes for those engaged in the industries.

In addition to the schemes that applied throughout the United Kingdom, some were introduced specifically for Northern Ireland. These schemes were aimed at addressing the particular economic circumstances on farms arising from 'the Troubles' and the political unrest. One particularly valuable scheme for County Fermanagh was the Agricultural Development Programme (ADP).

The Agricultural Development Programme (ADP)

This was the most successful scheme ever introduced as far as County Fermanagh was concerned. Meetings to promote the new scheme were held at centres throughout the county in March 1981. There were two parts to the scheme. Part 1 provided higher rates of grants for land improvement works (70 per cent drainage, 65 per cent for grassland improvement and fencing) and farm roads (60 per cent) in the LFAs. Fermanagh farmers were fortunate in that most of the county had this classification and could therefore benefit from the higher rates of grant payable under this scheme compared to those available under the national schemes. Grants on certain items, like concrete roads, could be claimed on a standard cost basis rather than actual costs. The standard costs were based on UK average figures which gave a major financial advantage in Northern Ireland and particularly in County Fermanagh where aggregates and other materials were available locally at much lower costs than those pertaining on the UK mainland.

Concrete roads provided excellent access to farms.

These costs together with the generally high rate of grant meant that grant supported work could be carried out at considerably lower prices than those indicated by the standard cost figures. The financial advantage was even greater where normal farm labour was used to carry out the work. This provided an incentive for farmers in the county to undertake major development work for a modest investment outlay.

Drainage schemes were an important element of land improvement.

Part 2 of the ADP Scheme was available to farmers under 55 years of age and who spent at least half their time on the farm. The scheme involved a plan which could be up to 6 years in length and under which a herd of between 5 and 40 suckler cows had to be maintained. A 30 per cent increase in production was required over the period of the plan with an income at the end of at least £2,000 (expressed as a Gross Margin). A premium amounting to £24 was payable (additional to other eligible payments) on each suckler cow with a grant of 37.5 per cent available for farm buildings under the scheme. A 10 per cent grant was also available on machinery purchases.

Suckler herds were important enterprises on Fermanagh farms.

The ADP Scheme was so successful that it was heavily over-subscribed and it was necessary to suspend it due to available funds having been allocated. It was re-introduced in July 1988 with lower rates of grant. The rate of grant for drainage renewal was reduced to 40 per cent with similar rates for reclamation, pasture improvement and fencing. Grants for farm roads and grass silos were reduced to 30 per cent, as was the rate for grass silos. Silage effluent and animal waste storage facilities still qualified for a 60 per cent grant. At the time of this announcement, it was pointed out that the scheme would close for applications on December 31st 1991 and investment work had to be completed by December 31st 1992.

Livestock scheme payments

Under the Common Market support arrangements for farmers, Hill Livestock Compensatory Allowances were introduced in 1976. These Allowances were to supplement the income of farmers in the Less Favoured Areas to take account of the permanent natural handicaps affecting farm activities. The objective was to ensure the continuation of livestock farming in these areas, thereby helping to maintain the population in the hills and uplands and to conserve the countryside. The payments were made to farmers who maintained regular breeding herds of cows, kept primarily for the production of calves and qualified flocks of breeding ewes, kept for the production of lambs.

Hill sheep in the Marlbank area.

The Suckler Cow Premium Scheme came into being in June 1980 and its purpose was to maintain incomes of specialist beef producers.

The boom years in Fermanagh

Because of the generous grant system and a reasonably prosperous time for agriculture tremendous strides were made in County Fermanagh farming in the 1980s. The availability of competent contractors and good promotion and efficient administration by the Department of Agriculture's staff contributed very significantly to this progress.

An examination of the statistics for 1982 gives an indication of the extent of the work undertaken in County Fermanagh under the various improvement schemes that were current at that time.

Table 33.1 Capital Grant Scheme Applications in 1982

	Applications	Grant paid £
Agriculture and Horticulture Development Scheme	93	116,760
Farm and Horticulture Development Scheme	-	2,996,187
Agriculture and Horticulture Grant Scheme	931	2,304,181
Farm Capital Grant Scheme	-	2,612,810
Agricultural Development Programme (Part 1)	5,466	7,017,737
Agricultural Development Programme (Part 2)	128	13,382
Total		15,061,057

The number of different improvement items applied for in 1982 under the Farm and Horticulture Development Scheme, Agriculture and Horticulture Grant Scheme, and the Agricultural Development Programme in County Fermanagh were as follows:-

Table 33.2 Farm Improvement items in 1982

Farm buildings	853
Electricity	41
Water supplies	188
Field drainage	2,679
Roads	3,033
Cattle handling facilities	119
Fences and gates	2,666
Grassland improvement	3,743
Reclamation	1,363

Land improvement works, particularly drainage and reclamation, combined with grassland improvement, transformed the face of the Fermanagh countryside and led

Improved grassland led to increased productivity. Mr Alan Warnock, Agricultural Adviser, discussing a grazing sward with Mr Eamon Kelly, Cavanacross.

Beef cattle attracted additional payments.

to a substantial increase in farm productivity and reduced the cost of production for grass based livestock enterprises.

The improvement of farm roads, mainly by concreting, greatly enhanced access to homesteads and farmyards. This development gave farm families renewed heart in living in the countryside and was a significant factor in contributing to the maintenance of the rural population.

In addition to the capital grant schemes support in 1982, Hill Livestock Compensatory Allowances (HLCAs) were a significant source of funds to the farming community in the county. Under that scheme there were 3,148 applications involving 39,013 cows and 10,852 sheep. The amount paid out in 1982 under HLCAs was £1,791, 905.

During 1982, the combined capital grants and the Hill Livestock Compensatory Allowances paid to Fermanagh farmers amounted to £16,852,962.

By 1984/85, the total amount paid out in the county had increased to £19.50 million. The Suckler Cow Premium Scheme and the Calf Premium Scheme together were worth £1.90 million and the amount paid out under the Agricultural Development Programme (Part 1) had increased to £11.82 million.

Support in the 1990s

Following the McSharry reforms of the CAP, support to the livestock sector was channeled more through direct payments to farmers rather than through market support measures. The Beef Special Premium Scheme (BSP) commenced in January 1993. Payment (60 ecu or £49.13 per head in 1993 rising to 90 ecu or £73.70 per head in 1995 and thereafter) was made at two stages in the male bovine's life – 10 months and 23 months. There was a headage limit of 90 per age group per holding per year. An Extensification Supplement (30 ecu or £24.56 per head) was payable on eligible animals up to the 90 headage limit at both stages of the BSP. A Deseasonalisation Premium (60 ecu or £49.13) was also payable to encourage slaughterings between 1st January and 30th April.

Rates of payment under the Suckler Cow Premium Scheme (SCPS) were: 70 ecu or £57.32 per cow in 1993 increasing to 120 ecu or £98.26 in 1995 and thereafter. In addition to these payments there was the potential for a national top-up of 25 ecu or £20.47. Quotas for suckler cows were also allocated in autumn 1993, with 1992 being the reference year. The Extensification Supplement was payable on eligible animals under BSPS and SCPS where stocking rates were under 1.4 Livestock Units (LU) per hectare.

The Sheep Annual Premium Scheme, as with the other schemes, started in January 1993 and quotas were involved which were based on sheep numbers paid on in 1991. There was a headage limit (1,000 ewes in LFA and 500 ewes in lowland) for payment of the full Premium.

Fencing and gates are essential for livestock control.

Quality beef

At the meeting Mr Moreland Ingram BAgr, Head of the Ministry's Fatstock Inspectorate, emphasised the importance of producing top quality beef. The important quality factors were tenderness, leanness, flavour and juiciness. He said that cutability (yield of saleable meat) was an important factor from the butcher's point of view. He went on to explain that in order to assist farmers in producing the right type of beef the Ministry had introduced the Carcase Quality Bonus Scheme in 1968. Under this scheme producers were given detailed information about the carcases graded at deadweight certification centres. Beef farmers could then gain experience with successive marketings of cattle and obtain helpful pointers as to why cattle were awarded certain grades. Mr Ingram pointed out that the main reason for down-grading carcases was the lack of proper fleshing. This condition was primarily caused by poor thrive as a result of wrong feeding and management at some stage in the animals' lives. The importance of orderly marketing was also stressed. Mr Ingram said that there was normally a glut of cattle in the autumn and early winter with a corresponding shortage in late winter and spring. The Ministry had introduced headage payments to encourage farmers to even-out the production cycle. An incentive of £7 per head had been introduced and would be paid on animals marketed during the seven-week period from late March. Mr Ingram concluded by encouraging farmers to produce what the market wanted – a medium weight, well-fleshed animal which was sold at a stage of only moderate fat finish.

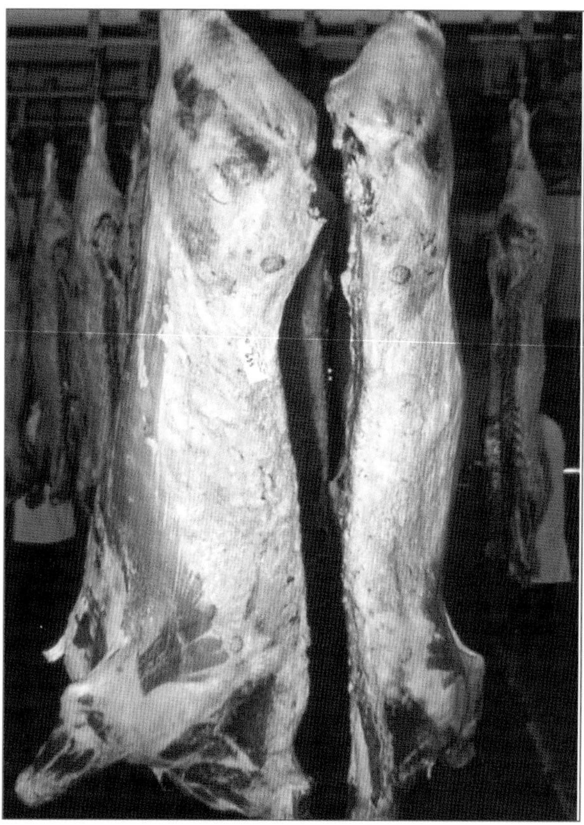

Quality beef carcases.

Planning for beef production

The next speaker Mr Milby Gregg BAgr, Director of the Ministry's Loughgall Livestock Husbandry Farm, took the theme *"Plan for Beef"* as his topic. He believed that '18 month beef' from autumn/winter born calves making use of high quality fodder offered considerable potential. Target growth figures were: indoors 1.50 lb per day going out to grass at a liveweight of 210 lb; then 1.60 lb per day at grass giving a liveweight of 680lb going into the house for finishing with a daily gain of 1.75 lb resulting in a final total weight of 940 lb. In conclusion, Mr Gregg referred to suitable breeds. He said it was generally agreed that Aberdeen Angus x Shorthorn Cows crossed with a Hereford bull gave the type of animal that grew into the type of beef that had all the desirable qualities. However, he pointed out that he was convinced that in future suckler herd replacements would come from beef crosses on the dairy herd which was largely Friesian.

Angus x Shorthorn cow with Hereford calves.

Beef production on a Fermanagh farm

Mr Sam McEwen, the Ministry's local Agricultural Adviser, then spoke about feeding and management and gave the example of a Fermanagh farmer who was at present finishing 27 bullocks on high quality silage made from 14½ acres of grass. The grass had received 102 units of nitrogen, 51 units each of phosphate and potash per acre and was made into high quality silage using a forage harvester in late May. Nine acres of this area received 81 units of nitrogen and 18 units each of phosphate and potash in early June and were made into silage in mid July. Half a gallon of formic acid was applied to each ton of grass ensiled. The two cuts of grass produced 155 tons of silage, enough to fatten 27 light-weight bullocks. The bullocks were purchased in October and housed in early November. The bullocks weighed on average 833 lb at the beginning of the fattening period and were then weighed at intervals. During the first ten weeks the animals gained on average 2 lb per day using only 4 lb of barley per head. It was expected that the animals would be finished in March at around nine and a half hundredweight giving an average return per head of £108 17s 9d (including guarantee and

£7 headage payments) leaving a margin over feed costs of about £30 per head. Mr McEwen said that the results being achieved by this farmer could be obtained by many farmers in County Fermanagh if they planned properly.

Mr Sam McEwen.

This public meeting was followed up by many press articles on the subject of beef production and also by a farm demonstration on Mr William West's farm at Feugh, Newtownbutler, conducted by Mr David Todd, Agricultural Adviser. Mr West had a suckler herd of 49 mainly Shorthorn cows which he crossed with a pedigree Hereford bull. The cows were housed in winter in a cubicle court.

The suckler herd

During the winter of 1972/73 the Ministry's main advisory campaign was entitled *'More from Sucklers'*. Its purpose was to inform and encourage farmers to expand beef production by keeping more and better suckler cows. Well attended meetings were held at centres throughout County Fermanagh.

At a meeting in Churchill in December 1972, Mr W. T. McClintock, County Agricultural Executive Officer, stated that the beef cow herd was the most important enterprise on Fermanagh farms. He said that suckler cows were the main or subsidiary enterprise on almost 5,000 farms in the county and outnumbered the number of dairy cows by a considerable margin. He continued: "*There was not only a need to expand beef cow numbers to meet the increased demand for suckled calves but there was also the need to ensure that the calves produced were of a size and quality which would command good prices in the market. Income from the suckler herd was determined not only by the price received for the weaned calf but also by the subsidies attracted by both the cow and the calf*". He stated: "*under Common Market conditions income would be determined more and more by the price of the weaned calf at the autumn sales.*"

Rearing replacements

At the meetings Mr Donagh O'Neill, Director of the Grassland Experimental Husbandry Farm, Castle Archdale, described a system to bucket rear Aberdeen Angus/Friesian cross heifer calves which would calve down at two years of age. He said they cost £75 to rear to that age allowing £35 for the purchase price of the calf. He also detailed the benefits to be derived from September calving of the suckler herd.

Mr Donagh O'Neill.

Breeding

Mr Sam McEwen, Agricultural Adviser, gave details of the results of a survey in County Fermanagh which was carried out by the Ministry's staff during the summer of 1972. It indicated that the farmers' breed preference for suckler cows was: first choice – Shorthorn; second choice – Hereford cross Friesian; third choice – Angus types. The survey also showed that Angus and Shorthorn type cows comprised 65 per cent of the suckler herds in the county.

Charolais potential

The meetings around the county stressed the need for quality replacements for the suckler herd. The potential benefit of using AI dual purpose Shorthorn and Simmental bulls, which were provided free of charge under the newly introduced Beef Herds Replacement Scheme, was emphasised. The benefits of using the newly introduced breed, Charolais, were being promoted by the Agricultural Advisers at the meetings. A restricted licence had been granted in certain circumstances for the use of three-quarter bred Charolais bulls.

Charolais cattle at Loughgall in the 1960s.

Profit from Beef Cattle

Aspects of management and economics of over wintering beef cattle were the subjects for discussion at a meeting organised by the County Advisory Service in Enniskillen Agricultural College in November 1979. Dr Raymond Steen, of the Agricultural Research Institute, who was the guest speaker stated that if the price of stores in the spring exceeded the anticipated price of beef by £4 per 100 kg then it would be better to treat the animals as stores over the winter and fatten them off grass. For fattening purposes it was stated that the amount of meal feeding required depended on the quality of silage. With good silage 1 kg of barley could be fed economically to Hereford heifers and for Charolais, Simmental and Friesian steers the amount could be increased to 2.5 kg per day. With poorer silage, the amount could be increased to 2.5 kg per day for the other classes of cattle. Dr Steen then explained the value of different feeds. If barley cost £110 per ton then silage was worth between £11 and £17 per tonne depending on quality and hay was worth between 80 pence and £1.20 per bale. He then went on to explain the value of *Romensin* as a feed additive. This additive influenced the type of fermentation in the rumen. The inclusion of *Romensin* in the diet, at the recommended rate of two grams per day, cost £1.50 for a five-month period. A typical response to the inclusion of *Romensin* was an extra 9 kg of carcase gain worth £14. With regard to silage making, Dr Steen said that very early cutting only showed benefits where little meal was fed to fattening cattle. He recommended cutting in the first week in June followed by further cuts at eight-week intervals. He said wilting before ensiling did not increase animal performance yet the intake of wilted silage was greater than direct cut material. He did say that wilting reduced the need for silage additives and it also reduced the amount of effluent produced. Dr Steen said that precision chop silage offered no advantage in animal performance over single chop material.

Dr Raymond Steen.

Crisis in the beef industry

In most decades farmers face a serious challenge of one sort or another. The 1970s was no exception. In the early years of the decade farmers were concerned about low incomes. However, these concerns were small in relation to what was to come in 1974. That year witnessed a collapse in beef prices and in farmers' confidence. The situation was further aggravated by a poor fodder conservation season. Increased feed costs arising from a world shortage of grain, combined with higher oil prices, added further to the economic gloom on farms. The beef crisis and the fodder problems had a very significant impact on Fermanagh agriculture due to its heavy dependence on grass based enterprises – 95 per cent of its farm income being generated from cattle and sheep.

Despite the earlier predictions of a beef shortage, increased production had resulted in a beef surplus with a sharp fall in prices. Northern Ireland as a major beef exporter was particularly badly hit. Mr James T. O'Brien, from the Livestock and Meat Commission, attributed the problem to excessive imports of beef into the UK. Farmers were losing a lot of money, beef cattle prices were halved and dropped calves could hardly be sold. Protests by farmers throughout the Province were widespread.

Bad hay year

The problems arising from the collapse of beef prices in 1974 were compounded in that the summer of that year was extremely poor leading to great difficulty in getting adequate fodder conserved on many farms. Land conditions were difficult for silage making and as a result reduced quantities were made. Hay was still an important element in winter fodder in County Fermanagh at that time. Only small quantities of hay were saved and it was of very poor quality. Advice was offered by the Department's Advisory Staff through press articles on the value of rationing fodder where it was scarce and supplementing it with bought-in meal. Farmers who depended on hay as winter fodder were faced with selling stock or purchasing fodder or supplementing fodder stocks with additional meal purchases. Meal costing £80 per ton was regarded as equivalent in value to hay at 63p per bale or silage at £9.80 per ton at that time.

The Department of Agriculture responded to the fodder crisis in another way by making a grant of £4 per cow to help with the additional feed costs. To be eligible farmers had to be benefiting under the 1975 Hill Cow, Beef Cow or Breeding Herd Subsidy. In addition, the farmer had to purchase feedingstuffs of a type which the Department considered to be suitable for supplementary feeding to the value of at least £12 for each eligible cow on which grant was being claimed. The grant was payable on a maximum of seven cows in the herd and the first two cows in any herd were ineligible as were dairy cows. This payment was regarded as derisory by the farming organisations. Advisers spent a good deal of time during the winter advising those farmers who were short of fodder on the most economic ways of maintaining their stock over the winter.

Difficult silage making conditions.

Drought Serious in Fermanagh

Whilst 1974 was an extremely difficult year for Fermanagh farmers due to the collapse in beef prices and the atrocious summer weather, the 1975 season was the very opposite in terms of weather. On 10th July 1975 a report in *The Impartial Reporter* quoted Sam Morrow, the Deputy County Agricultural Executive Officer, as saying: "*The next week or fortnight will be critical for farmers as the drought was reaching the serious stage in County Fermanagh. It was claimed that the danger point was now approaching. Grass was getting very scarce and unless ample rain comes quickly there will be very poor after-grass to maintain livestock.*" It was stated that, despite the shortage of grass, livestock were very content and were thriving well.

Lowering costs of production

Throughout the decade emphasis was placed on lowering costs of production on farms. It was anticipated that with entry to the Common Market the best hopes were for those enterprises which were grass based. The best preparation for the future was therefore low cost production based on improved grassland productivity combined with efficiency of utilisation. The conservation of winter fodder was regarded as a significant challenge at that time as hay was still the main method of conserving winter fodder on many farms. During 1971 and 1972 particular emphasis was placed on grassland and fodder conservation in the Ministry's advisory campaigns.

'More from Fodder' Campaign

This initiative placed emphasis on the need to make more and better quality silage. The *'More from Fodder'* campaign was launched in January 1971 at Greenmount Agricultural College by the Minister of Agriculture, the Rt Hon Phelim O'Neill MP PC. At that time it was pointed out that only 6,000 out of the 19,000 farmers in Northern Ireland made silage. In Fermanagh the opening meeting in the *'More from Fodder'* campaign was held in Enniskillen Agricultural College on Thursday 28th January 1971 followed by meetings at eight other centres in the county. The conservation of winter fodder in the form of silage was a continuing feature of the Ministry's advisory activities for the remainder of the century.

'More from Grass' Campaign

Mr Harry West, Minister for Agriculture, when launching the *'More from Grass'* campaign at Greenmount Agricultural College in January 1972 said: "*While our best grassland farmers are amongst the best in the world, too many Northern Ireland farmers still consider grass as a natural growth on the farm, rather than a crop from which they should try to obtain the maximum yield.*"

One hundred farmers attended the first of a series of four meetings in the *'More from Grass'* campaign held in Enniskillen Agricultural College. In his introduction the chairman, Mr Sam Morrow, Deputy County Agricultural

Officer, said that while the subject was of widespread interest in Northern Ireland it was of particular importance to County Fermanagh. He said that while the soil and climatic conditions in Fermanagh did not suit arable cropping grass can be grown as well as in any other part of Northern Ireland. He continued: "*We are now on the threshold of the Common Market where one of the basic philosophies is that commodities should be produced in the regions where there is a natural advantage for production. We have a natural advantage in so far as grassland is concerned and it is up to us to exploit and make the most of this advantage. The ability to grow grass is one matter but turning it into a saleable and profitable commodity is another. Our two main products from grass are beef and milk. The prospects for beef appeared to be excellent as there was a scarcity in the Common Market and it was likely that this shortage would continue for some time. Mr West at the Greenmount launch of the campaign said that there was immediate scope for increasing the suckler herd by 25 per cent. As for milk the Milk Marketing Board appeared to be confident that there would be scope for expansion under EEC conditions and that prices would increase.*" Mr Morrow went on to say that it was likely that meal prices would increase under Common Market conditions, so it was therefore essential to reduce dependence on concentrates to an absolute minimum. He said: "*Fortunately our dependence on meal for beef and milk can be reduced considerably if we produce grass of the right quality for both grazing and fodder. Therefore, if we are to make the most of market opportunities which are presented to us we must get more from grass in terms of both quantity and quality.*"

Mr Bob Haycock, Director of the Grassland Experimental Husbandry Farm at Castle Archdale then spoke on increasing stocking rates and Mr David Todd, Agricultural Adviser, dealt with cattle housing. Mr Haycock, speaking at a subsequent meeting in the series, said that Fermanagh had the best conditions for growing grass in Northern Ireland. He said that grass yields obtained at Castle Archdale were higher than at any other centre in the country. Mr Haycock described two beef production systems in operation at Castle Archdale where stocking rates were one cow equivalent per acre using up to 230 units of nitrogen per acre.

'More from Your Land' Campaign

This campaign was introduced at Greenmount Agricultural College in December 1973 by Mr Peter Mills MP, the second Direct Rule Minister with responsibility for agriculture to serve in Northern Ireland. Mr Mills referred to the success of the previous campaigns in the series but emphasised that there was still unexploited potential for better and more production from the land. In County Fermanagh the emphasis was placed on increasing the output from grassland. This involved reclamation of waste areas, hedge removal where fields were too small, better grassland management, drainage and the provision of housing for cattle.

Mr Bob Haycock detailing the yields of grass plots at Castle Archdale.

Good news in 1974

Whilst 1974 was a dreadful year in so far as livestock prices and weather conditions were concerned there was one item of particularly good news. That was the achievement of having 92 per cent of County Fermanagh classified as Severely Disadvantaged Land under the terms of the EEC Less Favoured Area Directive. Many believed that the EEC definition of less favoured land extended beyond that covered by the definition of hill land as had applied under the UK farming support regime. A delegation to the Minister, Mr Peter Mills, from the Ulster Farmers' Union in Fermanagh, led by Mr Robert L. Thornton, achieved this very valuable outcome which would mean many additional millions of pounds to Fermanagh farmers in the following years. This was a great boon to Fermanagh farmers. Those farming within the newly designated area would in future qualify for preferential rates of grant under the various capital grant schemes and livestock support schemes. The Farm Capital Grant Scheme (FCGS), which had been introduced in 1971, offered attractive rates of grant for farm improvement work in the Less Favoured Areas (LFAs). Those items of particular interest to Fermanagh farmers were drainage attracting a 70 per cent grant, farm roads, fencing, stock handling facilities and grassland improvement all attracted a 50 per cent grant. The provision of silage accommodation, livestock housing, and slurry accommodation attracted a 30 per cent grant. Milking machine equipment earned a 20 per cent grant.

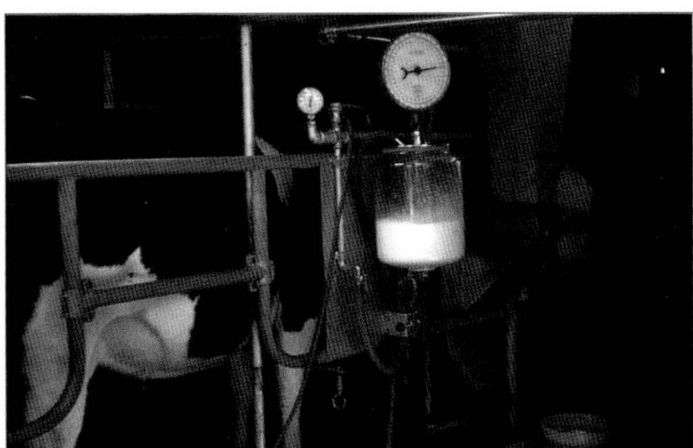

Milking parlour equipment attracted grant aid.

The new Farm and Horticulture Development Scheme (FHDS) offered higher rates of grant (40 per cent) for those items attracting 30 per cent under the FCGS. In addition, the FHDS had a 25 per cent grant for milking equipment and 15 per cent for machinery and equipment and for the purchase of livestock. The demand for advice on the development of farm businesses and on farm grant schemes put a tremendous pressure on the staff resources of the County Agricultural Executive Office. At that time the County Agricultural Executive Officer had one deputy and three full-time advisers and one part-time agricultural adviser together with a complement of field and office staff.

Profitable milk production

Milk production was an important enterprise on Fermanagh farms. In order to ensure that milk producers were informed of the latest developments in the feeding and management of dairy cows meetings were organised involving not only the local advisers but experts from the Agricultural Research Institute at Hillsborough and Loughry and Enniskillen Agricultural Colleges.

Demonstration at the Agricultural College

In 1972 a well attended demonstration was held at Enniskillen Agricultural College on the topic of *'The feeding of dairy cows'*. The Principal of the College, Mr Robert H. Houston, in welcoming the visiting farmers, stated that with the likelihood of entry to the Common Market the future for milk production looked good with the possibility of a high price per gallon but at the same time meal costs could rise. He said it was important therefore that the feeding of dairy cows should be based on high quality grass during the grazing season and high quality silage during the winter feeding period. He said farmers should aim to get maintenance plus five gallons of milk from grass and maintenance and two gallons from silage. The lecturers from the College then dealt with the various aspects of economic milk production using the College dairy herd and facilities for demonstration purposes.

Hillsborough experience

In March 1979, Dr Fred Gordon, of the Agricultural Research Institute at Hillsborough, was guest speaker at Enniskillen Agricultural College. Mr Rayner McKinley, Agricultural Adviser, set the scene by stating that only 24 per cent of the monitored dairy herds in Co Fermanagh were achieving yields in excess of 1,000 gallons per cow. Furthermore, some of these higher yielding herds were of low profitability due to excessive meal feeding.

Dr Gordon emphasised, that irrespective of the system of management, a high yield of milk was required for high profitability. He said that mid-winter was the most profitable time to calve cows provided a strict system of feeding and management was practised. He said that each month delay in calving after 1st January resulted in the loss of 50 gallons per cow and that the key to a profitable mid-winter calving herd was a plentiful supply of good grass and good quality silage. A good grass sward was a pre-requisite and adequate amounts of fertiliser must be applied and that some form of controlled rotational grazing system was required. He said that silage making at seven-week intervals was regarded as ideal in practice with the first cut being taken during the last week in May. The first cut received 100 units of nitrogen per acre and subsequent cuts about 80 units. He said wilting reduced

A Border bridge that had been blown up.

bombing or burning of farm houses and farm buildings, were recorded on properties throughout the county. Farmers who owned land on both sides of the Border found farming activity difficult as in most cases Border roads were cratered or blocked by the security forces to prevent terrorist movement between the two jurisdictions. These farmers also found difficulty in getting contractors to undertake work on their farms due to vulnerability to attack or intimidation.

Deaths

While intimidation and associated strife took their toll in terms of farming activity and community and social life, this was a small sacrifice in comparison with those families whose loved ones lost their lives. The book *Lost Lives,* written by David McKitterick, Seamus Kelters, Brian Feeny and Chris Thornton, chronicles the deaths and circumstances of the deaths of all who were victims as a result of *'The Troubles'* during the period 1966 to 1999. According to the book 3,636 people lost their lives in Northern Ireland during that period. One hundred and ten of these died in County Fermanagh. A list of those who died on their farms or who were involved directly in farm work, or were murdered after moving from their farms as a result of intimidation, is shown below. Both communities are represented in the list.

Tommy Fletcher, a part-time member of the UDR, Frevagh, Garrison, was shot by IRA terrorists on 1st March 1972 after being taken from his small farm (he was also a forestry worker).

William Herbert Trotter, Newtownbutler, killed on 28th August 1972 when he triggered an IRA booby-trap bomb on his farm when he was going to inspect grazing cattle. His dog was lying dead near his body.

Thomas Bullock, a part-time member of the UDR, and his wife Emily were shot dead on 21st September 1972 by the IRA at their farmhouse at Killynick, Aghalane.

Robin John Bell, 21 years of age, a part-time member of the UDR, was shot on 22nd October 1972. His father who was travelling with him to an out-farm was injured in the attack.

Michael Naan and Andrew Murray who died on 23 rd October 1972 were found with multiple stab wounds on the Naan farm at Aughnahinch, Newtownbutler, on the following day. Nine years later two soldiers from the Argyll and Sutherland Highlanders were sentenced to life imprisonment for their murder.

Patrick J. Duffy, 19 year old farm worker, was killed on 5th September 1973 when he drove his tractor over an IRA landmine left close to his home at Greaghnaglera near Belcoo. The 100 bomb was targeted at members of the security forces.

Matthew Lilley, milk lorry driver and part-time member of the UDR, was shot by the IRA on 7th September 1973 shortly after 9am when he called at a farm in Kellagho to collect milk.

Gordon Liddle, civilian, aged 28, was killed on 17th July 1976 on the farm lane leading to his residence at Drumgole, Lisnaskea. He was a postman and also helped on the family farm.

Richard Latimer, a part-time member of the UDR, aged 39 years, shot on 9th June 1980 by the IRA in his hardware store in Main Street, Newtownbutler. The Latimer family lived at Lisnaskea Road having been intimidated out of their farmhouse home near the Border after gun attacks.

Ernest Johnston, a member of the RUC Reserve, shot at Lisrace, near Magheraveely, on 23rd September 1980. He was previously injured in an IRA landmine explosion which killed two other RUC Officers. At the time of his death he had put his farm, situated very near the Border, up for sale because he feared for the safety of his family. A local councillor said that Ernest and his father were 'quiet, decent hard-working people who made a living out of their land. This is just another one of the tragedies around here and it is the government to blame ----'

Albert Beacom, aged 42, a part-time member of the UDR, was shot by the IRA in his farmyard at Boyhill, Maguiresbridge, on 17th November 1981 as he returned from leaving his two young sons to a Boys Brigade meeting in Brookeborough.

Ronald Funston, a former member of the UDR, 28 years of age, shot by the IRA on 13th March 1984 as he was preparing to feed cattle on the family farm at Lowry, Pettigo.

John W. McVitty, Cloncarn, Newtownbutler, a member of the RUC, was shot by the IRA on 8th July 1986 while working on a farm at Drumady, near Rosslea. His murder was witnessed by his 12 year old son.

William Burleigh, aged 51, was killed on April 6th 1988 when an IRA bomb exploded under his car as he left an auction of farm machinery at Tirraroe, Derrylin.

Retirement of Mr W. T. McClintock

No record of agricultural activity and related matters during the 1970s would be complete without reference to the retirement of Mr W. T. McClintock. He retired at the end of July 1977. The report in the press covering his retirement, headed: '*W.T. Became The Farmers' Best Friend in Fermanagh*' stated: *he had set a record during the past 42 years which has never been achieved before anywhere in the Province and is unlikely to be achieved in the future*'. The feature article covered his appointment as Organiser and Secretary to the Fermanagh County Committee of Agriculture in 1935. It then traced the challenges faced by the industry from the time of his appointment until his retirement. There were the issues of livestock improvement and the education of farmers in the value of fertilisers. His appointment as County Agricultural Executive Officer by the Ministry of Agriculture on the outbreak of the Second World War brought the challenge of compulsory tillage. The campaign to have grass silage made rather than hay lasted for a number of decades. He was instrumental in having the Marginal Land Scheme introduced in 1943 under which generous grants were available for fertilisers and the erection of farm buildings in County Fermanagh. Another milestone was his role in the designation of most of County Fermanagh as a Less Favoured Area which brought tremendous benefits to the county.

When Mr McClintock was in his 91st year he wrote an account of his life entitled *Memories of W. T. McClintock.* This history covered every aspect of his life but concentrated on his adoption of *God's Way of Salvation* and his experience of Christian life.

Mr W. T. McClintock.

New County and Deputy County Agricultural Executive Officers

Mr Samuel B. Morrow, BAgr, who had been the Deputy County Agricultural Executive Officer in Fermanagh from 1966, was appointed by the Department of Agriculture as Mr McClintock's successor. Mr Stanley Lytle, BAgr, a farmer's son from County Londonderry, who had been an Agricultural Adviser with the Department in County Tyrone was appointed as Deputy County Agricultural Executive Officer for Fermanagh at that time.

Death of Lord Brookeborough

The death of Northern Ireland's second Minister of Agriculture, and later Prime Minister, occurred at Colebrooke on 6th August 1973. Sir Basil was born in

1888 and was the eldest son of Sir Arthur Douglas Brooke, 4th Baronet, who farmed at Colebrooke and was the first Chairman of the Fermanagh County Committee of Agriculture on its formation in 1901. After his education in France and England Sir Basil served in the Royal Fusiliers from 1908 but transferred to the 10th Hussars in 1911. He was awarded the Military Cross and Croix de Guerre with Palms for his service during World War I. In 1920 he left the British Army to farm on his estate at Colebrooke. In 1921 he was appointed CBE and was elected to the Northern Ireland Senate but resigned the following year. In 1921 he was elected to the Northern Ireland Parliament to represent Lisnaskea. He served as President of the Ulster Farmers' Union during the year 1930/31.

Sir Basil succeeded Sir Edward Archdale as Northern Ireland Minister of Agriculture and was appointed a Privy Councillor in 1933. He served in that capacity until 1941 when he was appointed Minister of Commerce. He became Prime Minister of Northern Ireland in 1943 and served in that role until 1963.

During his time as Prime Minister of Northern Ireland Sir Basil was raised to the House of Lords as Viscount Brookeborough in 1952. He was appointed a Knight of the Garter in 1965 and served as Her Majesty's Lord Lieutenant for County Fermanagh from 1963 until 1969.

Two of Lord Brookeborough's sons, Lieutenants Basil Julian David and Henry Alan, were killed in action during World War II. His surviving son, Captain The Hon John W. Brooke, made a significant contribution to agricultural development in the post war period and served for a number of years as the Chairman of the Fermanagh County Committee of Agriculture. Later, as the Second Viscount Brookeborough, he contributed very significantly to the work of the House of Lords Agricultural Committee. Following the Second Viscount's death in 1987, his son Alan, the Third Viscount Brookeborough, subsequently served on the Agricultural Committee in the House of Lords.

References:

Issues of the Department of Agriculture's *Agriculture in Northern Ireland.*

Records of the Fermanagh County Agricultural Executive Office.

Files of *The Impartial Reporter* and *Fermanagh Herald* held in Enniskillen Library.

Barton, Brian, *Brookeborough – The making of a Prime Minister.* The Institute of Irish Studies, The Queen's University, Belfast (1988).

Chapter 35
The 1980s

This decade was one of challenge and opportunity. The weather provided some extremely difficult conditions for farming and also some very good seasons. The introduction of milk quotas placed a constraint on dairy herd expansion. The use and subsequent ban on growth implants in beef production impacted on the profitability of the enterprise. The potential for farm diversification was being explored. The importance of the farmers' role as custodians of the countryside was taking on a new significance. Superimposed on all of this was the importance of farmers running good businesses through cost controls and efficient production methods. During the decade, despite many handicaps, tremendous progress was made in terms of farm improvements and increased stocking rates for cattle and sheep. Profitability of farm enterprises also showed a significant advance.

'Challenge of the eighties'

The Department of Agriculture's Advisory Service set the scene at the beginning of the decade when it launched a province wide advisory programme entitled 'Challenge of the Eighties' in the autumn of 1980. The programme concentrated on 'good housekeeping to cut costs'. Mr T. A. Larmour, Chief Agricultural Officer of the Department, launched the programme at Greenmount College of Agriculture. He said that while farmers must cut costs by improving efficiency and making better use of resources to maintain and where possible increase incomes during this difficult period, it would be false economy to attempt savings on items like fertilisers and even feedingstuffs where such reductions would lower output.

Mr Larmour went on to say: "*This is proving to be a difficult year for farming. Many costs have been increasing and incomes have been under pressure. In such a situation farmers must examine costs carefully. Fixed costs have been increasing even more rapidly than direct production costs and, where possible, farmers should attempt to control their fixed costs and aim to spread them over as large an output as possible*". Mr Larmour concluded by saying that the advisory programme was aimed at helping farmers to face the challenges that would arise during the decade.

Mr Sam Morrow, County Agricultural Executive Officer, explained that the major problems facing Fermanagh farmers were increasing costs of production and the extremely poor weather conditions throughout the summer and autumn of 1980. The advisory programme planned for that year had taken these factors into consideration and the meetings, demonstrations, and other activities would focus attention on ways of increasing efficiency at farm level and also the importance of making silage.

Priorities

Throughout the decade the Agricultural Advisory Service concentrated on what was considered to be the four major priorities which would contribute most to farm business development in County Fermanagh. These were grassland improvement, fodder conservation, livestock improvement and the encouragement of agricultural education and training. The allied needs of inadequate forage accommodation, insufficient cattle housing, poor slurry facilities and field drainage were addressed during the ten year period. Despite progress made with silage making in Fermanagh 35 per cent of fodder was still conserved as hay in 1981. In August 1981 Mr Walter Keag, Senior Deputy Chief Agricultural Officer of the Department, when commenting on County Fermanagh's programme stated: "*In my own mind I feel strongly that there is nothing will contribute more to overall improvement of agriculture in Northern Ireland than a massive concentrated and long term programme on the improvement of grassland and silage and I am sure that it will take a number of years to make a significant impact in this field.*"

Farm business development made great strides during the decade. A number of schemes with relatively generous grant aid gave great encouragement to farmers to invest in their businesses. The Agriculture and Horticulture Development Scheme (AHDS), introduced on 1st October 1980, offered attractive rates of grant for silos, cattle housing and farm waste facilities. Under the Agricultural Development Programme (ADP) a tremendous volume of farm improvement work including field drainage, reclamation, grassland improvement and farm roads, was carried out. The development of the gravel tunnel drainage system and the existence of competent contractors in the county gave a new impetus to land drainage and land improvement.

Mr Ken Conn, Area Officer, discussing land improvement with Mervyn Dane, Shanco, Lisbellaw.

The Department's Advisory Service was deeply involved in promoting and advising on these schemes as an aid to farm business development. In addition to general promotional meetings, the County Agricultural Executive Officer and his Deputy addressed most branches of the Ulster Farmers' Union on an annual basis throughout the decade. Consultations were held with the farmers' organisations representatives in the county in order to find out the needs of the industry and then advisory programmes and activities were designed to meet those needs.

Cattle housing

Early in the decade alternative systems for housing cattle were featured at a conference for farmers held in Enniskillen Agricultural College. The conference held on 4th March 1980, attracted a large audience where Mr David Magill BAgr, Dip Ag Eng, the Department's farm buildings specialist, together with Mr Donagh O'Neill of the Grassland Experimental Centre, Castle Archdale, were the main speakers, along with local Agricultural Adviser, Mr Alan Warnock. An item of particular interest was a description of the topless cubicle facilities at Castle Archdale for over-wintering mating and in-calf heifers. Mr Magill detailed the costs of different types of new cattle housing as follows:

- **A self-feed unit consisting of a covered silo, ramp, lean-to cubicle house, covered yard and lagoon for 42 beef cattle - £530 per head.**
- **The same self-feed unit with a calf creep for 36 beef cows and calves - £685 per cow.**
- The same self-feed unit only with slatted tanks instead of the lagoon for 42 beef cows - £550 per head.
- An easy feed-unit with slatted house, concrete apron and open silo for 54 cattle - £416 per head.

Topless cubicles at Castle Archdale.

Large attendance of farmers at the livestock housing meeting.

Farm business development

Advisory activity in 1980/81 and in 1981/82 concentrated mainly on advising farmers on the development of their businesses, taking advantage of the incentives under the Farm and Horticulture Development Scheme (FHDS) and its replacement, the Agriculture and Horticulture Development Scheme (AHDS). Improving the efficiency and competitiveness of milk production and suckled calf production was a priority. Meetings and demonstrations were held. The financial results obtained by those farmers who kept farm management accounts in Fermanagh were used to show how feeding and management impacted on profitability of the enterprises. Profitability of the suckled calf enterprise was found to be largely determined by the sale price of the calf combined with low feeding costs. The most successful producers received over £200 for their calves with feed costs kept under £30 per cow. Similarly for dairying, of the 240 dairy farmers who kept

farm management accounts in the county, profitability was shown to be determined largely by the value of the output which was mainly milk yield. Irrespective of whether low cost feeding was employed, yields in excess of 4,000 litres were necessary for reasonable profitability. The highest gross margins in the county were obtained by those producers with over 4,500 litres of milk per cow and low meal usage of 0.76 to 1 tonne per cow.

Feeding the dairy cow

IIn November 1980 Dr Fred Gordon, of the Agricultural Research Institute, addressed a meeting of 200 dairy farmers at Enniskillen Agricultural College. He said that autumn calvers on medium quality silage required approximately 18 lb of meal per day for the first three months of their lactations after which time meal could be reduced to 12 lb per day. For spring calvers 16 lb should be used as a threshold only to be exceeded in exceptional circumstances. He emphasised the importance of a plentiful supply of leafy grass for grazing and recommended a three cut silage system with six to seven weeks between cuts. He stated that neither the fineness of chop nor dry matter affected the feeding value of silage.

Top AI bulls

In December 1980 a large attendance of farmers met in Enniskillen College when they were up-dated on the Artificial Insemination (A.I.) Service. Mr Bob Cooper, Veterinary Officer in charge of the Northern Ireland AI Service, explained the benefits of AI in controlling and eliminating venereal disease and in livestock improvement. He stated that a bull could provide 15,000 services through AI in a year compared to 70 by natural service. Mr John Wilson, Deputy Chief Livestock Officer, stated that: *"Now, more than ever before it is vital to invest in good breeding to counter higher production costs and maintain profit margins."* He then dealt with merits of the bulls on offer. Among those mentioned was *"Winton Equator 5th"* which was raising yields by 415 kg (91 gallons) and yields of fats and proteins by 19 kg; *"Normead Wondale"* was breeding good all-round dual purpose Friesians and raising butter fat by 10 per cent; *"CBS King Henry"* was being introduced into the 'Premium Bull of the Day' category and was particularly good for raising butterfat percentage.

Profitable milk production

A major demonstration was held at Enniskillen Agricultural College in February 1981 when over 250 milk producers attended. Mr Rayner McKinley, Agricultural Adviser, quoted from the results being achieved by 200 milk producers in County Fermanagh who were keeping detailed farm accounts. He showed that there was a large variation in gross margins being obtained. Yield per cow and the amount of meal fed had the biggest influence on profit margins. He emphasised that while high milk yields were important they should not be achieved by using excessive amounts of meal or feeding at the wrong stage of lactation. The main topics discussed during the demonstration were: breeding to improve milk yield; production and utilisation of grass and silage; feeding and management of the dairy cow; rearing herd replacements and hygienic milk production.

Alan Warnock, Agricultural Adviser, discussing grazing management of the dairy herd with Maurice Owens, Sessiagh, Arney.

Poor weather

The year 1981 was remembered as a most difficult year for Fermanagh farmers. Generally, the county could expect a six or six and a half month in-wintering and feeding programme but that winter programme extended to as much as eight months on many farms. This inevitably led to higher costs, lower levels of animal performance and more work for farmers. The month of June was so wet grazing stock caused severe damage to pastures through poaching. The poor summer weather, particularly in June, made for difficulties in fodder conservation. The weather improved in August which enabled good yields of second cut silage to be harvested under suitable conditions. This period of good weather enabled many farmers in the late hill areas to harvest their hay crops. The good weather was not to last and heavy and persistent rain resulted in rapid deterioration in ground conditions which led to poor utilisation of autumn grass and to the early housing of cattle. Livestock prices had shown an improvement over the previous year. At the end of 1981 fat cattle averaged £99.17 per 100 kg compared to £83.15 for the corresponding week in 1980. Fat pigs were 99.6p per kg compared to 83p in the previous year. Inflation, unlike the 1970s, had been brought down to a comparatively reasonable level at around 4 per cent.

Growth implants

The economic benefits in using growth promoters in beef cattle were brought to the attention of cattle finishers from the early years of the decade. An EU ban on their use was imposed in 1988 but the UK government banned their use from December 1986. Dr Raymond Steen of the Agricultural Research Institute, Hillsborough, whose research speciality was in beef production, was the guest speaker at a number of meetings in the county when the use of implants was the subject for discussion. Dr Steen emphasised that economic winter beef production depended on the feeding of high quality silage which brought about a considerable saving in the amount of meal that had to be fed. With regard to the use of implants a good response could only be obtained if cattle were well fed. Best responses were obtained with finishing steers. The licensed growth promoters (trade names) for use in beef cattle in Northern Ireland in 1984 were Ralgro, Finaplix, Compudose 365, Implixa BM, Implixa BF, Romensin, Flavomycin and Avotan. The first five named products were implants which were injected under the skin at the base of the ear while the other three products were feed additives. The hormone implants were not permitted to be used later than three months before slaughter. The response from the feed additives was only half that obtainable from the implants. Dr Steen stated that providing cattle were well fed and managed the use of implants could result in an increase of about 15 kg in carcase weight with an expected increased profitability of £25 to £30 per animal.

Suckler herd demonstration

Enniskillen Agricultural College beef unit was the centre for well attended sucked calf production demonstrations in February 1982. The 50 Aberdeen Angus cross Friesian suckler cows were divided into two herds – 30 autumn calving and 20 spring calving. The calves born in the autumn were weaned in June or July at 350 kg while the spring herd, calving in January/March, were weaned in September/October at 275 kg. The Gross Margin per cow (including Suckler Cow Premium and Hill Livestock Compensatory Allowance payments) was £189 for the autumn born calvers and £149 for the spring calvers.

Form filling

Increasing responsibility was being placed on the farming community under EC rules in relation to the accuracy of form filling. Failure to present the correct information on some very complex application forms could lead to serious penalties being imposed or indeed the total loss of payments under the various schemes. An important feature of the Department's advisory activity during November 1981 was the holding of courses to train those interested in providing a form filling service for the farming community. There was a very good response to the two courses that were held with a total attendance of 56.

BSE

The recognition of 'Mad Cow Disease', or Bovine Spongiform Encephalopathy (BSE), in England in 1986 and its appearance in Northern Ireland would, in time, have serious consequences for the agricultural industry in the United Kingdom. Up to this time the disease was regarded as a condition which only affected cattle. As will be seen in the next chapter this disease had a very serious impact on the agricultural economy throughout the United Kingdom and particularly in Fermanagh during the second half of the 1990s.

The difficult years

Weather was also a significant factor in the fortunes of farmers later in the decade as well as in 1981. The years 1985 and 1986 had poor summers resulting in shortages of fodder and difficult grazing conditions. The summer of 1985 was worse than that of 1981 for fodder conservation. At the end of the growing season it was estimated that only 65-70 per cent of fodder needs had been saved. In September the County Agricultural Executive Officer stated that only five per cent of hay had been saved. The Department's County Agricultural Advisory Service responded by holding 44 fodder clinics where farmers were advised on the best way to cope with the shortages in each individual's circumstances. These were well attended with over 800 farmers receiving advice on how to deal with the fodder shortage in the most cost effective manner. The relative economic value of various bought-in alternatives to hay and silage was one aspect which received particular consideration. At the same time farmers were being encouraged to make more and better silage in future years. Mr Harold Hamilton from Kesh, who was president of the Ulster Farmers' Union at the time, stated that farm incomes fell by 50 per cent in 1985 and it was anticipated that 1986 would not be any better.

Less sunshine

The year 1986 was another very poor season with high rainfall (543mm compared to 559mm for the preceding year). The month of May was especially wet with 190 per cent of normal rainfall for the month. June and July had 25 and 22 rain days respectively. In addition to the rain, there was a very dull and cool summer with 24 per cent less sunshine than normal. The wet, dull and cold weather had an adverse effect on grass growth, efficiency of grass utilisation and animal performance. Both milk

production and beef cattle were affected. Milk production in Fermanagh in May was down by 13.1 per cent compared to 1985 which was also a bad year. At Castle Archdale suckled calves and store cattle had shown 10 per cent and 15 per cent less weight gain respectively. First cut silage was on average delayed by three weeks. The situation was redeemed to some extent in September and early October when rainfall was very low (12 per cent of 30 year average). This enabled silage and hay to be gathered in reasonable quantities. However, it was considered that fodder quality was poor with a 20 per cent deficiency in nutrients. The situation facing farmers was again addressed by the Advisory Service by holding 38 fodder clinics in the more disadvantaged areas of the county.

The good years

The spring and summer of 1982 were excellent for Fermanagh. At the end of July the weather was likened to that of the Costa Brava. Mr Sam Morrow, County Agricultural Executive Officer, was quoted in the *Fermanagh Herald* of 31st July as stating: "*From April onwards the weather conditions had been so much above average that silage making, hay making, livestock performance and farm improvement work had all prospered. Second cuts of silage had already been made; yields were good and the quality excellent. As for hay, the recent spell of exceptional weather had meant that over 90 per cent of the crop had been saved and because of the good underfoot conditions hay balers could be used on most of the land.*" The good weather also helped animal production. He stated: "*Milk production in June was up by 11 per cent in the county compared to the previous year and that this was, no doubt, largely due to the good weather.*" The excellent weather coupled with the introduction of a new scheme at the beginning of 1982, the Agricultural Development Programme (ADP), encouraged farmers to get on with farm improvement work. By the end of June 1982 the County Agricultural Executive Office had received a normal year's intake of applications. The County Agricultural Executive Officer was asked by the *Fermanagh Herald,* in an interview in 1982, to comment on the large intake of scheme applications. He said: "*This is an indication that farmers want to get on with their work and all the evidence is that they are getting on with it because the contractors – whether involved in reclamation work, farm roads, drainage etc – are being pushed to the limit and not only them but also the suppliers of the raw materials like the quarry owners. This all helps the whole economy of the county.*"

The years 1984 and 1987 were very good in so far as weather was concerned and this favoured farming in Fermanagh. After one of the wettest winters for many years April sunshine in 1989 brought relief to farmers and the following summer months were extremely dry. Ground conditions were so dry that by July rain would have been welcomed by farmers.

Milk Marketing Board initiative

Following a presentation by the County Agricultural Executive Officer to the members of the Milk Marketing Board at its headquarters in Belfast on what had been achieved on the milk producing farm of Mr George Moore, Tiraroe, Derrylin, the Board decided to have a campaign on milk production in County Fermanagh. In October 1982, the County Agricultural Advisory Service in partnership with their Milk Division colleagues and Milk Marketing Board staff mounted a series of meetings at the processing plants of Fermanagh Creameries Ltd at Lisnaskea and at West Ulster Farmers Ltd in Irvinestown. These meetings and demonstrations on milk production on farms and processing at the creameries were aimed at encouraging producers in the west to increase the quantity and quality of milk produced. At that time 29 per cent of the milk produced in Fermanagh was processed into butter with 66 per cent going into cheese manufacture. In 1970/71 there were 2,560 producers in Fermanagh and by 1981/82 this number had dropped to 1,676 although cow numbers remained roughly similar at around 26,000.

Fermanagh Creameries factory at Lisnaskea.

Milk quotas

Milk quotas were introduced on 31st March 1984 and Northern Ireland producers were allocated nine per cent below 1983 production levels (1,322 million litres). Representations regarding Northern Ireland's special circumstances resulted in the European Community (EC) awarding an additional 65,000 tonnes to the Province, which despite a lot of debate as to whether the full amount was ever received, meant that individual milk producers gained a small amount in their quota allocation. The imposition of quotas created a considerable challenge to milk producers and the Agricultural Advisory Service took a leading role in informing producers about the new arrangements. Two public meetings on the subject were held, 200 producers took advantage of office consultation facilities and 225 specific farm visits relating to quotas were made. The challenge for producers and advisers was the maintenance of farm income when production levels were reduced. The options were to keep fewer cows, feed less

Sheep housing eased winter management.

Mr Patrick McGurn BAgr, Agricultural Adviser, discussing cattle housing and farm waste management with Mr Gabriel Shannon, Drumdoney, Derrylin.

Mrs Diane Stevenson, Agricultural Adviser, discussing land improvement with Mr Malachy Corrigan, Rossavalley, Bellanaleck.

concentrates and generally lower production costs. The EC imposed further regional cuts and by 1993/94 the quota was 1,283 million litres. The possibility of buying or leasing quotas was also an aspect for consideration as quota was available for purchase from England. This aspect of advice would be a continuing feature throughout the remainder of the century and into the next decade. By 2003/04 the Northern Ireland milk quota, mainly through purchase, was over 1,760 million litres which was a 37 per cent increase on the 1993/94 figure.

Tremendous progress

The shortcomings resulting from the poor summers during the 1980s were to some extent offset by other developments which enabled tremendous progress to be made in agriculture in County Fermanagh. The productivity of grassland increased significantly through an intensive programme of land drainage, reseeding and pasture improvement. Substantial strides were made in the construction of grass silos, livestock housing and in improving animal performance through advances in breeding and better husbandry. During 1985/86 fifty-three new silos were erected together with 177 new cattle buildings. One hundred and sixty-eight slurry tanks were constructed. The development of big bale silage and associated wrapping put an end to dependence on hay for many small farmers. Sheep numbers increased rapidly during the decade in Fermanagh showing an increase of 50 per cent between 1983 and 1985. During the decade there was over a six-fold increase in total sheep numbers in the county. The use of sheep housing during winter helped this expansion to take place.

Specialist Advisers

Changes in the Department's Advisory Service were announced in October 1986 when greater specialisation took place. From the beginning of the twentieth century Agricultural Advisers had responsibility for giving advice on all agricultural enterprises to be found on the farm, apart from horticulture and poultry. In announcing the changes Lord Lyell, Minister with responsibility for Agriculture in Northern Ireland, stated: "*Times change and the service we provide must change to meet new needs. Farming has long since ceased to be a way of life. It is now a business requiring business decisions and business acumen. It involves a great degree of hard work and more than ordinary business risks. The right choice of enterprise, wise capital investment, good husbandry, an adequate return on capital and a carefully planned cash flow are all vital components in today's farm business. A more specialised service has been developed in direct response to the changes which have taken place in farming in recent years. To meet the needs of the industry and in particular the increasing importance of farm business management we have decided that our main*

emphasis should be on advisers with a specialism in a particular kind of enterprise. These specialist staff have been well trained in their respective fields, for example, dairying, beef and sheep production, crop husbandry, pigs, poultry and horticulture."

Advisers based at Crown Buildings

Farming activity in County Fermanagh was mainly centred on grass based enterprises. In announcing the impact of the new arrangements, Sam Morrow, the County Agricultural Executive Officer stated that the Advisory Service would continue to be based in Crown Buildings, Enniskillen. The service would be led by Mr Alex Cromie BAgr, Senior Agricultural Adviser, who had previously been an Agricultural Adviser in County Armagh and had been transferred to Fermanagh on promotion. There would be three dairying advisers, Messrs Alan Warnock BAgr, Connor Maguire BAgr and Eric Strahan BSc and each would have a specific area in the county. Mr Frank Tisdall MA BAgrSc and Mrs Diane Stevenson BSc BAgr would have responsibility for beef and sheep production advice. The pig enterprise in County Fermanagh at this time was quite small and Mr Colin Rea BAgr Dip Agr Comm, who had responsibility for specialised pig advice in County Tyrone, would also serve Fermanagh. Commercial aspects of advice on poultry and horticulture, both small enterprises in the county, would be obtained through the County Agricultural Executive Office from the Specialist Divisions of the Department. Mr Stanley Lytle BAgr, Deputy County Agricultural Executive Officer, from the date of the introduction of the new Advisory Service took responsibility for managing the greatly increased volume of work associated with the introduction of new schemes which were popular with the farming community.

Inishkeen House

The Department of Agriculture's service to the farming community was considerably enhanced in August 1989 when Inishkeen House, situated in the Killyhevlin Industrial Estate in Enniskillen, was opened. This new purpose-built building was designed specifically to meet farmers' needs and accommodate all the field and office staff of the County Agricultural Executive Office, the Divisional Veterinary Office, Forest Service and other Departmental Divisions that interfaced with the farming community. The new building had excellent reception areas and adequate car parking space which were greatly welcomed by the farming community.

Diversification and the environment

The 1987 advisory programme for farmers incorporated the possibilities for diversification on farms in order to maintain the viability of rural communities. This approach was in response to the spectre of agricultural surpluses in most agricultural commodities. In the meantime, Mr Colin Rea, responsible for advice on pigs in the county, was encouraging producers to use feed recording systems to reduce the amount of feed required per pig produced.

Environmental improvement and the farmers' role as managers of the countryside were increasingly being appreciated at this time. This aspect was specifically addressed in the 1987/88 advisory programme featuring tree planting and pollution prevention.

New challenge for Advisory Service

A decision was taken in Great Britain and in the Irish Republic in 1987 to charge farmers for the advisory service, which had been free in the past. The Department of Agriculture in Northern Ireland followed suit in 1988. The advisory services provided for the farming community were to be charged for from 10th October 1988. In announcing the introduction of charging for services Lord Lyell, Minister responsible for Agriculture in Northern Ireland, said: *"To meet customer needs the Department's Advisory Services has put together a comprehensive range of services. These will be available in three different categories."* He then went on to give details of the different categories. These were an enterprise information service, off-the-shelf packages to meet specific needs of farmers, and customised packages to cover any particular requirements. Lord Lyell estimated that income to the Department for the first financial year of the charged services in Northern Ireland would be £250,000.

Inishkeen House.

In County Fermanagh the Advisory Service had extensive consultations with the farming community, including the Ulster Farmers' Union, The Northern Ireland Agricultural Producers' Association and the Young Farmers' Clubs, in advance of the introduction of charging for services. A survey carried out by a firm of private consultants for the Department of Agriculture, before the introduction of charging for services, indicated that Fermanagh farmers would not be prepared to pay for services to any appreciable extent. This proved to be far from reality. Fermanagh farmers, who over the years had been used to a good service, responded positively and the income for the Advisory Service in Fermanagh was considerably in excess of its fair share of the Northern Ireland income.

This new development changed the approach to advisory work in that it was much more targeted and aimed at individual farmers rather than farmers in general. However, in Fermanagh the Advisory Service still maintained a range of public meetings which kept the industry well informed on general developments.

An excellent concrete farm road.

Financial support

Throughout the 1980s Fermanagh farmers, despite the many challenges in relation to weather problems, took full advantage of the financial incentives given under the various schemes that were available. The helpful technical inspection staff and a user-friendly administrative system ensured that farmers were able to make the most of the opportunities that existed to improve their farm businesses.

Farmers took good advantage of the grants available for improvement work under the Agricultural Development Programme and the Farm and Horticulture Development Scheme in the early years of the decade. The grants and other support measures earned by Fermanagh farmers were substantial with funding peaking at £20.46 million in 1984 with the years 1982 and 1983 earning £19.49 and £17.32 million respectively.

Increased productivity

The improved economic climate and advisory activity, combined with the financial incentives under the various schemes, had a significant impact on farm productivity in County Fermanagh. The trend in terms of cattle and sheep output is indicated in the following table. Cattle and sheep numbers have been converted to livestock units for purposes of illustration.

Table 35.1 Agricultural Production 1982 – 1990

Year	Livestock Units (1000s)	Index
1982	109.5	100
1983	113.9	104
1984	118.4	108
1985	123.0	112
1986	121.0	110
1987	117.2	107
1988	120.3	109
1989	131.8	120
1990	137.0	126

Whilst the above figures represent quite an impressive improvement based on standard livestock unit conversions, they do not convey the advances made in livestock productivity. During this period milk yields increased substantially. Improvements in breeding, feeding and management of the suckler herd and in the breeding ewe flock resulted in much heavier animals of better conformation. Taken together it would not be unreasonable to claim an additional ten per cent, over and above the standard livestock unit conversion, to show the additional animal productivity.

Change in profitability over the decade

Some indication of the changes in profitability of farming can be gained from examining the results from the Farm Management Standards published each year by the Department of Agriculture. Farm accounts are kept by a substantial number of farmers in each county under the supervision of the Department's Economics and Statistics staff. At the end of each year the results are published mainly for the benefit of other farmers who could compare

Mr and Mrs Maurice Hurst hosted a visit by Mr Douglas Hurd, Secretary of State for Norhern Ireland, to their farm in 1985. Mrs Edith Hurst, Maurice's mother, and Jonathan, Maurice and Marlene's son, complete the picture.

Contentment. Mr John James Robinson relaxing in his comfortable farmhouse kitchen at Tower Beg, Garrison.

their own financial and physical performance measures for each enterprise on their farm with the published standards. Standards for most enterprises are quoted for four levels of achievement: 'Excellent', 'Good', 'Moderate' and 'Poor'. Generally 70 to 80 per cent of results fell into the 'Good' or 'Moderate' standards. For the purposes of comparison the 'Moderate' standard has been used, for grass based enterprises, which most likely corresponds to the bulk of Fermanagh farmers due to difficult land conditions. The main enterprises on Fermanagh farms during the decade were: suckled calf production, cattle fattening, milk production, and pigs. For pigs, which are not land based and do not have to cope with the handicaps of the land based enterprises, the 'Good' standard has been used.

Table 35.2 Economics of Farming in the 1980s

Enterprise	Gross Margins		
	1970/1971	1980/1981	% increase
Suckled calf production (LFA) per cow	£44	£100	218
Fattening cattle (per acre)	£20	£57	185
Sheep (per ewe)	£6	£29	383
Milk production (per cow)	£80	£215	169
Pig rearing and fattening (per fat pig)	£5.50	£7.50	36

Fixed costs during the decade (on mixed farms) increased from £10.8 per acre to £13.76 per acre or a 27 per cent increase.

References:

Reports and other records of the County Agricultural Development Office.

Department of Agriculture's *Agriculture in Northern Ireland.*

Files of *The Impartial Reporter* and *Fermanagh Herald* held in Enniskillen Library.

Chapter 36
The 1990s

In a number of respects this decade had similarities to those that had gone before especially in relation to weather patterns. However, the agricultural industry faced a crisis from the middle of the decade of monumental proportions in relation to BSE. The economic implications flowing from this had a most serious impact not only in Fermanagh but in farming throughout the United Kingdom. Further reform of the Common Agricultural Policy had an influence on practically every aspect of farming. Changes in the arrangements for the administration of agricultural affairs were introduced by the Department of Agriculture for Northern Ireland (DANI) which transformed a system which had remained basically unchanged for most of the twentieth century.

CAP Reform

The 1992 Cap Reform Agreement had as its central feature a radical change in the basis of support for the Community arable sector. Reduced cereal prices and compulsory set aside were the significant changes. Cereal prices, over a three year period, were to be brought closer to world prices with compensation to farmers to offset the reduction in returns. Beef prices and butter prices were to be cut by 15 per cent and five per cent respectively. The reduction in cereal prices had the potential to benefit Fermanagh farmers through lower input costs in terms of bought-in feeding stuffs. For beef producers there was a significant shift from intervention end price support to direct premia payments. Furthermore, measures were introduced to give higher levels of returns to beef producers finishing cattle over the winter period. In relation to sheep production quotas for ewe premia were introduced from January 1992 in an effort to restrict further growth in the flock.

Challenge of the new arrangements

Issues arising from CAP Reform posed a serious challenge for farmers and also for those tasked with its administration. From the beginning of 1993 there was a tremendous increase in applications under the various schemes especially those associated with the Beef Special Premium Scheme (BSP). In January large numbers of farmers arrived at the Department's County Office in Inishkeen House seeking information and assistance in connection with the beef schemes. There followed a very substantial number of applications which had to be dealt with within a short period of time. Office staff in Inishkeen House abandoned most other duties to deal with the large volume of BSP applications.

Mr Leslie Long of the Department of Agriculture and Rural Development's office staff at Inishkeen House explaining details of a new scheme to Mr Sean McAleer, Eshnadara, Rosslea.

Financial support for farmers

The financial support flowing from the CAP Reform schemes was substantial. Payments under the Livestock Schemes and Capital Grants not only helped to maintain farm incomes and sustain rural communities but also contributed significantly in increasing competitiveness of farm businesses, improving the countryside and making farms safer as workplaces.

Table 36.1 Payments made to County Fermanagh farmers during the year 1994/95

Scheme	Amount of payment (£ millions)
Hill Livestock Compensatory Allowances	2.720
Suckler Cow Premium Scheme	6.830
Beef Special Premium Scheme	2.620
Deseasonalisation Premium Scheme	0.160
Sheep Annual Premium Scheme	1.220
Farm and Conservation Grant Scheme	0.570
Agricultural Development Operational Programme	4.170
Agricultural Development Programme (ADP88)	0.200
Agriculture and Horticulture Development Scheme	0.120
Other Capital Grant Schemes	0.790
Total	19.400

A modern above ground slurry tank.

A very successful farm diversification enterprise.

Mr Sean Nugent (centre), DARD Rural Development Division, in discussion with from left: Messrs Michael Kiernan, Killycramp; Ivan Moran, Drumkillen; James McBarron, Manager, South West Fermanagh Development Organisation, Teemore, and Leslie Campbell, DARD.

Payments under the livestock schemes amounted to 70 per cent of the total. The investment made by County Fermanagh farmers, which attracted capital grant payments during 1994/95, amounted to almost £12,000,000. The purposes of those capital grants are summarised as follows.

Farm and Conservation Grant Scheme (FCGS)

This scheme helped farmers to maintain efficient farming systems and assisted in meeting the cost of combating pollution and conserving the countryside and its wildlife. The scheme focussed on works which stimulated new investment, cut costs of updating existing resources and helped to achieve good countryside management. Waste handling facilities were a special priority. The rates of grant under this scheme varied from 20 – 25 per cent.

Agricultural Development Operational Programme (ADOP)

The aim of this scheme was to improve efficiency and competitiveness of farm businesses, enhance the environment and improve produce quality and encourage diversification where feasible. Grant rates were 35 per cent in the Disadvantaged Areas (LFA) and 25 per cent elsewhere. However, the rate of grant for environmental improvement was 50 per cent.

Agricultural Development Programme (ADP88)

This Scheme was the predecessor of the Agricultural Development Operational Programme. It closed for applications in January 1991 but grant for work carried out under the scheme was being claimed during 1994/95.

Other schemes which had terminated in previous years and where payments were made for work completed or claimed in 1994/95 were: Agriculture and Horticulture Development Scheme, Agriculture Improvement Regulations (Plans), Farm Diversification Grant and Innovation/Diversification Schemes.

This pattern of financial support continued to the end of the century as summarised in the following table.

Table 36.2 Financial support to Fermanagh farmers (£millions) 1995 – 1998

Year	1995/96	1996/97	1997/98
Livestock	15.370	25.380	17.331
Other	2.074	2.816	4.321
Total	17.444	28.916	21.652

Teemore Quality Assured Suckled Calf Scheme

This scheme involved 77 farmers with over 1,000 suckler cows and was aimed at the production and marketing of quality assured calves. It was a community based rural development project funded by the International Fund for Ireland, EC Intereg and the Agricultural Development Operational Programme. The Agricultural Development Service provided advice on building design on each farm for the cattle houses which were an integral part of the project. In addition, advisers were involved in the education and training programme which was a part of the initiative for producing quality suckled calves. A comprehensive monitoring package to record the physical and financial performance of each herd was provided.

Farmers attending a lecture at Teemore.

BSE – a serious crisis

Most decades in agriculture experience at least one crisis of lesser or greater magnitude. The arrival of Bovine Spongiform Encephalopathy (BSE), or 'Mad Cow Disease', in Northern Ireland dwarfed most crises in other decades. BSE was first noticed in the United Kingdom in 1986. In Northern Ireland from 1988 until November 2000 there were 1,800 cases of BSE recorded with consequent slaughterings amounting to 2,300 animals. It was claimed in 1996 that humans who consumed BSE infected meat were at risk of developing new variant Creutzfeldt-Jakob Disease (CJD). Because of the relatively high levels of BSE cases in the United Kingdom, the European Union imposed a world-wide ban in March 1996 on the export of bovines and bovine products from the United Kingdom. The ban remained in place until March 2006. This crisis led to lost beef exports and damage to consumer confidence not only in beef but also in other meats. Tight controls on feeding stuffs and other measures were introduced. The cause of the disease was an infectious form of a type of protein, called prions. It was considered that the most likely source of this agent was from meal fed to cattle which contained some meat and bone meal that was infective. Meat and bone meal, derived from the brains and spinal cords of animals that had not been rendered at a sufficiently high temperature, was regarded as the most likely source of the prions. From July 1988 there was a ban on bovine material being fed to cattle entering the food chain. The implications associated with this disease for Fermanagh farmers, like everywhere else, led to a drastic reduction in the price received for stock and consequently in income.

Income crisis for farmers

Following the McSharry reforms of the Common Agricultural Policy in 1993 the weakness in Sterling, for a time, masked the reductions in support prices envisaged under the reform. The impact of BSE from 1996 with the ban on livestock exports, together with the problems arising from the strength of Sterling, had a serious effect on cattle prices which reached extremely low levels in 1998. Beef prices in Northern Ireland in 1998 were the lowest in Europe. Beef prices in the Province fell from an average of 226.8p per kg in 1994 to 143.4p in 1998 – a fall of 37 per cent in four years.

In Fermanagh the problems were compounded by an abnormally wet season in 1996 resulting in poor grass growth with associated depressed performance of grazing livestock. Furthermore, the amount of fodder saved was well below requirements. Fermanagh was particularly badly hit because of its dependence on suckled calf and beef production. Eighty per cent of Fermanagh farmers had these as their main enterprises compared to 68 per cent for Northern Ireland as a whole. The prices received for suckled calves at Enniskillen Mart during the period 1995 to 1998 gives an indication of the severity of the crisis. In 1995 the average price in October was £436. In the following two years prices were down by the order of £100 per head averaging £335 per suckled calf. The big drop came in 1998 when the average price per suckled calf in October was only £198.

Very difficult silage making conditions.

The severity of the weather in 1998 and its impact on production in Fermanagh can be gleaned from the following facts. During the months of April to September rainfall was 31 per cent above the long-term average for the county. Rainfall in the critical months of June and July was 63 per cent and 115 per cent higher respectively than the long-term average. Lack of sunshine was also a major factor. There was 66 per cent less sunshine in July and 97 per cent less in September compared to the 30-year average. Fodder conservation was difficult. Because of the wet June many farmers postponed taking the first cut of silage to July only to find that July was even wetter. In some cases cutting was postponed until August resulting in low feeding-value silage. Poor seasons were nothing new for Fermanagh farmers but when this was combined with a collapse in prices for a main item of produce a difficult time lay ahead.

Poor prices were not confined to beef cattle as milk and pigs were also affected. In the late 1990s pigs suffered a collapse in prices falling from a peak of 149p per kg in 1996 to 48p per kg in 1998.

Trend in profitability from 1995/96 until 1999/00

An indication of the impact of BSE and other factors on the profitability of the main Fermanagh farm enterprises can be established from the following data relating to the Gross Margins for the various enterprises as published by the Department of Agriculture and Rural Development (DARD) in the annual Farm Management Standards. The published standards relate to Northern Ireland as a whole. The profitability of the grass using enterprises in Fermanagh would have been somewhat poorer than the Northern Ireland figures during these years, due to the adverse weather and difficult farming conditions, particularly in 1998/99.

Gross Margins represent the difference between the value of outputs and the direct costs of production related to a particular enterprise. The income figures include the payments made to farmers under the livestock support schemes detailed in the earlier paragraphs headed 'Financial Support for Farmers'. The other costs associated with farming activity are the Indirect or Fixed Costs such as machinery depreciation and running costs like insurance, electricity, building repairs and farm fuel. These costs rose marginally over the period 1995/96 until the end of the century. In the Farm Management Standards published in January 1996 Fixed Costs on Less Favoured Area farms amounted to £185 per hectare and these had risen to £194 by the year 2000. This meant that farm running costs over the period were maintained but the income generated by the farm enterprises was drastically reduced.

Boost for small milk producers

A welcome introduction for some dairy farmers in 1996 was a Small Milk Producers' Scheme. It was developed by Fermanagh Local Action Group (FLAG) in association with the Department of Agriculture and Rural Development (DARD). Its aim was to enable participants to increase their competitiveness in terms of milk quality and reduce production costs. FLAG was a partnership of private business people, voluntary groups, and local government bodies formed to administer the EU Leader II funding. The Small Milk Producers' Scheme during its four years' existence had 53 participating farmers with milk quotas of between 40,000 and 100,000 litres of milk. Participants had been given technical and financial assistance of up to £2,500 with a further £1,500 paid when all objectives of the scheme had been achieved. During the scheme participants entered into educational and training programmes organised jointly by DARD's Rural Enterprise Division and the locally based Greenmount College Development Advisers. Milk quality had been improved through upgrading of equipment such as the installation

Average Gross Margins

Table 36.3 Average Gross Margins 1995/96 – 1999/00

	1995/96	1996/97	1997/98	1998/99	1999/00
Suckler cows (per cow)	**£329**	**£375**	**£345**	**£240**	**£219**
Sheep (per ewe)	**£53**	**£67**	**£52**	**£46**	**£38**
Dairy cows (per cow)	**£986**	**£855**	**£758**	**£677**	**£633**
Pigs – birth to bacon (per pig)	**£27**	**£30**	**£17**	**£-3**	**£7**

Source: Economics and Statistics Division, Department of Agriculture and Rural Development.

of hot water boilers for washing and sterilising milking equipment. Regular testing and upgrading of milking equipment was a feature of the scheme. The development of practices to keep cows and equipment clean together with the individual testing of cows to identify those with high cell counts all helped to improve milk quality.

Planning for a better future in beef production

It would be depressing to leave the twentieth century without some positive indicators about a reasonable future for agricultural production in County Fermanagh. This was provided through a major event held at Enniskillen College of Agriculture in September 2000. *'Suckler 2000'* was an event staged with the aim of giving Northern Ireland's important suckler cow beef sector a timely tactical boost by lifting the quality of breeding stock in readiness for a stronger, export led, market for finished cattle. Enniskillen was chosen as the centre for this event as almost half of Northern Ireland's suckler cows were to be found in counties Fermanagh and Tyrone and because of the excellence of the suckler herd enterprise at the College. A ban on beef exports had been imposed in March 1996 but there were now prospects that the ban could be lifted if Northern Ireland's claim to be a low incidence BSE area was successful. In the year 1999 there had been only six BSE cases in Northern Ireland. While the export ban was in place 80 per cent of the Province's production was exported to GB. Whereas, prior to the ban in 1995, 50 per cent of Northern Ireland's beef had been exported outside GB.

In readiness for export opportunities opening up again *'Suckler 2000'* was aimed at getting breeders from across the Province to make a united effort to improve both cow and calf quality. Concern had been expressed at the genetic decline in the suckler herd arising from the use of bigger, more extreme dairy type and less durable Holsteins combined with less use of AI and a drift into the use of inferior crossbred bulls of dubious quality. The staging of *'Suckler 2000'* in an effort to introduce better beef genetics involved a collaborative approach involving the Department of Agriculture and Rural Development (DARD), AI Services, the breed societies and the Livestock and Meat Commission (LMC).

The exhibition and demonstration featured all aspects of the breeding, feeding and management of the suckler herd including: winter management, breeding which highlighted bull and cow selection, rearing replacements, grazing management, weaning and weanling management and bench marking targets. Eight Breed Societies mounted demonstrations of a range of commercial beef cross cattle to highlight the merits of each breed in producing quality beef.

Quality beef cattle at grass.

Organising committee for Suckler 2000. Back row from left: Dr Lewis McClinton (DARD), Dr Sam Campbell (AI Services), Mr Cormac McKervey (DARD), Mr John Herron (DARD), Mr Neville Forsythe (Armagh, Aberdeen Angus Breed Society), Mr Harry Marquess (Antrim, Charolais Breed Society).
Front row from left: Mr Stanley Lytle (DARD), Dr Noel Lavery (LMC), Mr Alex Cromie (Enniskillen College of Agriculture), Mr Jack McGowan (Armagh, Limousin Breed Society).

Quality beef cattle on the farm of Mr Andrew Wilson, Lisnaskea.

End of county based administration

During the decade two major reviews were carried out regarding the Department of Agriculture and Rural Development's (DARD'S) arrangements for providing advisory services and scheme administration for the farming community. In 1991 a new emphasis was placed not only on the development of the agricultural industry, but also on the environment and on the rural community. The Agricultural Development Service, previously called the Agricultural Advisory Service, had now three main responsibilities:

- To assist farmers and growers to maximise their contribution to the rural economy through the operation of successful businesses
- Promoting the adoption of positive measures for the enhancement of the countryside and
- Sustaining the viability of rural communities and improving the quality of life for all those who reside in rural areas.

The County Agricultural Executive Office and Officer, titles in existence from 1939, became the County Agriculture Development Office and Officer respectively. The Deputy County Agriculture Development Adviser with responsibility for the development work undertaken by the Development Advisers was Mr Stanley Lytle. The Senior Agricultural Development Officer, Mr Graeme Melville, who had been transferred from a similar post in County Tyrone, had responsibility for scheme work development in the county. Mr Melville replaced Mr Alex Cromie who had been transferred to a senior position in Enniskillen Agricultural College.

A further review of the organisation of DARD's Agriculture Service was carried out in the mid-1990s and its out-workings were implemented during the 1995/96 year. New structures would replace the system which had been in place from the beginning of the Second

The County Agriculture Development Office staff in 1996.
Back row: Mervyn Simpson, Paddy McGurn, Dessie Carson, Mark Whitely, Leslie Long, Joe Rice, Leslie Campbell, Malcolm Finney, John Marshall, Bertie Morrison, Ronnie McIlwaine.
Third row: George Thompson, Daphne Robinson, Alan Warnock, Reggie Aiken, Frank Tisdall, John Armstrong, Paul McCaffrey, Brendan Gilroy, Tom Crudden, Nicholas Coyle.
Second row: Norman Noble, Albert Knox, Bernard McGirr, David Moore, Connor Maguire, Cahal Murphy, Gerry McGirr, Niall Maguire, Martin Shannon.
Front row: Catherine McQuade, Mrs Olive Bruce, Patricia Maguire, Stanley Lytle, Sam Morrow, Graeme Melville, Mrs Dympna Mohan, Mrs Sandra Ellis, Grainne McAvoy.

World War in 1939. Under the county based system the County Agricultural Executive Officer had responsibility for providing an advisory service for farmers in relation to all aspects of production and farm management and marketing of produce. In addition, a grant and subsidy inspection and information service was provided. Grant applications and claims for payment were also processed in the county office. Another important role was to keep the Ministry or Department informed of local conditions and problems and to suggest how these might be addressed. From the year 1900 the officer responsible for agricultural administration in the county (from 1939 the County Agricultural Executive Officer) had responsibility of serving as Secretary of the County Committee of Agriculture. This body, which in its time had provided a most valuable service to the farmers of County Fermanagh, ceased to exist in the 1970s when it was replaced by a short-lived Province wide General Agricultural Advisory Committee.

Increased specialisation in farming and the increased emphasis on the environment, together with the challenge of greater accountability, and streamlining in relation to the administration of farming support measures were factors indicating need for change. The benefits of a closer relationship between the Agriculture Development Service and the education and training provided at the Colleges were also very clear. As part of the transition to the new structures the County Agriculture Development Officer in Fermanagh, Mr Sam Morrow, was appointed Principal of Enniskillen College of Agriculture, in succession to Miss Ann Mallon, who transferred to a senior headquarters role in the Department, in January 1994. Sam Morrow, on retirement from the Civil Service, vacated his position as Principal of the College and relinquished County Staff responsibilities at the end of June 1996. This brought to an end an administrative system which had functioned from the year 1900, when the Department of Agriculture and Technical Instruction set up a county based system for the provision of an agricultural advisory service and the administration of support schemes for the benefit of the agricultural industry.

In County Fermanagh during the 96-year period three people had responsibility for this work in County Fermanagh. These were Mr W. H. West (1900 to 1935) who also had the responsibility of being Secretary of Fermanagh County Council in the later years, Mr W. T. McClintock (from 1935 until 1977) and Mr S. B. Morrow from 1977 until 1996.

From 1996 senior staff based in the agricultural colleges, or at the Department's headquarters divisions, took responsibility for the work previously undertaken by the County Agriculture Development Officers. However, in County Fermanagh the all-important Agriculture Development Advisers, now part of Greenmount Agricultural College's (later CAFRE) staff, the field and office staff who dealt with farm support measures, together with their professional supervisors, remained based in Inishkeen House. They continue to provide a high class service which is available to the entire farming community in Fermanagh.

References:

Department of Agriculture and Rural Development's *Agriculture in Northern Ireland.*

Reports of the Fermanagh County Agricultural Development Office.

Stewart, T. A. And Morrow, S. B., A report prepared for Fermanagh District Council in 1999 entitled: *Fermanagh Farming in Crisis.*

Chapter 37
Reflection

Throughout the decades of the twentieth century there was constant change as those engaged in getting a living from the land coped with the challenges that confronted them. In the early part of the century there was a pattern of small owner-occupied farms together with a limited number of larger holdings and then the large estates. Throughout the century farmers in Fermanagh depended very largely on livestock as the main enterprise. Cropping has always been on a limited scale because of the natural handicaps of soil and a generally unfavourable climate. In the first half of the century necessity dictated a large degree of self sufficiency especially on the smaller farms. Expenditure was limited to those items which could not easily be produced on the farm. Maize was an exception in that it was a high quality feed, particularly suitable for pigs and poultry, and it was cheap as substantial quantities were imported into the British Isles from North America and elsewhere. The two world wars put an even greater emphasis on self sufficiency as far as home grown feeds and other products were concerned. Compulsory tillage was a feature of Government policy during the two wars.

Farmers enjoyed reasonable prosperity during the First World War but this was followed by years of depressed farm incomes. Efforts to improve marketing of farm produce offered promise but had a limited beneficial impact on farm incomes. A renewed emphasis on home production of food with reasonable prices, which were guaranteed by Government, opened up some new opportunities for farmers during the Second World War.

Period of expansion

The value of home production of food was appreciated by Government following the difficult experience of two world wars. The 1947 Agriculture Act was a significant milestone following World War II. The Act gave farmers guaranteed prices for their produce encouraging increased production so that the United Kingdom became more self sufficient in food supplies. As well as guaranteed prices, schemes for land improvement and farm infrastructure were introduced to aid increased production and efficiency. This was accompanied by very effective initiatives in the marketing of agricultural produce.

In the post war period a revolution in farm mechanisation commenced and continued with increasing intensity to the end of the century. Farmers appreciated the value of agricultural education and research findings which were applied to good effect particularly from the 1960s. Eradication programmes for Tuberculosis and Brucellosis brought great benefits to farmers and assurance to consumers.

Farm business development and rationalisation

Major expansion in livestock numbers occurred in the post Second World War period. The increase in the size of the livestock population was accompanied by a reduction and almost total elimination of arable cropping. In addition, increased economic pressures on farming and social developments led to other changes. The number of farm businesses in County Fermanagh, as elsewhere in the Province, has shown a steady decline. Over the years farm family members had better off-farm employment opportunities together with better remuneration and improved life styles and this led to the drift from the land.

In so far as cattle are concerned, the acceptance of suckler cows as a major source of quality beef animals gave a great boost to this enterprise. The expansion of the suckler herd was encouraged over the years by the Northern Ireland and United Kingdom Governments through subsidies. This support was continued under the Common Agricultural Policy of the European Union. The dairy enterprise, which was once the main stay on most Fermanagh farms, has increasingly become specialised with tight financial margins and very high standards of production required to meet quality requirements.

The sheep enterprise showed an even more dramatic increase than cattle in County Fermanagh. Again this was encouraged through subsidies and technological developments that enabled sheep to be kept on the rather difficult farm lands found in the county. Pigs and poultry as enterprises on the family farm were victims of specialisation and low profit margins.

The following table summarises the major changes in cattle and sheep numbers and farm holdings in County Fermanagh during the period 1930 to 2000.

Table 37.1 Farming trends in County Fermanagh 1930 - 2000

Year	1930	1940	1950	1960	1970	1980	1990	2000
Dairy cows					29,400	26,674	24,693	21,535
Number of dairy herds					2,600	1,591	938	623
Beef cows	#33,293	#34,706	#40,436	#40,242	33,002	39,538	47,701	55,906
Number of suckler herds					3,815	3,195	2,868	2,707
Total cattle	83,976	94,721	119,814	120,854	146,000	165,144	167,998	179,184
Total sheep	15,655	18,142	15,839	36,030	18,860	17,868	115,869	118,853
Number of farm holdings	12,711	11,118	9,956	8,295	7,231	6,044	4,904	3,525
Agricultural labour force					8,795	7,103	5,650	6,161

 # Includes dairy cows

Source: Economics and Statistics Division, Department of Agriculture and Rural Development.

The Common Market

A very significant policy change took place with entry to the Common Market in 1972. Since then agricultural policy has been increasingly determined by the European Union with prices and other aspects of production being decided in Brussels rather than in Westminster. The basic philosophy of the Common Market was that commodities should be produced in those areas where natural advantages for production of the commodity existed. Over time this meant that the agricultural economy in Northern Ireland, and in County Fermanagh in particular, became increasingly dependent on grass based enterprises. With developments in large scale production methods for pigs and poultry these enterprises only survived on a small number of highly efficient units. Financial support from EU funds was directed at supporting farming enterprises and enabling food costs for consumers to be kept low. Moving into the twenty-first century a major policy reform resulted in subsidies to farm businesses being no longer linked to production but rather made through a Single Farm Payment based on historic levels of subsidies paid to the farm. Under this de-coupling support mechanism farmers have greater freedom to produce to meet the demands of the market. The main conditions associated with the payment are that the land should be kept in good agricultural condition and that the environment is protected.

The Environment and Rural Development

Until the end of the 1970s Government and EU agriculture policies placed the emphasis on food production. Thereafter, environmental and rural development considerations became increasingly important. There was recognition of the farmers' role as managers of the countryside. This led to the introduction of schemes to reward farmers for the protection and enhancement of features of environmental and conservation interest. Furthermore, a linkage was developed between production support measures and environmental protection referred to as cross-compliance. With increasing productivity and fewer people engaged in farming, grant aid under agricultural schemes was introduced to encourage diversification projects which would create employment, generate income and help maintain the rural population.

Food security and animal welfare

A number of food safety scares, culminating in the BSE crisis in the 1990s, put immense pressure on farmers, suppliers of feedingstuffs and food processors to comply with the highest production and traceability standards. Consumers of milk, meat and eggs are no longer satisfied with cheap food. They require assurance that it is produced by safe and welfare friendly methods.

The future

It has been estimated that in the world there will be an additional 1.5 billion people over the next 20 years resulting in many more people to feed. No doubt traditional farming methods will help to meet this increased demand for food but on a global scale resources for food production are limited. Increased efficiency of utilisation of these limited resources will have to be addressed. During the First World War the Irish Department of Agriculture's advertisement promoting increased tillage emphasised the value of crops as a food source. It pointed out that an acre of potatoes would feed 220 people for a week, whereas an acre of oats would feed 100 people for the same period. More significantly, it was stated that an acre of grass devoted to beef production would feed eight people for a week. These relativities can be debated but the point is clear, crops as a food source utilise resources more efficiently than livestock.

In recent times a new argument against livestock as a food source has emerged in that it is claimed they contribute very significantly to global warming through the production of greenhouse gases. However, the grass that they eat in its own right has a significant carbon collection and storage capability. In terms of livestock, poultry, pigs and fish are much more efficient converters of vegetable material into flesh than ruminants, like cattle and sheep. Beef and lamb are therefore more expensive and tend to be increasingly regarded as luxury food items.

County Fermanagh is not suited to arable cropping on a significant scale unless, of course, there is significant global warming and less rainfall in the future. The best prospects for agricultural production in the county would appear to be for grass fed enterprises like milk, beef and lamb production targeted at markets in parts of the world which are comparatively affluent. Marketing of these products will need to capitalise on the region's clean green welfare and environmentally friendly image and on the traditional farming and livestock management skills of the farmers. Organic methods of production will pay dividends in certain situations.

Production and marketing need to embrace the latest technologies and business principles in order to maintain competitiveness and sustainability in an increasingly global marketplace. It has been clearly demonstrated that intensive enterprises, like pigs and poultry which depend on purchased imported feed, can thrive in the county where efficiency and business management skills are of the highest standard.

The beautiful countryside with its wide range of habitats has potential for all sorts of recreational activity and will continue to offer opportunities for those who wish to provide services for the increasing number of visitors coming to Fermanagh.

Fermanagh has some of the fastest growing forests in Europe. The potential for tree growth has not been fully exploited. A move from agriculture to forestry requires careful economic consideration. It must be rememberd that it is an expensive operation to revert from forestry to agriculture and involves major reclamation. As well as the potential to make a positive economic contribution, forestry is valuable in terms of carbon collection and storage in the battle against global warming.

Finally, there is increasing emphasis on renewable sources of energy. As well as land providing sites for wind generation it has the very substantial potential to produce energy crops. Fermanagh has shown that willow can produce high yields of energy per hectare. The technology for turning this and other crop material into useable energy is steadily developing. Whether or not these crops will be grown on a significant commercial scale as an alternative to normal farm enterprises will depend on energy prices. Energy prices would need to be such as to yield better financial returns than traditional agriculture. There would also need to be reasonable prospects of sustainability for such an enterprise. Farm waste can also be harnessed to produce energy which can be utilised for heat and power. Again the economics of this process will depend on the net cost of the energy produced being competitive with the cost of other sources of energy. The level of Government subsidisation will have a significant influence on farming's contribution at least in the short term.

Index

List of Illustrations with page numbers

List of Tables with page numbers

Page numbers are shown in brackets

Imperial/Metric Conversions/Decimalisation

1 acre = 0.4047 hectares (ha)
1 gallon = 4.456 litres(l)
1 pound (lb) = 0.4536 kilograms (kg)

£1 = 100 pence (p)
£1 = 240 pence (d)
£1 = 20 shillings (s)
1 shilling (s) = 12 pence (d)